Depression in Children and Adolescents: Guidelines for School Practice

John E. Desrochers & Gail Houck

National
Association of
School Nurses

DEPRESSION IN CHILDREN AND ADOLESCENTS: GUIDELINES FOR SCHOOL PRACTICE

John E. Desrochers & Gail Houck

TABLE OF CONTENTS

4: RECOGNIZING, SCREENING, AND ASSESSING STUDENTS WITH DEPRESSION

5: SYSTEMS, COLLABORATION, AND ADMINISTRATIVE STRUCTURES

6: SPECIAL TOPICS

Kelly Vaillancourt, PhD, NCSP, Katherine C. Cowan, & Anastasia Kalamaros Skalski, PhD

APPENDIX: HANDOUTS

A. Universal Interventions for Preventing Depression

B. Targeted Interventions for Students at Risk for Depression

C. Intensive Interventions for Students With Depression

D. Building Effective Programs to Prevent Depression

E. Approaches to Temperament Risk Factors for Depression

F. Students and Grief

G. Signs of Depression in Children and Adolescents

H. Mental Health Screening in Schools

I. Talking With Students About Depression

J. Talking With Parents About Their Adolescent With Depression

K. Providing Mental Health Services Within a Multi-Tiered System of Supports

L. Professional Advocacy Planning Worksheet

ACKNOWLEDGEMENTS

We would like to take this opportunity to thank some of the people who were so generous with their time and expertise in helping to create this book.

Jon Lemich, MA, of the National Association of School Nurses (NASN) served as managing editor for this project and deserves special thanks for providing leadership, encouragement, and a firm sense of direction for everyone involved. Other members of the NASN editorial staff who made major editorial contributions to this book on many levels were Nichole Bobo, MSN, RN; Donna Mazyck, MS, RN, NCSN; and Kenny Lull, MA.

Kathy Cowan and Denise Ferrenz of the National Association of School Psychologists likewise deserve thanks for organizing NASP contributions to the project and providing invaluable editorial advice all along the way. Special thanks to Kathy, who made many of the initial suggestions regarding the structure and format of the book, and who deserves much of the credit for its present form. We also thank Janine Jones and the NASP Publications Board for their unwavering support of this project.

Thank you to Kelly Vaillancourt, PhD, NCSP (NASP Director, Government Relations), Katherine C. Cowan (NASP Director, Communications), and Anastasia Kalamaros Skalski, PhD (NASP Director, Professional Policy and Practice) who wrote Chapter 16: Advocating for Comprehensive and Coordinated School Mental Health Services, making this a much stronger book in the process.

External reviewers read chapters and provided expert advice that vastly improved the content of this book. We thank them all for their hard work and encouraging words. These reviewers included:

- Ann Bannister, MS, RN, NCSN, CRRN
- Nichole Bobo, MSN, RN
- Marie DeSisto, MSN, BSN, RN
- Megan O'Reilly Foran, PhD, NCSP
- Julia K. Lesiczka, EdM, NCSP
- Donna Mazyck, MS, RN, NCSN
- Nancy A. Peterson, MA, NCSP
- Deb Robarge BSN, RN, NCSN

Everyone involved in this project provided support, encouragement, and expertise that helped to bring this book to publication. We are extremely grateful for their collaboration.

Finally, we would like to thank our mentors and teachers who helped to shape us personally and professionally over the years. John would like to thank John Girdner, Mary Alice White, Jan Duker, Barbara Lynch, and Ed Lynch. Gail would like to thank Jan Hootman, Mary Catherine King, Sheila Kodadek, Kathryn Barnard, and Cathie Burns. We also want to acknowledge the students and families who continue to teach us, as well as school counselors, nurses, psychologists, and social workers who seek to make a difference in the lives of students.

DEDICATION

For Sarah and Elizabeth, who mean the world to me.

John

For Mike and Katey, with all my love.

Gail

JOHN E. DESROCHERS, PHD, ABPP

John Desrochers has worked in public schools as a school psychologist for more than 30 years. During this time, he has also worked as a consultant with school districts on emotionally and behaviorally disturbed students and a therapist working with children and their families. He earned his doctorate in school psychology from Columbia University and holds graduate degrees in marriage and family therapy and applied behavior analysis. He is a licensed psychologist, board certified school psychologist (American Board of Professional Psychology–ABPP), board certified behavior analyst (Behavior Analyst Certification Board–BCBA), and is listed on the National Register of Health Service Providers in Psychology. He serves on the adjunct graduate faculties of Fairfield University (Connecticut) and the Massachusetts School of Professional Psychology, where he teaches courses in behavior therapy, psychotherapeutic techniques, and school psychology. He is the editor of the NASP *Communiqué* and a member of the editorial boards for *the Journal of Applied School Psychology and School Psychology Forum*. He is a former president of the Connecticut Association of School Psychologists (CASP) and Connecticut Delegate to the National Association of School Psychologists (NASP). A recipient of the CASP Distinguished Service Award and two Presidential Awards from NASP, he was named the NASP School Psychologist of the Year in 2007. His research interests are in behavioral assessment and intervention, psychotherapy, and professional issues in school psychology.

GAIL M. HOUCK, PHD, RN, PMHNP

Gail Houck has been a psychiatric-mental health nurse practitioner for 35 years, and is a professor in the School of Nursing at Oregon Health & Science University. Her experience as a psychiatric-mental health nurse practitioner working with women with a history of abuse and other factors that created deviations from normal development contributed to an intense interest in understanding the optimal ways to foster developmentally healthy and well-adjusted children who mature into healthy and well-adjusted adults. This interest has manifested in conducting research on how varying styles of socializing children foster self-regulation, social competence, and a positive self-concept rather than how they affect compliance. Other work has included research with ADHD children and their families, serving as a program evaluator for a day treatment intervention with substance abusing mothers and their infants and toddlers, and serving as a consultant and evaluator for a project to improve mental health assessment and intervention skills of school nurses for prevention and early intervention with students. She obtained her doctorate in nursing science from the University of Washington and holds a graduate degree in psychiatric-mental health nursing with licensure as a PMHNP. She has served on faculty at OHSU School of Nursing for 25 years, and teaches in the Psychiatric Mental Health Nurse Practitioner Program and doctoral programs. In the PMHNP program, she teaches theories of psychosocial development and intervention courses. She serves as a reviewer for *Journal of Pediatric Nursing, Archives of Psychiatric Nursing, Nursing Research,* and *Research in Nursing and Health.*

ESSENTIALS

- Depression is preventable.

- School mental health professionals (school counselors, school nurses, school psychologists, school social workers, and others) have the skills needed to implement most interventions for depression.

- This book is not a textbook; it contains key information about working with students who are experiencing depression and provides easily accessible resources for further study.

- Few practitioners or districts will implement every recommendation in this book, but we hope that all will improve their programs for students with depression and other mental health problems.

There are too many students in our schools who are depressed. Some experts have estimated that up to six students in any given high school classroom may be experiencing symptoms of depression (Huberty, 2012). Except for the more severe cases, most of these students do not receive treatment for these symptoms and can experience suffering, failure, and lifelong negative consequences as a result. We wrote this book in the hope that we could motivate school-employed mental health professionals to take a closer look at students with depression and feel empowered to use the full extent of their skills in helping them.

Recent research demonstrates that, to a surprising degree, depression can be prevented.

It is also clear that early intervention—from elementary through high school—can significantly reduce the number of cases of depression during the school years and even into adulthood. The same interventions implemented to prevent depression will prevent a variety of other mental health issues, too, and in the process improve the behavioral and academic outcomes of our schools. Moreover, school mental health professionals have the skills needed to successfully implement most of these interventions.

Who This Book Is For

This book is written primarily for school-employed mental health professionals. In most school districts, these include school counselors, school nurses, school psychologists, and school social workers. Some districts may also employ other mental health professionals such as behavior therapists, expressive therapists, and family therapists. We also hope that this book finds its way into the hands of school administrators, who are key players on any collaborative team with an interest in preventing depression.

We did not set out to write a textbook (there are several outstanding ones already available). This is a book for practicing school mental health professionals to use in their everyday work. Each chapter contains a brief review of the main issues and provides resources and referrals to other sources. It is a compendium of information that should allow readers to immediately improve their understanding of how to intervene with depressed students. Because the book is designed for immediate use by practitioners who do not have ready access to professional libraries, every effort was made to find references and resources that were readily available online, often possessed by school mental health professionals, or otherwise easily acquired. Of course, we would love it if people would read this book cover to cover. However, we also understand that school mental health professionals are extremely busy people. Therefore, each chapter is more or less self-contained, allowing readers to go directly to the topics that they most need to learn about.

Main Themes of the Book

Ten major themes are woven throughout the book. These themes are:

- Depression among children and adolescents is under-recognized and inadequately addressed.

- Services for students with depression need to be comprehensive in scope, integrated with other programs in the school and community, and delivered in a coordinated manner.

- Depression is best understood from a developmental perspective.

- Depressive symptoms occur on a continuum.

- School mental health professionals are front-line service providers.

- Collaboration is critical to effectively address depression.

- Response to intervention can be an effective framework for delivering mental health services.

- Improving student mental health improves academic outcomes.

- Depression is preventable.

- Advocacy is part of our job.

We are aware of the constraints under which schools operate. We are also aware that some of the recommendations in this book are aspirational. Change is difficult and resources are tight. Not every school will implement every recommendation. But we sincerely hope that every reader of this book will be compelled to begin the process of improving programs for students with depression and, for that matter, other mental health problems, in their own schools and districts.

CHAPTER 1

Depression in Childhood and Adolescence: A Quiet Crisis

Depression among children and adolescents represents a quiet crisis for those students and their families, for schools, and for society as a whole. By the time they turn 18 years, approximately 11% of children and adolescents will have experienced some form of diagnosable depressive disorder (National Institute of Mental Health [NIMH], 2012). If one considers subclinical levels of depression, the percentage is even higher (Avenevoli, Knight, Kessler, & Meridangas, 2008). Studies have found that 10% to 30% of adolescents either show significant subclinical depressive symptoms or would meet clinical cutoffs if self-reports were considered, suggesting that "if 20% is considered a 'middle ground' approximation, the data would indicate that, in a classroom of 30 adolescent students, approximately six would have serious depressive symptoms or disorders" (Huberty, 2012, p. 151). These students exhibit significant depressive symptoms and functional impairment and are at increased risk for the later development of clinical levels of depression (Rudolf, 2009).

THE COST TO STUDENTS, ADULTS, AND SOCIETY

Students with depression frequently exhibit difficulties in academic performance and social interactions. Their motivation, initiative, and persistence can suffer, and teachers sometimes misperceive them as lazy or not caring about their work. This can result in fewer positive student–teacher interactions followed by further student disengagement from school and increased depressive symptoms. In a similar way, students exhibiting depression frequently also have difficulty maintaining social connections with peers. They sometimes exhibit irritability, indifference, or behavior problems that alienate their classmates, contributing to feelings of disconnection and depression. Tardiness and absence from school can reinforce this downward cycle with teachers and peers.

In adulthood, these students often experience low educational and occupational accomplishment (with correspondingly low income), early marriage and parenthood, and marital dissatisfaction. Negative outcomes are more pronounced for those with more severe depression (Avenevoli et al., 2008). The World Health Organization (WHO) reports that major depressive disorder is the leading cause of disability among Americans age 15 to 44 years (WHO, 2011, as cited in NIMH, 2012).

Depression that is left untreated in childhood and adolescence results in significant suffering to these individuals as adults. It also makes later treatment more lengthy and costly and places greater demands on family, healthcare, welfare, educational, business, and justice systems down the road, causing significant and preventable costs to society (NIMH, 2004).

The most tragic cost associated with depression is suicide. Suicide is the third leading cause of death among children and adolescents ages 10 to 24 years of age (NIMH, 2010). In 2009, this country lost 4,636 young people ages 5 to 24 years to suicide; 1,934 of those who died were between the ages of 5 and 19 years (CDC, 2012).

ESSENTIALS

■ In a classroom of 30 students, approximately 6 might have serious symptoms of depression.

■ Depression is associated with impaired school performance; negative interpersonal, vocational, and mental health outcomes in adulthood; and death through suicide.

A QUIET CRISIS

Notwithstanding the huge, long-lasting cost to students, families, and society, the prevention and treatment of depression is discussed very little in schools. The reasons for this include (a) the nature of depression and other internalizing disorders, (b) lack of knowledge among educators about student depression, (c) the stigma associated with depression, and (d) limited resources. Given the long-standing consequences, it is imperative that we begin the discussion.

CHALLENGES TO DISCUSSING DEPRESSION IN SCHOOLS

■ Depression is mostly internal to the student and hard to observe.

■ Knowledge about depression is lacking.

■ Stigma and denial about mental health problems exists in society.

■ People may hold the mistaken belief that mental health is not the responsibility of the schools.

■ School personnel may be concerned that addressing depression would overwhelm resources.

THE NATURE OF DEPRESSIVE SYMPTOMS

The nature of depressive symptoms does not make them easy to observe or talk about. The symptoms, like those of other internalizing disorders, are internal to the student; that is, the key symptoms of depression are usually internal thoughts and feelings not easily observable by others. Many depressive symptoms that are observable behaviors (e.g., restlessness, agitation, irritability, classroom misbehavior) are often misinterpreted by adults as a lack of motivation or as discipline problems. As a result, the true problems of students suffering from depression are often not recognized or treated appropriately.

LACK OF KNOWLEDGE ABOUT DEPRESSION

Most educators are not taught to identify signs of depression. Most people, including educators, are also not aware that depression has a significant effect on academic performance, that it can be prevented, and that school staff can effectively implement programs that prevent and reduce depressive symptoms. Moreover, very little attention is paid to this issue in educators' professional development. This lack of knowledge makes it less likely that teachers and other school personnel would realize that the topic of depression was even within their professional purview, making it very unlikely that they would feel comfortable or empowered to talk about issues of identification and intervention in their classrooms or schools.

STIGMA AND DENIAL

Despite continuing gains in this area, there is still a stigma associated with mental illness in general and depression in particular among a significant portion of society. This stigma operates to keep students, school personnel, and family members from talking openly about these issues, regardless of whether it concerns an individual student's suffering or school-wide programs to address mental health. Denial can also sometimes be at work with depression, much as it is with a variety of mental health problems. In addition, people often hold the mistaken belief that mental health is not the responsibility of the schools and that, instead, it is the responsibility of the family to find services outside of the school system.

LIMITED RESOURCES

The problem of limited resources, including inadequate numbers of school mental health professionals, often exerts subtle pressure to avoid looking too closely into these problems. The unspoken fear is that if school personnel were to become involved in addressing depression and anxiety to the same extent that they now address mental health issues such as aggression, conduct problems, and other externalizing disorders, they would not be able to handle the additional work.

WHO ARE SCHOOL MENTAL HEALTH PROFESSIONALS?

- School counselors
- School nurses
- School psychologists
- School social workers

MAJOR THEMES OF THIS BOOK

Several major themes are addressed throughout this book. One central theme is that depression is an under-recognized problem among children and adolescents that causes them and their families significant suffering, and results in immense cost to schools and society at large. Another is that, to be most effective, services for students with depression need to be comprehensive in scope, integrated with other programs in the school and community, and delivered in a coordinated manner. Other themes central to this book are introduced in this section and are elaborated in subsequent chapters.

Depression is Best Understood From a Developmental Perspective

Recent information about the developmental nature of many mental health problems (National Research Council and Institute of Medicine, 2009) is refocusing the attention of school mental health professionals on the necessity for early identification, prevention, and early intervention. Important concepts from this understanding of the development of mental disorders include the following:

- The most effective programming for addressing mental health requires an equal emphasis on mental health *problems* and on mental health *strengths* (Miles, Espiritu, Horen, Sebian, & Waetzig, 2010). This move away from a disease-oriented perspective may be especially relevant for children and adolescents.

- While there may be some risk factors specific to depression, there are also more general risk factors that contribute to a variety of mental problems, including depression (National Research Council & Institute of Medicine, 2009).

- A child's ability to successfully negotiate developmental stages depends on his or her prior history of success or failure. Moreover, the effects of these successes or failures is cumulative, resulting in a cascading effect whereby a preponderance of successful earlier experiences results in success with later experiences which, in turn, results in subsequent cascades of successful adaptation to each developmental stage. The reverse is also true: a history of difficulty with adaptation at one stage makes it more likely that the child will have difficulty with a later stage, with the effect cascading through multiple developmental levels. In fact, a child's level of resilience is now seen not exclusively as a trait inherent to the child, but as a developmental effect of the interplay of risk and protective factors in that child's life history (Edwall, 2012).

The implications of this view of mental health problems are profound for the prevention and treatment of depression and other mental health problems. For school mental health professionals, it means that they have both a great responsibility (because depression and other mental health problems should be addressed during the school-age years) and a great opportunity (because they have access to students for a long stretch of time) to prevent and treat depressive symptoms during a critical period of child development. Some of the most important implications of this point of view include the following:

- School mental health professionals are ideally situated to deliver a coordinated, integrated set of mental health interventions from a developmental perspective, offering a continuum of services from mental health promotion through interventions for mental health problems— starting at the preschool level and extending through high school.

- It is not sufficient to simply look for symptoms of depression and other mental health problems; we have to pay attention to risk and protective factors and develop programs for prevention. Depression (and many other mental disorders) exists on a continuum of severity from subclinical behaviors and symptoms to a diagnosable disorder. It is important to treat subclinical levels not only because they cause functional impairment in themselves, but also because, left untreated, they lead to more serious problems later.

■ Consider the cascading effect (in either a positive or negative direction) of successful or unsuccessful adaptation in childhood and adolescence for subsequent mental health. It is critical to begin mental health services as early as possible and to take a longer-term, more developmental view than we are generally accustomed to doing. The outcomes of what we do in second grade may not necessarily show up in end-of-year data, but may very well manifest in twelfth grade or even early adulthood.

Depressive Symptoms Occur on a Continuum

Rather than being an all-or-nothing phenomenon, depression refers to a continuum of emotions and behaviors that vary in frequency, duration, and intensity. Temporary behaviors and emotions typically associated with depression (e.g., feelings of sadness) come and go in most people's lives. As these states increase in duration, they can be considered as *symptoms* of a disorder. As the number of such symptoms increase, they may be considered as constituting a *syndrome* existing below the level of formal diagnosis (e.g., a major depressive episode as defined by the *Diagnostic and Statistical Manual of Mental Disorders* (*DSM-IV-TR*; American Psychiatric Association, 2000). Finally, the exis-

tence of a syndrome of sufficient intensity and duration may result in a diagnosis of a *disorder* (e.g., major depressive disorder).

Given the developmental nature of depression and the cascading effect of early symptoms of depression on later development of depressive disorders, prevention of depressive disorders should focus on interventions that prevent the emergence of symptoms and the development of syndromes such as major depressive episodes. The logic is irrefutable: preventing major depressive episodes would prevent major depressive disorders (Muñoz, Beardslee, & Leykin, 2012).

"The logic is irrefutable: preventing major depressive episodes would prevent major depressive disorders."

School Mental Health Professionals Are Front-Line Service Providers

In the United States, most mental health services provided to children are provided in school, primarily by school-employed mental health professionals. These professionals include school counselors, school nurses, school psychologists, and school social workers. Each has a unique contribution to make to the mental health team and all are critical providers of mental health services to children and adolescents with depression.

ESSENTIALS

■ Most mental health services for children are provided by school counselors, school nurses, school psychologists, and school social workers.

■ School mental health professionals have the training to prevent and treat depression.

School mental health professionals provide a comprehensive range of mental health services including the following:

- Education about depression for students, parents, school personnel, and members of the community.

- Formal and informal screening for depression and suicide.

- Psychological and functional behavioral assessment.

- Group and individual counseling.

- Behavioral and cognitive-behavioral approaches to managing depression.

- Referral and case management involving community providers such as therapists and medical personnel.

Moreover, a great deal of research has shown that school mental health professionals have the capability to effectively design, implement, and monitor a number of programs that prevent and treat depression and other mental health problems (see, for example, Durlak, Weissberg, Dymnicki, Taylor, & Schellinger, 2011).

Collaboration Is Critical to Effectively Addressing Depression

While schools and school mental health professionals have a critical role in interventions for depression, school personnel cannot do it alone; authentic family–school–community collaboration is a key component of any effective intervention program for students with depression. Schools and school mental health professionals are at the nexus of these systems and are in an excellent position to coordinate an integrated continuum of services for students.

ESSENTIALS

■ Family-school-community collaboration is a critical component of intervention for students with depressed behavior.

■ RTI frameworks that exist in schools should be used as frameworks for assessment and intervention with depression and other mental health problems.

Response to Intervention Can Be an Effective Framework for Delivering Mental Health Services

Delivery of services for students with depression is best provided through a multi-tiered problem-solving model. In schools, this model is often represented by the framework known as response to intervention (RTI). RTI is an educational reform that has been adopted by the majority of states in a relatively very short time.

RTI "is a practice of providing high-quality instruction and interventions matched to student need, monitoring progress frequently to make decisions about changes in instruction or goals, and applying child response data to important educational decisions" (National Association of State Directors of Special Education, 2006). Certain procedures have made RTI a powerful force for reform in the delivery of academic services: multi-tiered problem solving model of service delivery, emphasis on prevention, use of evidence-based interventions, and assessment practices such as screening and progress monitoring. These procedures are the same ones that should be used as a framework for assessment and intervention of students with depression. Of particular importance is the idea that these services should be delivered in a comprehensive and coordinated way across three tiers of intervention:

- Tier 1—Universal Interventions: Universal interventions are provided to everyone in a given population (e.g., all students in the school, all parents, or all teachers) without regard to whether or not members of that population are at risk. Examples are social–emotional learning programs for students, staff education about depression, or teaching all parents about the signs of depression and suicide.

- Tier 2—Targeted Interventions: Targeted interventions are provided to individuals or groups of people at risk of developing depression. Examples are groups for children of divorce, social skills groups, and programs for parents of students at risk for depression.

- Tier 3—Intensive Interventions: Intensive interventions are provided to students who have symptoms of depression or who are at very high risk of developing depression. Examples of intensive programs include a variety of individual and group counseling programs for students with symptoms of depression.

Integrating mental health assessment and intervention with the academic side of the RTI framework offers the opportunity to improve services to students, reduce the marginalization of mental health services in schools, and allow school mental health professionals to more fully utilize all the skills in their clinical repertoires.

Improving Student Mental Health Improves Academic Outcomes

The primary mission of schools is education, and the argument is sometimes made that schools should invest only in strictly academic interventions and programs and not be distracted from that mission by providing student mental health programs. At this point in time, however, it is clear that students who participate in programs designed to promote social and emotional health perform significantly better on academic outcomes than students who do not have access to these programs. Indeed, schools that offer such programs typically have academic outcomes approximately 11 percentile points higher than schools that do not (Durlak et al., 2011). Providing comprehensive social, emotional, and behavioral support systems for students not only successfully prevents mental illness but also significantly improves academic outcomes.

Depression is Preventable

The hopeful conclusion emerging from the contemporary developmental understanding of mental health and research demonstrating the effectiveness of readily available interventions is that depression is preventable. It has been estimated that services provided over the course of a lifetime could prevent 22% to 38% of major depressive episodes (Muñoz et al., 2012). Schools have a critical role in this project because they have long-term access to students and adolescents at critical periods of their development, employ mental health professionals capable of delivering appropriate interventions, and are positioned at the nexus of the family–school–community system.

Advocacy Is Part of Our Job

Most ethical codes for the helping professions require that professionals advocate for programs and services needed to promote the welfare of their clients. School mental health professionals often address their advocacy efforts to the need for targeted and intensive services for students at risk of depression and other mental health problems. This continues to be an important focus given that services for students with depression are often marginalized, overextended, or even nonexistent.

> "Advocacy is part of our jobs; it is often the first step toward intervention for students with depression."

ESSENTIALS

- School that offer programs to promote social and emotional health typically have academic outcomes approximately 11 percentile points higher than schools that do not (Durlak et al., 2011).

- Depression is preventable.

Meanwhile, other school professionals (e.g., teachers, administrators) typically focus their advocacy efforts on services that enhance academic outcomes for the greatest number of students. This continues to be an important effort given that so many students are underperforming in this area. But research demonstrating the reciprocal relationship between mental health and achievement, along with recent conclusions about the effectiveness of social, emotional, and behavioral programs in improving academic outcomes throughout the school, creates the opportunity for all school professionals to unite in advocating equally for improving mental health *and* academic services in their schools. If improving academic services improves mental health outcomes and improving mental health outcomes improves academic outcomes, advocacy for these programs becomes a broader agenda of advocacy for *all* students, not just those with mental health problems or just those with academic problems. In fact, the two issues are so intertwined as to be indistinguishable. Advocacy is part of our jobs; it is often the first step toward intervention for students with depression.

ACTION PLAN

- As a school counselor, school nurse, school psychologist, or school social worker, reflect on your role as a member of a collaborative team of mental health professionals. What is the scope of practice permitted under your certification or licensure? What competencies do you possess as a mental health professional? How can you expand your role in preventing depression?

RESOURCES

This book will provide key information and resources for assessing, preventing, and intervening with depression. Professionals wishing to become more expert on this topic will require further study. One of the three comprehensive textbooks on depression among children and adolescents listed below would provide an excellent starting point.

- *Handbook of Depression in Children and Adolescents*, edited by J. R. Z. Abela and B. L. Hankin (2008; New York, NY: Guilford). Covering only children and adolescents, this edited textbook covers foundations, treatment, and prevention of depression in a very authoritative manner.

- *Anxiety and Depression in Children and Adolescents: Assessment, Intervention, and Prevention*, by T. J. Huberty (2012; New York, NY: Springer). Organized as a graduate-level textbook, this resource comprehensively covers foundations, assessment, prevention, intervention, and legal issues for anxiety and depression.

- *Helping Students Overcome Depression and Anxiety: A Practical Guide (2nd ed.)*, by K. W. Merrell (2008; New York, NY: Guilford Press). This highly readable book is written specifically for use by school mental health professionals in their treatment of students with depressed behavior. It covers the basics of assessment but is strongest in its descriptions of school-based interventions for depression.

For a more comprehensive textbook that covers depression from childhood to adulthood, the *Handbook of Depression (2nd ed.)* edited by I. H. Gotlib and C. L. Hammen (2009) is an authoritative edited volume covering theory, assessment, prevention, and treatment of depression. Although this book covers depression across the lifespan, there are several outstanding chapters devoted to children and adolescents.

The book edited by B. Doll and J. A. Cummings, *Transforming School Mental Health Services: Population-Based Approaches to Promoting the Competency and Wellness of Children* (2008; Thousand Oaks, CA: Corwin Press—a joint publication with the National Association of School Psychologists) is also highly recommended, in particular for its discussion of providing school-wide interventions for students. Chapters in this book of particular interest include the following:

- Doll & Cummings: Why Population-Based Services Are Essential for School Mental Health and How to Make Them Happen in Your School.

- Baker: Assessing School Risk and Protective Factors.

- Christenson, Whitehouse, & Van-Getson: Partnering With Families to Enhance Students' Mental Health.

- Merrell, Gueldner, & Tran: Social and Emotional Learning: A School-Wide Approach to Intervention for Socialization, Friendship Problems, and More.

- Mazza & Reynolds: School-Wide Approaches to Prevention of and Intervention for Depression and Suicidal Behaviors.

- Adelman & Taylor: School-Wide Approaches to Addressing Barriers to Learning.

REFERENCES

Abella, J. R. Z., & Hankin, B. L. (2008). *Handbook of depression in children and adolescents*. New York, NY: Guilford Press.

American Psychiatric Association. (2000). *Diagnostic and statistical manual of mental disorders* (4th ed., text rev.). Washington, DC: Author.

Avenevoli, S., Knight, E., Kessler, R. C., & Meridangas, K. R. (2008). Epidemiology of depression in children and adolescents. In J. R. Z. Abela & B. L. Hankin, *Handbook of depression in children and adolescents*. New York, NY: Guilford Press.

Centers for Disease Control and Prevention. (2012). *Underlying cause of death, 1999–2009 results*. CDC Wonder Online Database. Retrieved from http://wonder.cdc.gov

Doll, B., & Cummings, J. A. (2008). *Transforming school mental health services: Population-based approaches to promoting the competency and wellness of children.* Thousand Oaks, CA: Corwin Press (a joint publication with the National Association of School Psychologists).

Durlak, J. A., Weissberg, R. P., Dymnicki, A. B., Taylor, R. D., & Schellinger, K. B. (2011). The impact of enhancing students' social and emotional learning: A meta-analysis of school-based universal interventions. *Child Development, 82*(1), 405–432.

Edwall, G. E. (2012, Spring). Intervening during childhood and adolescence to prevent mental, emotional, and behavioral disorders. *The Register Report, 38,* 8–15.

Gotlib, I. H., & Hammen, C. L. (Eds.). (2009). *Handbook of depression, 2nd ed.* New York, NY: Guilford Press.

Huberty, T. J. (2012). *Anxiety and depression in children and adolescents: Assessment, intervention, and prevention.* New York, NY: Springer.

Merrell, K. W. (2008). *Helping students overcome depression and anxiety: A practical guide (2nd ed.).* New York, NY: Guilford Press.

Miles, J., Espiritu, R., Horen, N., Sebian, J., & Waetzig, E. (2010). *A public health approach to children's mental health: A conceptual approach.* Washington, DC: Georgetown University Center for Child and Human Development. Retrieved from http://gucchdtacenter.georgetown.edu/publications/PublicHealthApproach.pdf

Muñoz, R. R., Beardslee, W. R., & Leykin, Y. (2012). Major depression can be prevented. *American Psychologist, 67*(4), 285–295.

National Association of State Directors of Special Education. (2006). *Response to intervention: Policy considerations and implementation.* Alexandria, VA: Author.

National Institute of Mental Health. (2004). *Preventing child and adolescent mental disorders: Research roundtable on economic burden and cost effectiveness.* Retrieved from http://nimh.nih.gov/scientificmeetings/economicroundtable.cfm

National Institute of Mental Health. (2010). *Suicide in the U.S.: Statistics and prevention.* Retrieved from http://www.nimh.nih.gov/health/publications/suicide-in-the-us-statistics-and-prevention/index.shtml#children

National Institute of Mental Health. (2012). NIMH factsheet 2012 on depression. Retrieved from http://www.cmhnetwork.org/resources/show?id=315

National Research Council and Institute of Medicine [NRC & IOM]. (2009). *Preventing mental, emotional, and behavioral disorders among young people: Progress and possibilities.* Washington, DC: National Academies Press. Retrieved from http://www.nap.edu/catalog.php?record_id=12480

Rudolf, K. D. (2009). Adolescent depression. In I. H. Gotlib & C. L. Hammen, *Handbook of depression, 2nd ed.* (pp. 444–466). New York, NY: Guilford Press.

CHAPTER 2

SCHOOL MENTAL HEALTH PROFESSIONALS AS FRONT-LINE SERVICE PROVIDERS

Schools are experiencing an epidemic of depression (Seeley, Rohde, & Jones, 2010). Approximately 11% of all students are diagnosed with some form of depression by the time they turn 18 years of age (National Institute of Mental Health, 2012) and approximately 20% of adolescents have significant symptoms of depression (Huberty, 2012). Most of these students—especially minority or poor children—will not receive services for their problems, and those who do will receive them from school mental health professionals (Rones & Hoagwood, 2000). Schools are the de facto mental health care system for children in this country. If they do not receive mental health services through their school, most children will simply go without.

> *"If they do not receive mental health services through their school, most children will simply go without."*

STAFFING LEVELS ARE OFTEN INADEQUATE TO MEET THE NEEDS OF DEPRESSED STUDENTS

Unfortunately, the number of school mental health professionals positioned to fight this epidemic is often inadequate to meet the increasing prevalence and severity of mental health needs seen in schools. However, with adequate staffing and capacity building, these professionals can meet the treatment needs of most students with depression and other mental health disorders.

ESSENTIALS

- Schools are experiencing an epidemic of depression among students.

- Most mental health services for students in America are provided by school mental health professionals.

- Staffing levels of school mental health professionals in most schools are far below those recommended by national professional associations.

- Schools need to use staff more efficiently and build capacity within their schools using existing resources.

ESSENTIALS

■ It makes sense to assign roles and functions based on individual competencies rather than professional title.

■ School mental health professionals can provide a full continuum of services from prevention and supporting good mental health, to assessment and treatment of identified mental health problems, to providing crisis intervention and interventions for more serious mental illness.

Recommended Staffing Ratios

The professional associations of each of the school mental health professions set recommended minimum ratios of staff to students, with most recognizing that such ratios need to be lower for staff working with students with intense needs, such as those with clinical levels of depression. The vast majority of schools do not meet even the minimum ratios, forcing them to lean too heavily on already stretched community-based resources for services they could easily, and more efficiently, deliver themselves if they had adequate staffing.

The American School Counselor Association (ASCA) recommends that schools employ one school counselor per 250 students, yet for the 2009–2010 school year, the national average was one school counselor for 459 students. Ratios varied across states, ranging from 1:183 to 1:815 (ASCA, 2012).

The National Association of School Nurses (2011) recommends a school-nurse-to-student ratio of 1:750 when working with well students, 1:225 for students requiring spe-

cial education or daily nursing services, and 1:125 for students with complex health care needs. Most states (especially in the western and southwestern parts of the country) do not mandate school nursing or specific ratios (Robert Wood Johnson Foundation, 2009). Consequently, current ratios of school nurses to students vary across states from approximately 1:400 to 1:4,400.

The National Association of School Psychologists (NASP) recommends a ratio of one school psychologist per 1,000 students but notes that "when school psychologists are providing comprehensive and preventive services (i.e., evaluations, consultation, individual/group counseling, crisis response, behavioral interventions, etc.), this ratio should not exceed 500 to 700 students for 1 school psychologist." The association recommends that this ratio should be even lower when school psychologists are working primarily with students with intensive needs, such as those "with significant emotional or behavioral disorders" (NASP, 2010, p. 10). According to a national survey of NASP members (Castillo, Curtis, Chappel, & Cunningham, 2011), during the 2009–2010 school year, the average ratio nationally of school psychologists to students was 1:1383.

The School Social Work Association of America (SSWAA) recommends a ratio of 1:400. Again, similar to the NASP position, the SSWAA specifies that "in situations where a large percentage of the school social worker's caseload is comprised of students with heightened levels of needs or risk ... a significantly lower staff-to-student ratio is required in order for the school social worker to effectively deliver needed services" (SSWAA, 2005, p. 1).

Building Capacity in a World of Limited Resources

It is clear that schools are not staffed at the levels determined by various professional associations as necessary in order to fully implement the comprehensive services described in this book and other descriptions of best practices in the literature. Moreover, this situation is not likely to change soon, particularly during tough economic times. Providing necessary school mental health services without adequate staff is a challenge.

This reality notwithstanding, the problem can be approached as one of building capacity and fully utilizing the skills possessed by the mental health professionals already employed by the school. Many of the strategies and resources described in this book can be used to help to build capacity within schools:

- Reduce professional overspecialization and increase role flexibility among all staff.

- Work for cultural and attitudinal change within the school to help everyone understand that depression is preventable and that improving student mental health results in improved academic outcomes.

- Broaden the number of school professionals involved in providing mental health services. It is not only school mental health professionals who can provide evidence-based interventions to students with symptoms of depression; for example, most teachers can successfully provide evidence-based whole-class interventions designed to

prevent depression.

- Leverage existing structures with the school (e.g., response to intervention [RTI] frameworks) to organize mental health services for students.

- Improve collaboration among all stakeholders.

- Provide to all staff professional development in evidence-based interventions for preventing and treating depression.

- Reduce fragmentation, overlap, and gaps in services available to students with depression and other academic, social, emotional, and behavioral difficulties.

- Reduce the marginalization of mental health services from the mainstream of school structures and incorporate them into the fabric of school life.

- Invest in prevention and early intervention for depression in school-age children.

It is not only school mental health professionals who can provide evidence-based interventions to students with symptoms of depression; for example, most teachers can successfully provide evidence-based whole-class interventions designed to prevent depression.

ADVANTAGES TO PROVIDING MENTAL HEALTH SERVICES IN SCHOOLS

Despite the inadequacies in the system caused by understaffing, there are a lot of compelling reasons for why schools have become the home of mental health services for most children and adolescents.

Perhaps the most compelling argument in favor of basing mental health services in schools is that that is where the kids are! Students have ready access to mental health professionals in their schools and, in turn, mental health professionals have access to students for prevention activities. Students tend to access mental health services more frequently when they are located within their school. Stigma about utilizing mental health services is lessened when those services are woven into the mainstream of school life (Rivet-Duval, Heriot, & Hunt, 2011) and perceived by students and parents as simply another aspect of schooling.

Moreover, there is generally a high degree of contact between school mental health personnel and the student's parents/guardians and teachers, creating the potential for a higher degree of integration of services than is typically possible when the mental health component of a student's program is delivered by personnel not so intimately connected with the school. It is, for example, relatively easy in these settings to incorporate prevention activities throughout the school curriculum and work on social, emotional, and behavioral goals in individual and group counseling, design for generalization of skills learned in counseling to classroom interactions, moni-tor progress toward those goals, and involve the family in supporting and monitoring progress. All of the most important components of a student's life—peers, family, academic achievement, and physical, social, emotional, and behavioral health—find a nexus in the school. It is possible in this setting to coordinate and seamlessly bring to bear the influences of the people most needed to support these areas of development: peers, teachers, parents/guardians, and school mental health professionals. Because depression is simultaneously a social, biological, and psychological phenomenon, interventions that simultaneously address all of these areas will be the most effective. A home–school–community collaborative approach, with the school at its center, is capable of providing such a continuum of intervention.

School mental health professionals understand how to work with the unique culture of the school and home–school system.

Schools possess the capability for early identification and intervention with social, emotional, and behavioral problems. Using school mental health professionals to detect, monitor, and intervene early when a student is exhibiting problem behavior is a crucial component of a system that has as a primary goal the prevention of more significant problems. On the other end of the continuum, school personnel are often available on immediate notice for emergency or crisis intervention.

Finally, school mental health professionals understand how to work with the unique culture of the school and home–school system. When students are working with community providers, these school personnel act as a bridge, making referrals to appropriate community providers and helping students integrate and apply the progress made with those providers in their everyday functioning in school.

ESSENTIALS

The advantages of providing mental health services through the schools include:

- Easy access to students.

- Stigma is reduced.

- Pre-established means of collaboration among parents, teachers, and the mental health professionals employed by the school.

- Easy integration of a variety of programs, services, and personnel when all are under the same organizational umbrella.

- Schools have the capacity for early identification, prevention, and early intervention before problems reach a clinical level.

- School mental health professionals are immediately available for crisis response.

- School mental health professionals know how to work effectively within the unique culture of schools.

QUALIFICATIONS OF SCHOOL MENTAL HEALTH PROFESSIONALS

School counselors, school nurses, school psychologists, and school social workers are all qualified to provide mental health services. Moreover, each has specialized training in applying these skills within the unique environment and culture of schools.

School Counselors

School counselors hold a minimum of a master's degree in school counseling and state department of education certification/licensure for school practice. Requirements vary by state, but most states require graduate-level training in human growth and development, individual counseling, group counseling, testing and assessment, research and program evaluation, and career development. Supervised practica and internships are also typically required (ASCA, 2011).

School Nurses

School nurse qualifications vary by state, with the typical minimum consisting of a bachelor's degree and licensure as a registered nurse. Some nurses possess national certification and a few hold a graduate degree with the nurse practitioner credential. Their education includes child and adolescent development, general and abnormal psychology, and clinical courses in psychiatry and mental health. As Selekman, Diefenbeck, and Guthrie (2013) note, "The management of mental health issues is a large part of the school nurse's role regardless of the reason for a student's visit to the health office" (p. 934).

"The management of mental health issues is a large part of the school nurse's role regardless of the reason for a student's visit to the health office."

School Psychologists

School psychologists possess a minimum of a specialist-level degree (at least 60 graduate semester hours) including a yearlong internship and state department of education certification/licensure for school practice. Their education includes mental health interventions, child development, collaboration, assessment, consultation, and evidence-based interventions for promoting social–emotional–behavioral functioning (NASP, 2010; NASP, n.d.).

School Social Workers

Qualifications for school social workers vary by state, with most requiring the master's degree and state department of education licensure/certification for school practice (Usaj, Shine, & Mandlawitz, n.d.). Their education includes training in mental health, counseling, consultation, and behavioral supports.

Advanced Qualifications

In addition to these minimum qualifications, many school-employed mental health providers pursue areas of specialization and hold additional credentials such as licensed professional counselor, licensed clinical social worker, nurse practitioner, board certified

behavior analyst, and state department of mental health-licensed psychologist, among others. These professionals often bring additional competencies to the collaborative mental health team.

"School counselors, school psychologists, school nurses, and school social workers are all qualified to provide mental health services. Moreover, each has specialized training in applying these skills within the unique environment and culture of schools."

ROLES AND FUNCTIONS OF SCHOOL MENTAL HEALTH PROFESSIONALS

School mental health professionals have an ethical obligation to practice only within the realm of their competencies. In addition, they must work according to the scope of practice granted by their certificate or license for school practice. Although each profession offers specialized skills to the mental health team, there is considerable overlap in core competencies among these professions. Moreover, even within each profession, specific competencies and subspecialties vary across individuals. For these reasons, it usually makes more sense to assign roles and functions based on the competencies of an individual practitioner rather than on whether one happens to be a school counselor, nurse, psychologist, or social worker by profession. This approach is consistent with the calls to reduce overspecialization of functions within collaborative teams discussed in Chapter 11 and is likely to contribute to building capacity with the school. Assessing the competencies of everyone on the mental health team could not only help to assign staff to areas where they could be most effective, but also highlight strengths of the team, locate areas where professional development is needed, and pinpoint the gaps in a team's programs. Organizing services in this way is best done in the context of a strong collaborative team.

In general, school mental health professionals provide a continuum of services ranging from supporting wellness and good mental health, to assessing and treating mental health problems, to providing crisis intervention and interventions for more significant mental illness. Such services are not confined to counseling and psychotherapy. Instead, they comprise the broad array of activities prescribed by the public health model, including screening, prevention, assessment, and intervention at the universal, targeted, and intensive levels of prevention. As school mental health providers, counselors, nurses, psychologists, and social workers are charged with providing these services to the students in their schools. Table 1 provides examples of the kinds of mental health services provided by these professionals.

> *"Assessing the competencies of everyone on the mental health team could not only help to assign staff to areas where they could be most effective, but also highlight strengths of the team, locate areas where professional development is needed, and pinpoint the gaps in a team's programs."*

ACTION PLAN

- Use staff professional development activities and parent educational forums to inform people about the qualifications of and services offered by the mental health professionals employed by your school.

- Advocate for bringing school staffing levels up to those recommended by national professional associations.

Review suggestions found throughout this book for building capacity among the staff already existing at your school to provide services to students with depression and other mental health problems.

Table 1. Examples of Services Provided by School Mental Health Professionals

Universal (RTI TIER 1)	Targeted (RTI Tier 2)	Intensive (RTI Tier 3)
■ Design and delivery of school-wide positive behavior supports and social–emotional learning curriculum ■ Prevention services to strengthen families and school climate and prevent crisis ■ School-wide suicide prevention activities ■ Individual and group counseling for students in establishing personal and career goals ■ Universal screening for depression, suicide, and other mental health concerns ■ Parent education and staff development regarding depression and other mental health issues	■ Screening for depression, suicide, And other mental health concerns for at-risk students ■ Parent education and staff development regarding depression and other mental health issues ■ Group counseling for students exhibiting depressed or at-risk behavior ■ Social skills training ■ Support groups for parents of students at risk for depressed behavior ■ Teacher and parent consultation for students at risk for depressed behavior ■ Behavioral assessment and intervention for students at risk for depressed behavior ■ Progress monitoring of depressed behavior ■ Evaluation of intervention program effectiveness	■ Individual, small-group, or family counseling for students with identified depression ■ Crisis intervention and postvention: school, family, community ■ Comprehensive evaluation of depressed behavior and development of treatment plan ■ Individual, group, and family counseling and therapy ■ Alcohol and drug counseling ■ Individualized behavioral interventions, supports, and plans ■ Comprehensive family services ■ Coordinating collaboration between the family, school, and community resources ■ Management of hospitalization and return to school ■ Administration and monitoring of medication for depression ■ Intensive progress monitoring of depressed behavior ■ Case management ■ Referral ■ Evaluation of treatment program
Sources for most of the information in this table are the websites of the American School Counselor Association, National Association of School Psychologists, National Association of School Nurses, and School Social Work Association of America.		

RTI CONSIDERATIONS

School mental health professionals are well trained in assessment, data-based decision making, and research-based interventions—
all key components of an RTI framework.

RESOURCES

The website of the American School Counselor Association (http://www.schoolcounselor.org/index.asp) is a good starting point for information about school counselors and their role in providing mental health services to students. Examples include:

- *Student-to-School-Counselor Ratios* (http://www.schoolcounselor.org/content.asp?contentid=658)

- Provides state-by-state listings of student to school counselor ratios.

- *The Role of the School Counselor* (http://www.schoolcounselor.org/content.asp?pl=325&sl=133&contentid=240)

- *Why Elementary School Counselors* (http://www.schoolcounselor.org/content.asp?contentid=230)

The National Association of School Nurses website (www.nasn.org) features a number of resources of interest. In particular, the following publications about the role of school nurses as mental health service providers are relevant to the discussion in this chapter:

- *Role of the School Nurse* (Position Statement, 2011; http://www.nasn.org/PolicyAdvocacy/PositionPapersandReports/NASNPositionStatementsFullView/tabid/462/ArticleId/87/Role-of-the-School-Nurse-Revised-2011)

- *Mental Health of Students* (Position Statement, 2008; http://www.nasn.org/default.aspx?tabid=237)

- *Education, Licensure, and Certification of School Nurses* (Position Statement, 2012; http://www.nasn.org/PolicyAdvocacy/PositionPapersandReports/NASNPositionStatements).

- *Coordinated School Health Programs* (Position Statement, 2008; http://www.nasn.org/PolicyAdvocacy/PositionPapersandReports/NASNPositionStatements)

The National Association of School Psychologists maintains a website (www.nasponline.org) with a large number of resources, including handouts, articles, and other information freely available to the public. Of particular interest:

- *NASP Model for Comprehensive and Integrated School Psychological Services* (2010; http://www.nasponline.org/standards/2010standards/2_PracticeModel.pdf)

- Provides an excellent overview of the kinds of services provided by school psychologists.

The website of the School Social Work Association of America (http://www.sswaa.org) contains many resources for information about school social work. The following are some of particular relevance to the current discussion:

- *Definition of Highly Qualified Social Workers* (2012; http://www.sswaa.org/displaycommon.cfm?an=1&subarticlenbr=52)

- *School Social Work Services* (2012; http://sswaa.org/associations/13190/files/School%20Social%20Work%20Services%20One%20Page%202012.pdf)

- The National Association of Social Workers (http://www.socialworkers.org) and the school psychology division of the American Psychological Association (http://www.apadivisions.org/division-16/index.aspx) provide further information on the role of social workers and psychologists in the schools.

REFERENCES

American School Counselor Association. (2012). *Student-to-school-counselor ratios.* Retrieved from http://www.schoolcounselor.org/content. asp?contentid=658

American School Counselor Association. (2011). *State certification requirements.* Retrieved from http://www.schoolcounselor.org/content. asp?pl=325&sl=133&contentid=242

Castillo, J. M., Curtis, M. J., Chappel, A., & Cunningham, J. (2011). *School psychology 2010: Results of the National Membership Study.* Retrieved from http://www.nasponline.org/advocacy/Mbr_Survey_Results_2011_Conv_Session.pdf

National Association of School Nurses. (2011). *Healthy children learn better! School nurses make a difference.* Retrieved from http://www.nasn.org/Portals/0/about/press_room_faq.pdf

National Association of School Psychologists. (2010). *Model for comprehensive and integrated school psychological services.* Bethesda, MD: Author. Retrieved from http://www.nasponline.org/standards/2010standards/2_PracticeModel.pdf

National Association of School Psychologists. (n.d.). *What is a school psychologist?* Retrieved from http://www.nasponline.org/about_sp/whatis.aspx

Rivet-Duval, E., Heriot, S., & Hunt, C. (2011). Preventing adolescent depression in Mauritius: a universal school-based program. *Child and Adolescent Mental Health 16*(2), 86–91.

Robert Wood Johnson Foundation. (2009). *Unlocking the potential of school nursing: Keeping children healthy, in school, and ready to learn.* Retrieved from http://www.rwjf.org/files/research/cnf14.pdf

Rones, M., & Hoagwood, K. (2000). School-based mental health services: A research review. *Clinical Child and Family Psychology Review, 3,* 223–241.

School Social Work Association of America. (2005). *School social worker staffing needs* (Resolution). Retrieved from http://www.dpi.wi.gov/sspw/pdf/sswpgstaffing.pdf

Selekman, J., Diefenbeck, C., & Guthrie, S. (2013). Mental health concerns. In J. Selekman (Ed.), *School nursing: A comprehensive text (2nd ed.)* (pp. 927–969). Philadelphia, PA: F. A. Davis.

Usaj, K., Shine, J. K., & Mandlawitz, M. (n.d.) *Response to intervention: New roles for school social workers.* Retrieved from School Social Work Association of America, http://www.sswaa.org/userfiles/file/RoleofSSWinRTI.pdf

CHAPTER 3

School-Wide Interventions for Preventing Depression

Depression throughout the lifespan can be prevented through the use of an integrated continuum of interventions that includes (a) universal prevention programs, (b) universal screening for depression, (c) targeted interventions for students at risk, and (d) intensive programs for those identified with depression (Munoz, Beardslee, & Leykin, 2012). As is discussed throughout this book, one way to provide such services in schools is through a multi-tiered problem-solving team framework such as response to intervention (RTI).

Universal preventive interventions target a whole population group, such as an entire classroom, school, or district. In other words, universal preventive interventions are not targeted specifically to students identified as at risk for depression, although these students also participate and benefit. Within an RTI framework, these would be considered Tier 1 interventions. School-based universal prevention strategies tend to emphasize (a) building resilience within students, (b) raising awareness about depression, and (c) building protective schools. The most effective approaches to universal prevention address both of these strategies in an integrated way. Universal programs are positive and proactive and, since they are provided independent of risk status, the potential for stigmatizing participants is minimized (Greenberg, Domitrovich, & Bumbarger, 2000).

This chapter focuses on depression prevention efforts provided to the entire population of students in a school or district (i.e., universal prevention or Tier 1 of an RTI approach). There are numerous evidence-based universal prevention programs available for implementation in schools. Several such programs are described in this chapter. Note, however, that there are many others that could be considered. An additional source of universal prevention programs is the Collaborative for Social and Emotional Learning (http://casel.org), and a discussion of universal prevention programs for preschool children may be found in Squires (2010). Subsequent chapters will discuss interventions for students who are at risk for depression (Tier 2 of the RTI framework) or who are already experiencing symptoms of depression or at very high risk of developing depression (Tier 3).

"School-based universal prevention strategies tend to emphasize (a) building resilience within students, (b) raising awareness about depression, and (c) building protective schools."

UNIVERSAL PREVENTION PROGRAMS THAT BUILD STUDENT RESILIENCE

The following universal prevention programs target building resilience within students. Two very well researched programs, the Penn Resiliency Program and Strong Kids/Strong Teens, have been shown to be effective not only as universal prevention programs but also as targeted intervention programs (Tier 2) for students at risk. These will be discussed in Chapter 4.

The Resourceful Adolescent Program

The Resourceful Adolescent Program (RAP), a program for students in grades 7–10, has components for adolescents (RAP-A), parents (RAP-P), and teachers (RAP-T). The 11-session program, built on principles of cognitive behavior therapy, is designed to be integrated into the school curriculum. Significant reductions in depressive symptoms have been found for students who participated in the program compared to those who did not, and their improvements were maintained 10 months later (Shochet, Dadds, & Holland,

Examples of Universal Prevention Programs

Name	Age/Grade Range	Access
Resourceful Adolescent Program (RAP)	Ages 7-10	http://www.rap.qut.edu
Beyond Blue	Grades preK–12	http://www.beyondblue.org.au
Children and Youth Resiliency Program	Ages 12–18	http://www.corstone.org/html/solutions/programs.cfm
Program in Education, Afterschool, and Resiliency	Grades k-12	http://www.pearweb.org
Second Step (Student Success Through Prevention)	Grades K-8	http://www.cfchildren.org/second-step.aspx
Adolescent Depression Awareness Progam (ADAP)	High School	http://www.hopkinsmedicine.org/psychiatry/specialty_areas/moods/ADAP
School Transitional Envionment Project (STEP)	Ages 12-18	http://www.ojjdp.gov/mpg/STEP%20(School%20Transitional%20Envionmental%20Program)-MPGProgramDetail-428.aspx
Caring School Community	Grades 1-6	www.devstu.org

2001). Building on this work, Merry and colleagues developed the RAP-Kiwi program (Merry, McDowell, Wild, Bir, & Cunliffe, 2004). This program demonstrated similar short- and long-term benefits for 13- to 15-year olds: depressive symptoms were significantly reduced for program participants compared to students that participated in a placebo program, and the improvements were consistent at an 18-month follow-up. The RAP program has also been adapted for indigenous youth and their families. Information, resource materials, and further research results may be found on the RAP website.

beyondblue

The *beyondblue* initiative provides classroom-based skills instruction over a 3-year period. This initiative was developed by a national Australian not-for-profit organization whose mission is to increase the capacity of the broader community to prevent depression (*beyondblue*: the National Depression Initiative, 2008). Established in 2000, the *beyondblue* initiative is a bipartisan effort of the Australian State and Territory governments. Partnerships were created among health services, schools, workplaces, universities, media, community organizations, and those with depression. Together, they seek to raise community awareness about depression and reduce stigma. The goals of the program are to build protective strengths in students and to build a protective school environment. To enhance the resilience of students, the school-based program focuses on the skills of problem solving, coping, emotional regulation, stress reduction, social competence, conflict resolution, assertive-

ness, and building social support. Elements include enhancing constructive views of the self, the world, and the future as well as building self-efficacy and self-awareness. Learning about mental health and how to seek help for self and others are included as well. To deliver the program, a range of interactive methods is used, such as small group exercises and discussions, role-plays, learning tasks, and quizzes. Central to the implementation of the program is that it is taught within the context of a whole-school-climate approach that aims to support the acquisition and maintenance of individual protective skills. Initially, the program was designed for adolescents in grades 8 through 10, but the program has since been extended to the primary grades. Spence (2008) provides a detailed evaluative description of the program and the *beyondblue* website provides considerable information, evaluation, and resources for implementing the program. A version of this program that was conducted by teachers was evaluated and depression, hopelessness, self-esteem, and coping skills were all found to have improved in the short term; however, only the improvements in self-esteem and coping skills were sustained 6 months later (Rivet-Duval, Heriot, & Hunt, 2011).

Children and Youth Resiliency Program

The Children and Youth Resiliency Program (CYRP) is a program developed by CorStone in partnership with the University of California, San Francisco, Global Health Sciences program. The CYRP is designed for middle and high school students (12 to 18 years of age), and is flexibly constructed for school schedules and after-school programs. The full program is structured as 1-hour group sessions conducted weekly over a 26-week period; a shortened program over 12 to 16 weeks is also available. The program is strength-based and designed to build self-esteem, improve problem-solving skills and social functioning, and teach how to cope with adversity and conflict. It also provides knowledge, skills, and support to enhance students' resilience. To conduct the program, two group co-facilitators must be trained by CorStone in an intensive 5-day training, and periodic mentorship and support is provided. A component of the program is a 2- to 3-hour training for teachers and administrators. The CYRP has demonstrated measurable positive changes in students' optimism, internal control orientation, coping, and social connectedness. Reported school-level outcomes include more cohesive peer-group, classroom, and school communities, as well as a reduction in the number and severity of disruptive incidents and suspensions.

Program in Education, Afterschool, and Resiliency

The Program in Education, Afterschool, and Resiliency (PEAR) was developed in cooperation with Harvard University and McLean Hospital to address the need for high-quality afterschool programs that could provide a format for building resilience, contributing to success in school, and preventing risk behaviors. Education, health, public policy, and psychological perspectives provide the framework for the developmentally based programs. Programs have been implemented in Boston schools and replicated across the country.

The PEAR website offers research summaries and examples of how the program has been applied in schools. An example of one such application is the RALLY program (Responsive Advocacy for Life and Learning in Youth), a school-based inclusive model of intervention and prevention designed to provide integrated academic and emotional support to middle school students. The emphasis in this program is on building social competence and resilience through relationships with positive adults. A central strategy is to avoid stigmatization by bringing supports into the classroom rather than pulling students out of the classroom. A unique feature is the role of the "Prevention Practitioner," who works with at-risk students in the program across settings (school, home, community).

Second STEP

Second STEP (Student Success Through Prevention) was developed by the Committee for Children, a not-for-profit organization dedicated to providing social and emotional education to children from the preschool years through middle school. The Second Step program for kindergarten through 5th grade is a classroom-based curriculum designed to increase academic success and reduce behavior problems by promoting self-regulation and social–emotional competence, with separate sets of lesson plans by grade level. Skills are taught over as many as 28 lessons to strengthen students' learning, problem solving, empathy, and emotional management.

The middle school program (for grades 6–8) draws on theory and research about adolescent development and risk and protective factors. Through seven classroom-based lessons, the program uses a variety of group, partner, and other interactive activities to help students learn the knowledge and skills needed to address five themes: empathy and communication to enhance social skills and school connectedness; bullying prevention through changing the culture of the school by reducing social rewards for bullying and improving peer relations; emotion management using cognitive–behavioral strategies and emphasizing coping with situations that provoke strong feelings; problem solving, decision making, and goal setting; and substance abuse prevention.

The website provides reviews of the research on which the programs are based, as well as samples of lessons with videos, and guides for teachers and school mental health professionals. Training is not mandatory but available, and may be required if the implementation of the program has grant-based funding. Assessment tools and separate or bundled curricula can be purchased through the online store.

RAISING AWARENESS OF DEPRESSION

The Adolescent Depression Awareness Program (ADAP) was developed to educate high school students, teachers, and parents about depression. The program was developed in response to programs that focused exclusively on either suicide or depression rather than focusing on the *link* between them. The thrust of the program is to provide education about the identification and treatment of depression in order to reduce the stigma, morbidity, and suicide associated with adolescent depres-

sion. The core message is that depression (and bipolar disorder) is a treatable medical illness and that concerned individuals need evaluation and should seek treatment.

Developed in 1999 by two psychiatrists and a psychiatric nurse, the ADAP program consists of a 3-hour student curriculum (Swartz et al., 2010). The curriculum is designed to be taught in health class and can be presented in three 1-hour (or 45-minute) classes or two 90-minute classes. Multiple teaching approaches are included: interactive lectures, discussion, video, homework and video assignments, and group interactive activities. Topics for each of the three classes with videos can be reviewed on the ADAP website.

The curriculum addresses knowledge about depression and the symptoms of depression, the steps involved in diagnosis, and the difference between depression and bipolar disorder. An interactive video is used to show a portion of an evaluation for depression with a psychiatrist in order to familiarize students with the process of a psychiatric assessment. In the discussion about treatment, the importance of therapy with medication is emphasized and a range of options is presented, including psychotherapy and family therapy. Suicide is not isolated or emphasized, but it treated as a symptom of depression and in the context of an illness needing treatment.

Students are asked to complete the Adolescent Depression Knowledge Questionnaire (ADKQ) as a pretest and posttest (available on the website). It includes questions about symptoms of depression, mania, and attitudes toward treatment of depression (Swartz et al., 2010). Between 2001 and 2005, more than 3,500 students participated in ADAP and completed pre- and post-test surveys. The effectiveness of the curriculum is evidenced by the number of students scoring 80% or higher on the test having more than tripled from pretest to posttest. More than 100 schools have been involved in teaching more than 22,000 students at multiple states.

UNIVERSAL PREVENTION PROGRAMS THAT BUILD PROTECTIVE SCHOOL ENVIRONMENTS

A more comprehensive, ecological approach to prevention considers the context or environment of the student as a contributor to the student's problems, including depression. Rather than focusing primarily on the individual characteristics of students, ecologically focused programs address the contextual (risk and protective) factors in the school as an indirect means to build resilience. Protective factors within the school include such things as school security and safety, social support, positive relationships with teachers and peers, and a sense of connectedness and belonging. Risk factors include such things as troubled relationships with peers and teachers, poor school climate, and inadequate classroom management. Programs that focus on changing the school ecology seek to make the school setting less threatening (by decreasing risk factors) and more supportive (by increasing protective factors).

beyondblue's School Environment Program

The school environment program within the *beyondblue* schools initiative seeks to build a safe environment that promotes positive, supportive relationships within the school and to increase opportunities and encouragement for students to participate in various school experiences. These include not only opportunities to participate in the social, recreational, and sporting activities of the school, but also to play a part in policy development and decision making related to the classroom, cafeteria, recreational activities, and other aspects of school operations. The *beyondblue* program uses a whole-school change process to create a protective school environment. The process involves a collaborative team of school staff that may include school mental health professionals, teachers, administrators, and others with a specific interest and expertise in student health and well-being. In Australia, they include a facilitator from the *beyondblue* research team; a facilitator would need to be identified for U.S. schools, possibly a school psychologist or consultant. The key task for the team is to obtain an audit of school health-promotion activities and student and staff survey data. Student questionnaires assess social support, depression, anxiety, emotional and behavioral problems, risk-taking behavior, victimization experiences, social skills, thinking styles, interpersonal problem-solving and coping skills, stressful life events, mental health literacy, perceptions of school climate (safety, participation, and supportive relationships), and help-seeking behavior. Teachers respond to surveys about their emotional well-being, work stress and satisfaction, methods of dealing with challenging students, and their perceptions of school climate and environment. The data from these assessments provide feedback to inform the creation of an action plan, and the implementation and outcomes of the plan are reviewed every 6 months.

Enhancing School Connectedness

Although the *beyondblue* whole-school change program is very comprehensive and is designed to address a range of student resiliency factors, schools can focus their attention on increasing *school connectedness* and accomplish a great deal to enhance student well-being. A student's school connectedness comprises a commitment to school, a belief that school is important, satisfying relationships with teachers and peers, opportunities to be involved, and feelings of belonging. School connectedness can be readily assessed by simply asking students three questions: In your friendship group, do you have (a) someone to talk to, (b) someone to depend on when you are angry or upset, and (c) someone who could be trusted with private feelings and thoughts? Students who respond with yes to all three questions may be categorized as having good social connectedness.

Bond and colleagues (2007) found that the combination of good social and school connectedness was associated with the lowest risk of depressive symptoms among students in their study; any other combination of school and social connectedness put students at more risk for depressive symptoms. Assessment of student risk and protective factors found within the school can point in the direction of features that need to be addressed in order to strengthen students' school connectedness. Schools are accessible and relatively stable sites within which to locate interventions to promote connectedness at key times in students' lives (Bond et al., 2007). School connectedness requires a commitment on the part of the school to promoting satisfying relationships between teachers and students and to optimizing students' relationships with peers. Encouraging this commitment and providing the resources needed in order to focus on relationships among students and between students and teachers are keys to effective intervention.

ESSENTIALS

- Increasing students' sense of connectedness to the school can build resilience and decrease the risk of depression.

- Assessment of risk and protective factors within the school environment can point to features that need to be addressed.

"School connectedness requires a commitment on the part of the school to promoting satisfying relationships between teachers and students and to optimizing students' relationships with peers. "

School Transitional Environment Project

Another example of an intervention that focuses on changing the school ecology and facilitating school connectedness is one that seeks to make the environment less threatening to students during the transition from elementary school to middle school and from middle school to high school. The School Transitional Environment Project (STEP) has been widely adopted to reduce the complexity of the new school environment by defining a supportive role for the homeroom teacher and by creating a stable support mechanism (a consistent set of peers and classmates) through the transition. A series of evaluations and replication studies found that, through this restructuring of the school environment during transition, students had significantly lower levels of stress and less anxiety, depression, and delinquent behavior than students who did not experience this program (Greenberg et al., 2000). This strategy can be readily applied to facilitate the transition from one grade to another as well as from one school to another. The consistent experience of change accompanied by reduced stress, anxiety, depression, and acting out should have long-term preventive effects for depression.

Caring School Community

The Caring School Community program, designed by the Developmental Studies Center, is for elementary school students in first through sixth grade (6 to 12 years of age), and seeks to change the school ecology in order to enhance school connectedness by creating a caring community of learners. The program consists of four components: class meetings, a buddy program, parent involvement, and school-wide components. Orientation and training materials include books, reference materials, and videos. On-site workshops are available to schools and districts, and a train-the-trainer approach may be used.

The demonstrated effects of the program led to its listing by the U.S. Department of Education as an effective violence prevention program, and the U.S. Center for Substance Abuse Prevention has selected it as a model substance abuse prevention program. In addition, the program has been endorsed by the National Association of Elementary School Principals, the National School Board Association, the Character Education Partnership, and the National Council for the Social Studies (Lewis, Shaps, & Watson, 2003).

ACTION PLAN

- Create, join, or support a collaborative problem-solving team in your school or district and use it to advocate for the implementation of a universal prevention program. Consider this program as one segment on a continuum of interventions for depression that also includes targeted interventions for students at risk for depression and intensive intervention for those identified as depressed.

- Consider integrating such a program into the school's RTI framework.

- Investigate several prevention programs and choose one that most closely matches the needs of your school or district in terms of the skills it teaches and its affordability, feasibility, and acceptance.

- Provide professional development to school staff, parents, and members of the community regarding the preventability of depression and the need for school-based prevention programs. Broaden family–school–community collaboration and support for the program.

- Implement and evaluate the program.

RESOURCES

Two books by Adelman and Taylor provide very practical information and materials for building collaborative teams and implementing school-wide programs: *The Implementation Guide to Student Learning Supports in the Classroom and Schoolwide: New Directions for Addressing Barriers to Learning* (2006a) and *The School Leader's Guide to Student Learning Supports: New Directions for Addressing Barriers to Learning* (2006b).

The book by Doll and Cummings (2008) entitled *Transforming School Mental Health Services: Population-Based Approaches to Promoting the Competency and Wellness of Children* contains a wealth of information about school-wide prevention and intervention programs.

The website of the UCLA Center for Mental Health in Schools (http://smhp.psych.ucla.edu) has an immense store of materials and resources for improving the delivery of mental health programs in schools.

The Collaborative for Academic, Social, and Emotional Learning website (http://casel.org) is another excellent source of information. Look here for lists of evidence-based prevention programs.

REFERENCES

Adelman, H. S., & Taylor, L. (2006a). *The implementation guide to student learning supports in the classroom and schoolwide: New directions for addressing barriers to learning.* Thousand Oaks, CA: Corwin Press.

Adelman, H. S., & Taylor, L. (2006b). *The school leader's guide to student learning supports: New directions for addressing barriers to learning.* Thousand Oaks, CA: Corwin Press.

beyondblue: The national depression initiative. (2008). *Programs and strategies.* Hawthorn West, VIC, AUS: *beyondblue.* Retrieved from http://www.beyondblue.org.au/index.aspx?link_id=4.36&tmp=FileDownload&fid=1174

Bond, L., Butler, H., Thomas, L., Carlin, J., Glover, S., Bowes, G., & Patton, G. (2007). Social and school connectedness in early secondary school as predictors of late teenage substance use, mental health, and academic outcomes. *Journal of Adolescent Health, 40* (4), 357.e9–357.e18. doi:10.1016/j.jadohealth.2006.10.013

Doll, B., & Cummings, J. A. (2008). *Transforming school mental health services: Population-based approaches to promoting the competency and wellness of children.* Thousand Oaks, CA: Corwin Press (a joint publication with the National Association of School Psychologists).

Greenberg, M. T., Domitrovich, C., & Bumbarger, B. (2000). *Preventing mental disorders in school-age children: A review of the effectiveness of prevention programs.* Washington, DC: U.S. Department of Health and Human Services, Center for Mental Health Services. Retrieved from http://prevention.psu.edu/pubs/documents/MentalDisordersfullreport.pdf

Lewis, C., Schaps, E., & Watson, N. (2003). Building community in school: The Child Development Project. In M. Elias, H. Arnold, & C. Steiger Hussey (Eds.), *EQ + IQ: How to build smart, nonviolent, emotionally intelligent schools* (pp. 100–108). Thousand Oaks, CA: Corwin Press.

Merry, S. N., McDowell, H., Wild, C. J., Bir, J., & Cunliffe, R. (2004). A randomized placebo-control trial of a school-based depression prevention program. *Journal of the American Academy of Child & Adolescent Psychiatry, 43*(5), 538–547. doi:10.1097/00004583-200405000-00007

Munoz, R. F., Beardslee, W. R., & Leykin, Y. (2012). Major depression can be prevented. *American Psychologist, 67*(4), 285–295.

Rivet-Duval, E., Heriot, S., & Hunt, C. (2011). Preventing adolescent depression in Maruitius: A univerisal school-based program. *Child and Adolescent Mental Health, 16*(2), 86–91. doi:10.1111/j.1475-3588.2010.00584.x

Shochet, I. M., Dadds, M. R., Holland, D., Whitefield, J., Harnett, P. H., & Osgarby, S. M. (2001). The efficacy of a universal school-based program to prevent adolescent depression. *Journal of Clinical Child Psychology, 30*(3) 303–315. doi:10.1207/S15374424JCCP3003_3

Spence, S. H. (2008). Integrating individual and whole-school change in the prevention of depression in adolescents. In J. R. Z. Abela & B. L. Hankin (Eds.), *Handbook of depression in children and adolescents* (pp. 333–353). New York, NY: Guilford Press.

Squires, J. (2010). Designing and implementing effective preschool programs: A linked systems approach for social–emotional early learning. In M. R. Shinn & H. M. Walker, *Interventions for achievement and behavior problems in a three-tier model including RTI* (pp. 293–312). Bethesda, MD: National Association of School Psychologists.

Swartz, K. L., Kastelic, E. A., Hess, S. G., Cox, T. S., Gonzales, L. C., Mink, S. P., & DePaulo, J. R., Jr. (2010). The effectiveness of a school-based adolescent depression education program. *Health Education & Behavior, 37*(1), 11–22. doi:10.1177/1090198107303313

CHAPTER 4

EVIDENCE-BASED INTERVENTIONS FOR STUDENTS AT RISK FOR DEPRESSION

Universal approaches (Tier 1 of an RTI framework) to building protective factors and resilience in order to prevent depression will be effective for most students. However, environmental changes, such as stressful life events, can disrupt the functioning of a student and thereby create vulnerability to depression. These events may have an especially negative impact for students who have personal vulnerabilities to depression (e.g., a history of parental depression) or lack protective factors against depression, such as effective social, problem-solving, or coping skills. Targeted interventions (Tier 2) are designed to support these students. While universal prevention efforts for depression largely strengthen protective factors and resilience, at Tier 2 those factors may require remediation in the face of life events or personal vulnerability. Targeted interventions are designed to prevent depression by treating students' individual vulnerabilities (including characteristics that may predict or contribute to depression) or addressing contextual risk factors that affect students (e.g., loss and bereavement or divorce). The evidence-based interventions for students at-risk for depression described in this chapter entail mobilizing school personnel to respond effectively to students facing adverse circumstances that create risk or vulnerability. Meta-analyses have revealed that targeted programs are most effective when offered to at-risk youth, over a relatively brief duration, using homework assignments to facilitate application of skills to everyday life (Stice et al., 2009). Typically, these programs teach cognitive–behavioral strategies in a small-group format that can be readily integrated into the school setting. The Tier 2 interventions described in this chapter should be ongoing and readily available for referred students, and serve varying numbers of students at any given time (McIntosh, Campbell, Carter, & Dickey, 2009). They require little formal assessment and, in many cases, a life event or specific vulnerability will define the need for intervention. The interventions will generally require few additional resources and can be implemented by any of the mental health professionals employed by the school. Ongoing universal prevention programs at Tier 1 should continue to be provided for students who are receiving Tier 2 services.

This chapter will first discuss interventions for individual risk vulnerabilities and then describe interventions for contextual risk factors for depression.

RTI CONNECTIONS

■ Targeted interventions for students at risk for depression are Tier 2 interventions within an RTI framework.

ESSENTIALS

■ Tier 2 interventions for depression either address students' individual vulnerabilities or contextual risks in students' lives.

■ Most targeted interventions at Tier 2 utilize cognitive–behavioral strategies to reduce depressive symptoms or risk of depression.

■ Targeted interventions teach students new ways of thinking, social skills, problem-solving skills, and coping skills.

■ These interventions should require little formal assessment or additional allocation of resources.

INTERVENTIONS FOR INDIVIDUAL RISK VULNERABILITIES

Intervention for individual risk factors or vulnerabilities for depression are largely based on the premise that addressing those vulnerabilities will prevent the onset of depression. Such targeted intervention involves teaching at-risk students new ways of thinking, social and emotional problem-solving skills, and strengthening their repertoire of coping strategies. The goal is to provide them with some protection against the development of depression in the face of these vulnerabilities and the challenges and negative life events that can be encountered throughout the school years.

A variety of programs are available as targeted interventions for use at Tier 2. Examples may be found at the website of the Collaborative for Academic, Social, and Emotional Learning (http://casel.org). In addition, Tier 2 interventions may also be constructed from more intensive applications of relevant aspects of universal prevention programs. The programs described in this section are examples of those available for working with at-risk students in schools. The first two, the Penn Resiliency Program and the Strong Kids/Strong Teens program, have also been shown to be effective as universal prevention programs. The last one, the Adolescent Coping With Stress class, is effective as both a Tier 2 targeted intervention and a Tier 3 intensive intervention.

Examples of Targeted Intervention Programs Addressing Individual Risk Factors

Name	Age/Grade Range	Access
Penn Resiliency Program*	Ages 8–15	http://www.ppc.sas.upenn.edu/prpsum.htm
Strong Kids Series*	Grades preK–12	http://www.brookespublishing.com
Adolescent Coping With Stress Class (ACWS)**	Ages 9–18	http://www.kpchr.org/research/public/acwd/acwd.html
Interpersonal Psychotherapy–Adolescent Skills Training	Ages 12–16	http://www.cebc4cw.org/program/interpersonal-psychotherapy-for-depressed-adolescents

* Also proven effective as a universal (Tier 1) prevention program.

** Also proven effective as an intensive intervention (Tier 3) program for adolescents identified as depressed.

KEYS TO COLLABORATION

A collaborative team can help to develop targeted interventions for students at risk for depressed behavior and can help gain staff support for their implementation.

The Penn Resiliency Program

The Penn Resiliency Program (PRP) has been found to be effective as both a universal and targeted intervention for depression with students ages 8 to 15. It is based on principles of cognitive behavior therapy and the teaching of social problem-solving skills. Students learn the impact of thoughts on emotions and behavior, as well as assertiveness, negotiation skills, decision-making, social problem-solving, and relaxation skills. The PRP consists of 18 to 24 hour-long class sessions or twelve 90-minute sessions. The PRP pedagogical approach involves three steps (Gillham, Brunwasser, & Freres, 2008). First, a conceptual understanding is established for each skill, using skits, role plays, short stories, or cartoons; the goal is to ensure that students grasp the basic concepts. Next, the group works with hypothetical examples that demonstrate how the skill is used in everyday experiences. In the third step, the students apply the skills to their own lives and share examples of when they used or could have used the skill. Weekly homework assignments reinforce the use of the skills. The group leader's manual provides the curriculum, with a detailed outline of each lesson and instructions for each activity. Students are given an illustrated notebook with the activities described and homework assignments for each lesson. Teachers or school mental health professionals most often deliver the program and facilitate the groups.

> *"The Penn Resiliency Program (PRP) has been found to be effective as both a universal and targeted intervention for depression."*

The PRP has been extensively evaluated; a list of research studies supporting its effectiveness is available on the program website. A meta-analysis of outcomes found that students receiving the program had fewer depressive symptoms at the end of the program and at follow-up than control students who did not participate in the program (Brunwasser, Gillham, & Kim, 2009).

Strong Kids Series

The Strong Kids series of programs were developed at the University of Oregon and are designed to teach social and emotional skills, increase coping skills, promote resilience, and engage students in learning through an integration of behavioral, affective, and cognitive approaches. The programs include rather brief learning curricula designed separately for children in preschool (Strong Start Pre-K), grades kindergarten to 2 (Strong Start), 3 to 8 (Strong Kids), and 9 to 12 (Strong Teens). These programs may be presented by teachers or school mental health professionals and used as a universal or targeted program for students at risk for depression. Outcome research for the series is summarized at http://strongkids.uoregon.edu/research.html.

Interpersonal Psychotherapy–Adolescent Skills Training

Interpersonal Psychotherapy—Adolescent Skills Training (IPT-AST; Young & Mufson, 2003) is a program based on interpersonal therapy adapted for school use (ages 12–16). This program teaches communication and social skills to develop and maintain positive relationships. Three areas are emphasized: (a) adjusting to life changes (interpersonal role transitions), (b) conflicting role expectations and relationship conflicts (interpersonal role disputes), and (c) lack of communication and social skills for initiating and maintaining relationships (interpersonal deficits). The first three group sessions focus on teaching skills to address each problem area, sessions four to six focus on applying the skills learned using peer coaching, and the last two sessions involve establishing competence for dealing with problems independently.

Horowitz and colleagues compared this intervention and the Coping with Stress Course to a control group that attended health class and received the usual wellness curriculum (Horowitz, Garber, Ciesla, Young, & Mufson, 2007). Students in the intervention groups had significantly lower levels of depressive symptoms than the control group. Furthermore, the differences in the intervention and control groups were greatest for adolescents with high levels of depressive symptoms in the beginning of the study. The 8-week intervention effects were not sustained over time.

Adolescent Coping With Stress Class

The Adolescent Coping with Stress Class (ACWS) is a psychoeducational, cognitive–behavioral approach to intervention designed for adolescents (ages 9–18) at risk for depression but not currently depressed. It is based on the Coping with Depression Course, a treatment for depression developed in the late 1970s that has had robust clinical effects across intervention studies (Stice et al., 2009; Cuijpers, Muñoz, Clarke, & Lewinsohn, 2009). The program is based on the premise that teaching students new coping skills and strengthening their repertoire of coping strategies provides them with some protection against the development of depression even if they have vulnerabilities or experience negative life events.

The ACWS is designed to be offered in the classroom setting during regular school hours, as an adjunct to health class, or as an after-school workshop or group. The program consists of 15 1-hour sessions that can be offered at the pace of two to four sessions a week. The sessions are highly structured and closely follow a specified agenda. The school mental health professional who conducts the intervention functions as an instructor or teacher. These attributes make the CWS program less stigmatizing than other interventions.

"The ACWS is designed to be offered in the classroom setting during regular school hours, as an adjunct to health class, or as an after-school workshop or group. "

An important feature of the CWS is the concept of a toolbox of various skills that help students cope with stress (and thereby prevent depression). These skills include social competence, restructuring negative cognitions, and behavioral activation to increase pleasant events (activity scheduling). The training in cognitive skills includes increasing thoughts associated with positive mood and decreasing thoughts associated with negative mood. The Activating events–Beliefs–Consequences (ABC) model is used to show how beliefs about events affect emotions and behavior. Like in the Penn Resiliency Program, students learn to assess the accuracy of their thoughts and to challenge negative beliefs by considering alternative interpretations. The program concludes with students developing a plan (including specific coping and problem-solving strategies) for addressing problem areas as well as potential stressors that may occur.

The manual for the course is very complete and includes modifiable texts for the brief lectures, lists of required materials, and descriptions of activities. There is a great deal of structure to this program, but leaders are encouraged to modify the content and presentation as needed. Each student is given a workbook to use with each session. The manual and workbook can be downloaded from the website of the Kaiser Permanente Center for Health Research, free of charge.

INTERVENTIONS ADDRESSING CONTEXTUAL RISK FACTORS

Although the focus of Tier 2 targeted interventions is on the prevention of depression in children and adolescents with depressive symptoms or a family history of depression, general principles of these programs have been applied to the prevention of depression and other negative outcomes in students who face difficult life events such as parental death and divorce. The experience of divorce or the death of a loved one is rather common, and both experiences place children and adolescents at risk for adjustment difficulties. There are also crises or tragedies that bring grief and distress to large numbers of students and staff, such as natural disaster, an act of school violence, or the death of a student or staff member. Whether these adversities occur on a large or small scale, school personnel need to be alert to the potential for depression and the need for intervention.

Examples of Targeted Intervention Programs Addressing Contextual Risk Factors

Name	*Age Range*	*Access*
New Beginnings Program	Ages 3–17	http://www.nrepp.samhsa.gov/ViewIntervention
Children of Divorce Intervention Program (CODIP)	Ages 5–13	http://www.childrensinstitute.net/programs/codip
Cognitive–Behavioral Intervention for Trauma in Schools (CBITS)	Ages 9–18	http://www.soprislearning.com

Divorce

The high rate of divorce has led to the experience being considered common (Gladstone, Beardlslee, & O'Conner, 2011), yet the process of divorce is thought to be one of life's most stressful changes (Pedro-Carroll, 2005). The immediate family reorganization can include changes in residence, standard of living, and relationships within the family, extended family, and family friends. The family reorganization carries implications that are manifested in loss of time with parents and other family members, changes in family routines and traditions, loss of time with supportive family friends and, too often, ongoing conflict.

These changes in family patterns and dynamics have considerable impact on the school-age child and adolescent. Initial feelings of sadness and vulnerability are thought to underlie subsequent depression, anxiety, and interpersonal difficulties (Hoyt, Cowen, Pedro-Carroll, & Alpert-Gillis, 1990; Pedro-Carroll, 2005). Children of divorce are more likely to have mental health problems, lower academic achievement, and higher rates of drug use than children from non-divorced families (Wolchik et al., 2002), and the negative impact of divorce may persist into adulthood (Wolchik et al., 2002; Pedro-Carroll, 2005).

In spite of the recognition of the problems divorce presents for children and the benefit of programs to address these problems, few programs have been systematically evaluated, even if widely disseminated. Fortunately, the few prevention programs for children of divorce that have been evaluated extensively are effective for reducing mental health problems, including depression, in the short and long terms. These program evaluations provide an evidence base for practice. Two such programs are described for use in the school setting: The New Beginnings Program and the Children of Divorce Intervention Program.

The New Beginnings Program

The New Beginnings Program (Wolchik et al., 2002) is designed for divorced parents of children between 3 and 17 years old. The groups are co-led by master's-level clinicians using social learning and cognitive behavioral principles to promote resilience of children following parental divorce. During 10 weekly group sessions and two structured individual sessions designed to tailor activities to individual needs, the parents learn skills to improve parent–child relationship quality, improve effectiveness of discipline, reduce exposure to conflict between parents, and increase access between the non-residential parent and child. Each session includes a short lecture, skill demonstration and practice, and discussion about challenges with the homework assignments.

A detailed training program leads to a 2-year certification; support and supervision is provided during its implementation. These requirements may limit utility for implementation in schools, although through a partnership with the court, the program has been effectively implemented in the community (Wolchik et al., 2009). School mental health professionals are well suited to be trained to implement this program in the school setting. Costs and contact information can be found at the SAMHSA National Registry of Evidence-Based Prevention Programs website.

The Children of Divorce Intervention Program

The Children of Divorce Intervention Program (CODIP) is a specifically school-based intervention program for 5- to 13-year-old students. Like the New Beginnings Program, this program focuses on building resilience by strengthening protective factors in elementary and middle school students after divorce. Trained group leaders conduct the CODIP groups in the school or after school, over 12 to 15 sessions. Training and technical assistance are available. Four procedure manuals and specially designed board games target different age ranges or grade levels to ensure that each child receives age-appropriate information and skill-building activities. Books, manuals, games, and information about training are available through the website.

The program depends on a small-group format that creates a supportive environment for students in order to facilitate the following goals: free sharing of experiences, establishing common bonds, clarifying misconceptions, and acquisition of the skills for coping with the stressful changes imposed by divorce. The key components of the program are group support plus coping skill enhancement. Research evidence has been translated into the program objectives (Pedro-Carroll, 2005). These are:

1. *Foster a supportive group environment.* An atmosphere must be created where children can share their experiences and their fears that they are in some way responsible for their parents' divorce. Comfort and relief can come from hearing one's peers having similar experiences and feelings, and the group reduces feelings of isolation. Confidentiality is a major factor in creating a supportive group.

2. *Help identify and express feelings appropriately.* Games and activities are designed to help students identify, express, and manage a range of feelings. The curriculum is sequenced so that the focus is first on feelings in general—the universal nature of feelings, the range, and the acceptability of all feelings. Once this is understood, the focus shifts to divorce-related issues.

3. *Increase an accurate understanding of family changes and clarify divorce-related misconceptions.* Various games and activities, including role-play, are used to help students make appropriate attributions for the divorce to external realities, rather than internalizing responsibility for the divorce. Several sessions are devoted to reducing fears of abandonment as well as fantasies about responsibility for restoring their parents' marriage.

4. *Enhance coping skills and realistic perceptions of control.* Across several sessions, students are taught social problem solving, interpersonal skills, and anger management. Again, developmentally appropriate games and activities are used to help them learn the skills and apply them to everyday life. Central to this component is the differentiation between problems they can

and cannot control, a distinction that helps them master the task of disengaging from conflict and redirecting energy to age-appropriate pursuits.

5. *Enhance positive perceptions of self and family.* The final unit involves self-esteem building exercises designed to highlight students' positive qualities through feedback and support from the group participants and leaders. Consideration of positive changes in the family as a result of the divorce and family strengths in the face of divorce is facilitated. Students are assisted in identifying those to whom they can go for support once the group is ended. Booster sessions may also be provided.

The program recommends that the leaders should be mental health professionals. It is also recommended that there be two leaders for every CODIP group, preferably one female and one male. This leadership pairing makes it possible for students to observe a cooperative adult relationship as well as a positive same-sex role model.

This program has acquired a substantial evidence base since its inception in 1982 (see Pedro-Carroll, 2005 for a review). Six controlled studies have been conducted, as well as a 2-year follow-up that documented lasting benefits to children of divorce (Pedro-Carroll, Sutton, & Wyman, 1999). Evaluations of subsequent adaptations of the program model for urban and suburban school settings, low-income students, and grade levels from kindergarten to eighth grade substantiated the program's effectiveness. Tests of key components revealed that providing support without the teaching of coping skills was less effective than the full program with the coping skills component. The study and evaluation results have consistently demonstrated that the CODIP provides skills and benefits that enhance children's resilience and healthy adjustment over time and thereby prevents depression. In 2005, the U.S. Department of Health and Human Services Substance Abuse and Mental Health Services Administration (SAMHSA) acknowledged the success of the CODIP with a national Program Excellence Award. The program was also awarded the National Mental Health Association's Lela Rowland Award for outstanding prevention programs.

"This program has acquired a substantial evidence base since its inception in 1982."

Grief and Bereavement

Grief and bereavement during childhood is thought to constitute a risk factor for concurrent and chronic distress and has a later association with depression in adulthood (Currier, Holland, & Neimeyer, 2007). The role of school mental health personnel is to be alert to the needs of children and adolescents who experience a loss through death, and to work with teachers and classmates to facilitate the creation of a safe environment for the student to think about and work through their loss.

A Death in the Family

Typically, schools will be informed when a student's family member (particularly a parent) has died. Once the school is informed, a home visit to the family can help assess the circumstances of the death, the student's needs, and how to address them as the student returns to school. If a student's parent or sibling has had a terminal illness, such as cancer, there are psychosocial interventions or support groups available through social services or the hospice care organization. It is crucial to ascertain whether such resources have been offered to the family, to determine any challenges or barriers to the student participating in an intervention, and to explore potential solutions to those barriers.

A meta-analysis of bereavement interventions with children revealed that they respond more favorably to grief therapy the closer the intervention follows the time of the death (Currier et al., 2007). This makes sense in that the usual format of bereavement intervention includes education about loss and the expression of grief-related feelings (these strategies are more effective when delivered before the student and the family have accommodated to the loss, especially if the accommodation is less than optimal). If parents decide against having their child participate in bereavement intervention, they can be reassured there is evidence that only a minority of children will have lasting grief complications (Currier et al., 2007; Horowitz & Garber, 2006) and those tend to be children whose loss is attended by traumatic circumstances.

ESSENTIALS

- Assess the circumstances of the death, the student's needs, and how to address them in school.

- Most students can be guided through the grief process.

- School staff should provide a nurturing environment for the student.

- Classmates and friends need to be informed in a direct and supportive way.

- Additional services may be provided to students as needed.

Given that most children and adolescents can be facilitated through the bereavement process, the primary task is to create a safe school environment for grieving. Depending on the discussion with the family, information should be shared personally and directly with the student's teacher and, in turn, the teacher or school mental health professional can inform the student's classmates and other close friends. The information should be factual and brief, yet sensitively delivered. It can be helpful to acknowledge your own feelings about the loss or a similar loss, and/or your feelings of sadness for the student. It is helpful to allow students to express their feelings and reactions, even if harsh (e.g., anger, fear, relief it did not happen to them), and to validate those feelings. This can be an opportunity to provide developmentally appropriate education about the feelings that go with grieving, such as irritability or anger, sadness, guilt or self-blame, or denial. Prepare the teacher and students to welcome the student back to school and to acknowledge the loss. Teachers and students can be encouraged to invite the student to talk about it when they feel ready. A key role for the classroom teacher at this time is to provide a nurturing environment (Balk, Zaengle, & Corr, 2011). An excellent handout that summarizes these ideas was developed by the Center for Mental Health in Schools at UCLA to help school staff members respond to those experiencing grief and loss. A copy of the handout can be located at http://smhp.psych.ucla.edu/pdfdocs/practicenotes/grief.pdf.

During this period, it is important for school mental health professionals to discuss the student's usual level of functioning in terms of affect, academic performance, and social interaction with teachers, and alert school staff members to any potential signs and symptoms of traumatic or complicated grieving. In this way, staff members can be consulted regularly regarding their observations of the student's emotional responses, especially as manifested in mood, academics, and social relations. One role of the teacher is to help facilitate referrals to school mental health professionals if the student does manifest symptoms that require more intense intervention (Balk et al., 2011).

Developmental Issues of Grief and Bereavement

Most students will experience at least one important loss before they complete adolescence. It is important, therefore, to be alert to the vulnerability that loss creates for students, no matter when it occurs. Toddlers have no real cognitive understanding of death, and typically experience a sense of loss and abandonment if the loss is a parent and means a disruption in caretaking. Preschoolers to students 6 years of age tend to perceive death as a personification or as a punishment. From 6 to 11 years of age, students will grasp the irreversibility and finality of death, yet struggle with accepting and understanding the loss of the specific parent or other loved one. In comparison, preadolescents and adolescents are able to be more abstract and often have developed a philosophy about death. The point is that children can only resolve a loss at their own developmental level at the time when the death occurs. This means that bereavement resurfaces and the loss will likely need to be addressed at every subsequent developmental stage.

"It is important to be alert to the vulnerability that loss creates for students, no matter when it occurs."

Grief is a process that will unfold over time for children. Children may seem emotionally unmoved but this should serve as a point of concern. In a typical reaction to loss, children and adolescents will report sadness, crying, lack of appetite, trouble sleeping, guilt, and a sense of responsibility for the death. Nervousness may be expressed as fears of dying, disease, and growing old. Students may be irritable with their peers, which can add to a sense of alienation and inferiority. Idealization of and identification with a parent are common reactions to their death, and anger is usually directed at the surviving parent and other members of the family. This may actually be helpful to the mourning process but does need to be assessed to determine if development is inhibited. Adolescents can seem to suddenly mature, but numbness and regrets more often than not accompany this maturity.

School Crisis

Tragic events impact school communities. These events range from bus accidents to school shootings to natural disasters that may result in student and/or teacher deaths. Deaths during adolescence typically occur because of accidents and interpersonal or self-inflicted violence (Balk et al., 2011). Highly publicized events have resulted in nearly 95% of schools in the United States having a crisis plan in place to guide emergency response (Openshaw, 2011). School communities rely on well-trained crisis teams comprising school mental health professionals, administrative and teaching staff, and outside professionals as needed (James, Logan, & Davis, 2011).

The primary goals in school-based trauma and grief work are to help students to feel safe; to remain engaged with supportive peers, school staff, and family; and to cope with the resulting thoughts, feelings, and behavior. It is unrealistic to screen an entire student body for risk factors associated with complicated bereavement or depression. Hence, the initial emphasis is on general education about trauma, loss, and bereavement. Then support groups can be made available for students who chose to participate and individual grief counseling can be provided for students that self-identify or who are referred by teachers or parents for more intensive help.

Cognitive–Behavioral Intervention for Trauma in Schools

Early intervention for depression and anxiety related to trauma is typically provided by school mental health professionals in a small-group format. In addition, structured therapeutic activities can also be provided by teachers and school mental health professionals within the classroom. Teaching basic relaxation techniques can also be helpful to students (Openshaw, 2011). These efforts are directed at providing initial support for students exposed to trauma.

A more comprehensive approach to helping students cope with trauma is the Cognitive–Behavioral Intervention for Trauma in Schools (CBITS) program sponsored by the National Institute of Mental Health and endorsed by the National Child Traumatic Stress Network. It is highlighted here because it has specifically targeted the symptoms of posttraumatic stress disorder (PTSD) and depression for prevention and early intervention.

The CBITS program is a group intervention for students ages 9 to 18 years, and most commonly implemented in grades six through nine. Trauma exposures for participants have ranged from witnessing or experiencing violence, accidents, natural or manmade disasters, and physical abuse or injury. The program involves ten 1-hour sessions in small groups of 5 to 8 students, conducted weekly in the school. The group sessions allow students to process the traumatic memories and express their grief. In addition, six cognitive–behavioral areas are addressed:

- Education about common reactions to traumatic events

- Relaxation training to reduce anxiety

- Cognitive therapy (understand link between thoughts and feelings; challenge negative thoughts)

- Development of avoidance and coping strategies

- Processing of stress or trauma memories through use of drawing, writing, or imagination exercises

- Social problem-solving

Each new set of skills is taught using age-appropriate examples, exercises, and games. The extension of the newly learned skills to everyday problems is facilitated by homework assignments that are collaboratively developed between the student and the group leader. One to three individual sessions with each student allow for some individualization of strategies, especially homework. In addition to the small group intervention, the CBITS also provides a teacher-education session to help teachers assist students to apply, in the classroom and other school settings, the skills learned in the program. Similarly, two parent education sessions are conducted to help parents also understand the reactions to trauma and to reinforce their student's relaxation, cognitive, and social problem-solving skills.

Staff members who implement the program are required to attend a 2-day training session and, if they are not skilled in cognitive–be-havioral therapy, it is recommended that they receive ongoing supervision from a local clinician with expertise. The manual includes age appropriate lessons, examples, worksheets, and activities.

Two sizable studies have been conducted with the CBITS program (Kataoka et al., 2003; Stein et al., 2003), one with English-speaking students and one with Spanish-speaking immigrant students. Both studies found that, compared to waitlist controls, those who participated in the CBITS groups had decreased depressive symptoms and those with clinical depressive symptoms at baseline had a significant decrease in depression level. PTSD symptoms were also significantly reduced in both studies.

Death of a Student or Staff Member

Much of what has been described above certainly applies to the death of a student, staff member, or other member of the school community. Well-trained crisis teams composed of school mental health professionals, teachers, and administrators are crucial to helping school communities respond to the death of a student or staff member. Initially, a designated school mental health professional will want to reach out to the family of the deceased student or teacher not only to offer condolences but to learn what information can be shared with the school community, particularly the student's classmates and friends or the teacher's students (Balk et al., 2011). A prepared statement, developed and reviewed by the school mental health professional with the family, may be a useful way for teachers to disseminate information to classrooms. At the same time, formal rituals for the participation of the school community that the family would prefer can be identified. Options include a funeral, memorial service, flowers, school-based memorial site, or donations in the name of the deceased.

School mental health professionals should schedule staff meetings with teachers, administrators, and other school personnel in order to keep them informed and to process their feelings (Balk et al., 2011). In addition, teachers should be taught to observe the signs and symptoms of prolonged and complicated grieving, and to examine these in relation to students' typical level of functioning. Changes in academic performance, social interaction, or affect may signal potential difficulty with grief. Guidance regarding how to discuss the death of the student or staff member is important and should be educational in focus (Balk et al., 2011). Information should be provided, common reactions identified, and strategies for coping shared. Classroom discussion should make students aware of personal strengths and coping skills and leave them feeling they are not alone. Developmentally appropriate ways of sharing memories about the student or staff member can be used to facilitate bereavement, through writing or art. Information about grief and coping with loss can be distributed to parents and adolescents. Sources for such information are to be found in the Resources section of this chapter.

A safe space in designated health offices, school counseling rooms, a counseling or guidance office, or other spaces in the school can be made available for support to students during the school day. This safe place can be open all hours of the school day, and should be staffed by school mental health professionals. If needed, grief counseling sessions can be provided for students who self-identify or are referred by teachers as needing more support.

In the weeks and months that follow a death, a more traditional bereavement group can be offered to students. These are usually organized to bring together individuals coping with similar themes or having similar responses to the death (Openshaw, 2011). Although initially the focus may be on processing feelings about the death, the focus must address the underlying blame and anger, increase understanding of the loss, and ultimately foster acceptance of the death and loss (Balk et al., 2011).

ACTION PLAN

- Build capacity through staff training and professional development.

- Compile a library of resources to provide for students, parents, and teachers basic information when needed.

- Make sure a crisis team is operating in the school and that it is prepared to respond to crisis events.

- Screen students for individual factors that make students at risk for depression.

- Assess contextual factors within the school that may increase student risk for depression.

- Use a collaborative team to decide which risk actors to focus on and choose an evidence-based program that addresses these factors in a way that is feasible for your school.

- Integrate these Tier 2 targeted interventions into a comprehensive program for the delivery of mental health services. If possible, embed them into an existing RTI framework.

- Collect outcome data for the program.

RESOURCES

The National Association of School Psychologists provides a number of free handouts on divorce, crisis, coping with death, and many other topics for parents and educators at its website (www.nasponline.org/resources).

Other resources related to crisis, trauma, and grief include the websites of the Substance Abuse and Mental Health Services Association and UCLA (http://smhp.psych.ucla.edu/pdfdocs) and the National Child Traumatic Stress Network (NCTSN; http://www/nctsnet.org/nccts). The NCTSN website offers the *Child Trauma Toolkit for Educators*, which provides a list of symptoms by age group that may be observed in the classroom, classroom strategies for helping students cope with crisis, and a list of symptoms that suggest a student should be referred to school mental health professionals. The booklet additionally addresses self-care for school personnel working with students who have experienced trauma. (http://www.nctsnet.org/nctsn_assets/pdfs/Child_Trauma_Toolkit_Final.pdf).

REFERENCES

Balk, D. E., Zaengle, D., & Corr, C. A. (2011). Strengthening grief support for adolescents coping with a peer's death. *School Psychology International, 32,* 144–162.

Brunwasser, S. M., Gillham, J. E., & Kim, E. S. (2009). A meta-analytic review of the Penn Resiliency Program's effect on depressive symptoms. *Journal of Consulting and Clinical Psychology, 77*(6), 1042–1054.

Cuijpers, P., Muñoz, R. F., Clarke, G. N., & Lewinsohn, P. M. (2009). Psychoeducational treatment and prevention of depression: The "Coping with Depression" course thirty years later. *Clinical Psychology Review, 29,* 449–458.

Currier, J. M., Holland, J. M., & Neimeyer, R. A. (2007). The effectiveness of bereavement interventions with children: A meta-analytic review of controlled outcome research. *Journal of Child and Adolescent Psychology, 36,* 253–259.

Gillham, J. E., Brunwasser, S .M., & Freres, D. R. (2008). Preventing depression in early adolescence: The Penn Resiliency Program. In J. R. Z. Abela & B. L. Hankin (Eds.), *Handbook of depression in children and adolescents* (pp. 309–332). New York, NY: Guilford.

Gladstone, T. R.G., Beardslee, W. R., & O'Connor, E. E. (2011). The prevention of adolescent depression. *Psychiatric Clinics of North America, 34,* 35–52.

Horowitz, J. L. & Garber, J. (2006). The prevention of depressive symptoms in children and adolescents: A meta-analytic review. *Journal of Consulting and Clinical Psychology, 74,* 401–415.

Horowitz, J. L. & Garber, J., Ciesla, J. A., Young, J. F., & Mufson, L. (2007). Prevention of depressive symptoms in adolescents: A randomized trial of cognitive–behavioral and interpersonal prevention programs. *Journal of Consulting and Clinical Psychology, 75*(5), 693–706.

Hoyt, L. A., Cowen, E.L., Pedro-Carroll, J. L., & Alpert-Gillis, L. J. (1990). Anxiety and depression in young children of divorce. *Journal of Clinical Child Psychology, 19,* 26–32.

James, R. K., Logan, J., & Davis, S. A. (2011). Including school resource officers in school-based crisis intervention: Strengthening student support. *School Psychology International, 32,* 210–224.

Kataoka, S. H., Bradley, D. S., Jaycox, L. H., Wong, M., Escudero, P., Tu, W., … Fink, A. (2003). A school-based mental health program for traumatized Latino immigrant children. *Journal of the American Academy of Child and Adolescent Psychiatry, 42,* 311–318.

McIntosh, K., Campbell, A. L., Carter, D. R., & Dickey, C.R. (2009). Differential effects of a tier two behavior intervention based on function of problem behavior. *Journal of Positive Behavior Interventions, 11,* 82–93.

Openshaw, L. L. (2011). School-based support groups for traumatized students. *School Psychology International, 32,* 163–178.

Pedro-Carroll, J. L. (2005). Fostering resilience in the aftermath of divorce: The role of evidence-based programs for children. *Family Court Review, 43,* 52–64.

Pedro-Carroll, J. L., Sutton, S. E., & Wyman, P. A. (1999). A two-year follow-up evaluation of a preventive intervention for young children of divorce. *School Psychology Review, 28,* 467–476.

Stein, B. D., Jaycox, L. H., Kataoka, S. H., Wong, M., Tu, W., Elliott, M. N., & Fink, A. (2003). A mental health intervention for schoolchildren exposed to violence: A randomized controlled trial. *Journal of the American Medical Association, 290,* 603–611.

Stice, E., Shaw, H., Bohon, C., Marti, D. N., & Rohde, P. (2009). A meta-analytic review of depression prevention programs for children and adolescents: Factors that predict magnitude of intervention effects. *Journal of Consulting and Clinical Psychology, 77,* 486–503.

Wolchik, S. A., Sandler, I. N., Millsap, R. E. Plummer, B. A., Greene, S. M., Anderson, E. R., … Haine, R. A. (2002). Six-year follow-up of preventive interventions for children of divorce. *Journal of the American Medical Association, 288,* 1874–1881.

Wolchik, S. A., Sandler, I. N., Jones, S., Gonzales, N., Doyle, K., Winslow, E., … Braver, S. L. (2009). The New Beginnings program for divorcing and separating families: Moving from efficacy to effectiveness. *Family Court Review, 47*(3), 416–435.

Young, J. F., & Mufson, L. (2003). *Manual for Interpersonal Psychotherapy–Adolescent Skills Training (IPT–AST).* New York, NY: Columbia University.

CHAPTER 5

INTENSIVE INTERVENTIONS FOR STUDENTS WITH DEPRESSION

Intensive interventions for depression (those at Tier 3 of an RTI framework) are provided to students who are (a) at very high risk of developing depression or already diagnosed with a depressive disorder and (b) not responding adequately to less intensive (i.e., Tier 1 universal and Tier 2 targeted) interventions. Although the percentage of students who do not respond to universal or targeted social, emotional, and behavioral interventions is relatively small, the services they require are more specialized and must be delivered more frequently. School mental health professionals provide specialized assessments and interventions, case management, and collaboration with community providers at this level of service.

INTERVENTIONS FOR ADOLESCENT DEPRESSION

School-based interventions typically are similar to targeted interventions but are specifically designed for students with depression, and include psychotherapeutic approaches. Integrated into these more intensive efforts are strategies designed to enhance protective factors and build skills that are important components of therapeutic intervention. Examples of approaches that are considered evidence-based are cognitive–behavior therapy, the Adolescent Coping with Depression Course, and interpersonal psychotherapy for depressed adolescents (IPT-A).

RTI CONNECTIONS

- Intensive interventions for students diagnosed with or at high risk for depression are Tier 3 interventions within an RTI framework.

- Services at this level may include more intensive variations of Tier 2 interventions or are specifically designed for students with depression.

- Tier 3 services are individualized for each student and include the most comprehensive and specialized services available in the school–community system.

ESSENTIALS

- Cognitive–behavior therapy (CBT) has yielded the strongest and longest-lasting effects on student depression.

- A minimum of 10 hours of CBT is required to effectively reduce depression.

Cognitive–Behavior Therapy

Among school-based interventions for depression, cognitive–behavior therapy (CBT) is the most researched and has yielded the strongest effects and longest lasting benefits (Hilt-Panahon, Kern, Divatia, & Gresham, 2007). The most frequently implemented components within the CBT approach include several techniques. *Cognitive restructuring* involves teaching students to challenge distorted and negative cognitions about themselves and their environment, and to replace these with more realistic ones. *Problem-solving* training involves teaching students to evaluate situations or problems by gathering relevant information, considering alternative responses or options, and choosing the best response. *Pleasant activity scheduling* is the systematic planning of a student's daily activities to include pleasant and desirable events. *Anxiety management/relaxation training* is not as well researched, but the effects point to this intervention as a promising one (Hilt-Panahon et al., 2007). In addition to these strategies, *social skills training* has added benefit for adolescents (Kennard et al., 2009), likely due to the social problem-solving deficits that often accompany adolescent depression (Becker-Weidman, Jacobs, Reinecke, Silva, & March, 2010).

Generally, the more sessions provided, the better the response to CBT. In school-based intervention studies, an average of 10 hours of intervention was required to produce a beneficial result in reducing depression (Hilt-Panahon et al., 2007). Kennard and colleagues (2009) found that 10 or more CBT sessions more than doubled the likelihood of an adequate response to treatment with an antidepressant (selective serotonin reuptake inhibitor or SSRI), and treatment effects of CBT alone have been found to be sustained over a 9-month period (March, Silva, Vitiello, & The TADS Team, 2006; Rohde et al., 2008). Thus, 10 hours of cognitive-behavioral

intervention would appear to be the minimum required to have a meaningful impact on student depression. Moreover, schools must consider making intervention available throughout the school year. School-based CBT and anxiety management training delivered in a group format (which minimizes the time and resources required) was also found to be effective in reducing student depression (Hilt-Panahon et al., 2007).

Adolescent Coping With Depression Course

The Adolescent Coping with Depression Course (ACWC) is a cost-effective, nonstigmatizing, psychoeducational intervention for depression that can be delivered in schools (Clarke, Lewinsohn, & Hops, 1990). It is a cognitive-behavioral treatment program that addresses social skills as well. It is conducted with groups of four to eight students, age 14 to 18 years; the program can also be used with 12- and 13-year-olds but must be adapted to be developmentally appropriate. The program is taught as a class in 16 2-hour sessions conducted over an 8-week period. School mental health providers serve as the group leaders and teach adolescent students skills for managing depression. Parents may also participate in the program in a separate course that consists of nine 2-hour sessions held weekly. In the parent sessions, an overview of the skills and techniques being taught to the adolescents is provided in an effort to promote acceptance and reinforcement of positive changes. School mental health professionals could modify the program to reduce the time commitment required and still expect to see some positive outcome for students, although it is uncertain to what extent modifying the course could reduce its effectiveness (Merrell, 2008).

"The Adolescent Coping with Depression Course (ACWC) is a cost-effective, nonstigmatizing, psychoeducational intervention for depression that can be delivered in schools."

Materials for implementing the course include the *Leader's Manual*, with over 300 pages that detail the intervention, and a *Student Workbook* that is closely integrated with the course discussions and activities. The workbook consists of brief readings, structured learning tasks, forms for self-monitoring, homework assignments, and quizzes. Detailed guidelines for conducting the parent groups are available in a manual, and a workbook for parents supports their learning. All materials are free and may be downloaded at http://www.kpchr.org.

Group leaders are expected to have a certain amount of relevant experience and training, and a broad range of mental health professionals are considered to have the necessary skills. In the school setting, the list includes psychologists, psychiatric social workers, psychiatric-mental health nurse practitioners, and counselors. Teachers (or school nurses) who do not have training in counseling should be involved under the supervision of a school mental health professional with that back-

ground. The *Leader's Manual* provides detail and scripted lessons, and the *Student Workbook* is explicit and integrated with the lesson plans in the *Leader's Manual*. However, hands-on familiarity with the manual and practice is highly recommended in order to complete the lectures, tasks, and exercises in the time allowed. It can be difficult, especially for new leaders, to deliver the content and simultaneously track the clinical and process issues, so it may be advisable to have a co-leader. This can be an effective way to train an additional leader and work with a teacher or school nurse.

The first course session entails a review of guidelines for the course, the underlying rationale, and the social learning view of depression. The remaining sessions focus on teaching specific skills:

- The relaxation sessions teach progressive relaxation and, later in the course, teach a technique that involves repeating a word or phrase to induce relaxation; these skills facilitate the management of stressful social situations and anxiety reduction.

- Sessions that focus on increasing pleasant activities use the Pleasant Activities Schedule to enhance positive and reduce negative experiences and to teach basic self-change skills by monitoring behaviors to change, setting realistic goals, and developing a plan and contract for making changes in student behavior.

- Cognitive therapy sessions teach students to identify and challenge the negative and irrational thoughts associated with depression, and to use positive thoughts to counter the irrational negative beliefs through a series of progressively advanced exercises.

- Social skills lessons teach techniques such as active listening, planning social activities, and strategies for making friends; these are taught in a range of sessions to ensure they are integrated with other techniques and skills.

- Basic communication, negotiation, and conflict resolution skills are taught in several sessions. Communication training involves feedback, modeling, and behavior rehearsal and addresses both verbal and nonverbal behaviors. Problem-solving instruction teaches a four-step model in which students learn to define the problem, identify alternatives, decide on a mutually satisfactory solution through structured negotiation, and specify implementation details.

- Setting life goals and integrating skills learned to maintain gains and prevent relapse constitute the last two sessions.

Students monitor their feelings and mood throughout the program. Booster sessions, individual or group, can be made available for when students begin to observe a more sustained negative drop in mood. Homework assignments are designed to help students manage their depressed moods and are often related to real-life situations that are bothering them. In addition, they are designed to

be brief and readily integrated into everyday routines. Strategies for dealing with absences and other issues are included in the manual.

Interpersonal Psychotherapy for Depressed Adolescents

Interpersonal psychotherapy for depressed adolescents (IPT-A) is a program designed for adolescents 12 to 18 years of age with mild to moderate depression. IPT is a short-term therapy consisting of 12 35- to 50-minute sessions delivered weekly (if necessary, the sessions can be extended over 16 weeks). Unlike the ACWC, IPT-A is designed for individuals, perhaps making it especially advisable for students who are more introverted and less comfortable in group settings. The program was not designed nor has it been tested for a group format. Parent involvement is not required but is encouraged, especially if there is family or parent–child conflict.

The program is manual-driven but is distinguished from the Adolescent Coping with Depression Course in a couple of ways that make it a very good fit for some adolescents. It takes the perspective that biological and personality factors contribute to vulnerability to depression. However, the onset of depression is linked to conflicts and problems in interpersonal relationships; therefore, addressing interpersonal interactions is the thrust of the program (Mufson, 2010). The program focuses on four problem areas: grief, role disputes, role transitions, and interpersonal deficits. The student identifies the problem area that is currently associated with his or her depressive symptoms and this becomes the focus of treatment.

There are three phases of treatment. In the initial phase, a problem area is identified and the student is provided information about depression and the effects of interpersonal events and situations on their mood and other symptoms. In the middle phase, the student actively works on the problem area. Student work at this stage includes clarification, expression of feelings and emotions, and learning communication and problem-solving skills. Learning these new skills involves role-playing during the session, and students are given interpersonal assignments to test out and practice new skills and strategies between sessions. The termination phase includes a review of interpersonal and generalization strategies for future situations. In addition, the warning symptoms of depression are reviewed and strategies identified to prevent relapse. The need for future treatment is assessed and feelings about ending the treatment are processed as well.

IPT-A has a parent component. This component also provides education about depression, communication and interpersonal skills, and problem solving. Parents are encouraged to practice these skills with their adolescent. If the student's interpersonal problem involves a parent or both parents, joint sessions with the student and parent(s) are advised in order to implement the interpersonal skills with the facilitation of the therapist.

Research has revealed IPT-A to be an efficacious and acceptable treatment for moderate depression (see Mufson, 2010 for review). Significant decreases in depressive symptoms and significant increases in social functioning in both Caucasian and Hispanic youth, in-

cluding those from a low-income background, have been demonstrated. These benefits have been found to be sustained up to a year after the intervention. Notable about this treatment program is that it can be learned and delivered with reasonable adherence and competence by community clinicians with effective results in school-based health clinics (Gunlicks-Stoessel, Mufson, Jekal, & Turner, 2010; Mufson, 2010).

"Research has revealed IPT-A to be an efficacious and acceptable treatment for moderate depression."

Low income has predicted a poorer response to CBT, so IPT-A is an alternative treatment that should be considered in that situation. A better outcome with IPT-A has also been predicted by a higher level of parent–child conflict, whereas those with family conflict have had limited benefit from CBT (Mufson, 2010). This outcome is not surprising given the focus of IPT-A on improving interpersonal interactions. Furthermore, social and global functioning are improved with IPT-A (Mufson, 2010; Gunlicks-Stoessel et al., 2010).

The program materials include an IPT-A treatment manual that can be purchased from the developer (Laura Mufson, PhD; lhm3@columbia.edu). This intervention typically requires the therapist to have a master's or doctoral degree in clinical or counseling psychology, social work, or psychiatric-mental health nursing. In addition, implementation training (1- or 2-day training) at the school is required. Therapist certification and subsequent supervision are also required, and the fees can amount to several thousand dollars, presenting a barrier to widespread adoption of this program in schools.

INTERVENTIONS FOR CHILDHOOD DEPRESSION

Because the rate of depression in younger children is low, less is known about intensive treatments and their efficacy in this population. However, given the adverse psychosocial and educational impacts of depression on young students, school mental health providers must provide intervention (Stark, Arora, & Funk, 2011) despite inconsistent guidance from research about what best practices might be for this group.

Both CBT and interpersonal psychotherapy can be adapted for elementary school students. Attention must be paid to the developmental challenges with which school mental health providers in elementary schools are familiar. Young children are more concrete and have fewer meta-cognition skills than middle school or high school students. They are generally less verbally articulate about feelings and are not as readily engaged in a discussion of thoughts. With this developmental context in mind, adaptation of the basic elements of CBT and interpersonal psychotherapy can be made according to the student's developmental level, attention span, verbal skills, and reading abilities.

ESSENTIALS

- Less is known about intensive interventions for elementary students with depression.

- CBT and interpersonal psychotherapy can be adapted for younger students.

Adaptation of Cognitive– Behavior Therapy

Many of the same components of CBT used with adolescents are used with children, albeit at a simpler and more concrete level; for example, artwork, physical activity, games, and manipulatives are frequently employed. Education about feelings and their relation to depression or sad mood is important for this age group. Building a feelings vocabulary using a game format, using a graphic of a mood thermometer to differentiate positive and negative feelings, and linking these to triggers or experiences in the students' lives are examples of ways to begin teaching children to counteract negative feelings. Relaxation training might be simplified to consist of learning a deep breathing exercise by taking three to five breaths and exhaling slowly or going limp "like a floppy noodle." Social skills training and other CBT strategies can all be used.

The ACTION Program

One CBT program, the ACTION program, can be delivered in the school setting to students as young as 9 years old (Stark, Brookman, & Frazier, 1990). ACTION is a developmentally and gender-sensitive group intervention that consists of a number of cognitive, self-control, behavioral, and parent-training procedures.

The program consists of two individual meetings with each student and 20 1-hour group sessions provided twice weekly; after the first 4 weeks, the sessions can be offered weekly if that schedule will optimize attendance. Groups consist of four to eight children with two therapists; the program can be adapted individually as well (Stark et al., 1990).

The sessions are designed to be fun and engaging for younger children while teaching them about their depressive symptoms, stressors, and relationship difficulties. Both presentations and experiential exercises or activities are used to teach the skills to students. New skills are rehearsed in the group, and exercises and activities are assigned as homework; application is recorded and monitored through completion of workbook activities linked to rewards during the group session. There is also an 8-session parent training component; parent involvement is considered essential to successful treatment (Stark et al., 1990). Parents are encouraged to increase the number of pleasant activities in the child's life, support the child's new skills, and learn new parenting skills that will support the child.

"The ACTION program has been used extensively and effectively in public schools with depressed children."

There are four components of the intervention. The first component is education about the experience of depression, its potential causes, and how treatment can help. Students are also taught the vocabulary of feelings, recognizing internal cues, connecting feelings and thoughts, and connecting events with their meaning and associated feelings. In the second component, the students learn coping and problem-solving strategies for dealing with negative feelings or mood; the goal is to provide skills that can be used to repair or improve mood in general. These skills include re-engaging in behaviors that lead to pleasant mood, promoting mastery experiences, and increasing positive interactions. The key for the student is to learn to define the negative feeling as a problem to be solved, identify strategies for coping, and do something about it. Five categories of strategies are taught: doing something fun and distracting, doing something relaxing, doing something active that expends energy, talking to someone, or changing the thinking. Cognitive restructuring (the third component) is the component in which students learn to identify thoughts associated with feelings, recognize distortions in thinking, reconstruct thoughts and images linked to feelings, identify and counter thoughts that interfere with coping, and develop positive self-statements. The objective of cognitive restructuring is to change the underlying core beliefs that are associated with negative thoughts and sadness. Finally, the parent component includes positive behavior management, family problem solving, communication skills, conflict resolution, and changing behavior that supports depressive core beliefs. This component combines features of both CBT and interpersonal psycho-therapy. With the children and their parents functioning more adaptively, parents can collaboratively assess the ways they contribute to their children's negative beliefs and learn to communicate more positive messages.

The ACTION program has been used extensively and effectively in public schools with depressed children (Stark et al., 2011). There is a therapist manual for treating children and separate workbooks for girls and boys. In addition, there is a therapist manual for working with parents of depressed children and separate workbooks for parents of girls and parents of boys. These are relatively inexpensive and available at http://www.workbookpublishing.com/depression.html. A video about the school-based group treatment of depressed students can be purchased as well.

Stark and colleagues (Stark et al., 2011) recommend that school mental health providers participate in a 2-day training workshop during the summer when school is not in session. Weekly phone or online video supervision is also recommended for the first year of implementation. For more information about training, contact the developer, Kevin D. Stark, Ph.D., Department of Educational Psychology, University of Texas at Austin; e-mail: kevinstrk@mail.utexas.edu.

Adaptation of Interpersonal Psychotherapy

Recall that the perspective that guides interpersonal psychotherapy (IPT) is that the onset of depression is linked to conflicts and prob-lems in interpersonal relationships, particularly in those who are biologically vulnerable (Mufson, 2010). Given that younger children are particularly embedded in family as well as peer relationships, addressing interpersonal interactions is a central effort in this approach. This focus on interpersonal interactions is actually more concrete than a focus on cognitions, and the phases of individual treatment can be readily adapted for younger children. Whereas parent involvement in the program with adolescents was encouraged but not required, it is crucial to working with young students.

The therapy progresses in three phases. In the initial psychoeducation phase, the younger student is taught about depression and how relationship events and situations affect his or her mood and other symptoms. An interpersonal inventory is conducted to identify what is problematic for the child so that the problem area may be formulated. One of four problem areas can be mutually identified: loss, developmental and family transition, conflict, or interpersonal skills deficits. The second phase entails active work on the problem area. Expressing and clarifying feelings, communication skills, and problem-solving skills are taught. The final phase—termination—includes a review of new skills and teaching about warning signs of depression. Feelings about ending the treatment are processed. Each phase of treatment is built on a consideration of the child's developmental stage and an understanding of the family as the primary interpersonal context.

The parent component of IPT is designed to teach parents about depression and its consequences for educational and social functioning. They are taught child management, communication and interpersonal skills, and problem solving. Joint sessions with the child are held to permit coaching of the parent and to strengthen the parent–child relationship.

COLLABORATION AND CASE MANAGEMENT

Some, but not all, school mental health professionals have the training and experience needed to provide the kinds of intensive services described in this chapter. However, for a variety of reasons (e.g., lack of training in the specific intervention needed, lack of time required to implement the intervention), many of these intensive interventions, especially for more severely depressed or suicidal students, are not delivered by school personnel (Seeley, Rohde, & Jones, 2010). More typically, some interventions are delivered by school personnel and others by community providers. In these cases, the proportion of services delivered in the school and in the community is based on the needs of the student and available resources. Students with severe depression and those who have depression with substance use, history of child abuse, suicidal ideation, and complex family involvement often need all services available. Intensive interventions in these cases require school mental health professionals to engage in collaboration with community-based providers and partnerships with parents in order to provide a comprehensive, integrated program for the student.

> **ESSENTIALS**
>
> - Students with depression often minimize their symptoms to maintain the appearance of normal.
>
> - Issues that need to be addressed in working with adolescents include confidentiality, connection with the student, and the student's need for information.

TALKING WITH ADOLESCENTS AND PARENTS ABOUT DEPRESSION

Adolescents have been found to experience their own depression with a growing sense of distress that evolves into a period of "being in a funk," and then a time of wondering whether or not they are indeed depressed (Wisdom & Green, 2004). During this time, teachers, coaches, or school mental health professionals may begin to notice and observe changes in the student's behavior or screen for depression and find positive symptoms. School nurses often notice such changes first because the health office is a safe place to visit with more frequent or vague complaints. Moreover, there may be less stigma associated with a visit to the school nurse than to one of the other school mental health professionals.

However, most students have a pressing desire to be normal, and often minimize their symptoms to maintain the appearance of normal (Wisdom & Green, 2004). Much like adults with primary care providers, students are likely to be very cautious about disclosing depressive symptoms to school mental health professionals in order to avoid negative and unwanted consequences of their disclosure (Rogers, May, & Oliver, 2001). They may fear being considered more depressed than they are, perhaps being prescribed an antidepressant, or being considered weird, stupid, or crazy; alternatively, the adolescent may also carefully disclose in order to minimize the risk of not being treated or not having their symptoms legitimized (Wisdom & Green, 2004). To offset these concerns and to create a context of safety in which depression can be identified and treatment discussed, school mental health professionals must address three issues from the beginning of their work with an adolescent: confidentiality, a connection with the student, and the student's need for information about depression.

Confidentiality

Confidentiality is a paramount concern for adolescents and is an important prerequisite to helping depressed students (Wisdom, Clarke, & Green, 2006). All school personnel—teachers, coaches, mental health professionals—must appreciate that many students view their expressions of distress and feelings of inadequacy as privileged information and treat their disclosures accordingly (Wisdom et al., 2006). Therefore, while most students do understand that there are times when their information may have to be shared with others, this concept should be clarified at the very beginning of the relationship. It is especially important to discuss confidentiality and develop an agreement about what will and will not be shared with the parent. States and school districts may have different regulations or policies about confidentiality, but three situa-

tions are commonly recognized as requiring a breach of confidentiality: (a) when a student requests it, (b) when there is a risk of harm to the student or others, and (c) when required by a court. School mental health professionals need to explain the limits to confidentiality at the beginning of a relationship with a student—what information will be shared, why and with whom it will be shared, and how it will be shared.

ESSENTIALS

Three situations may require a breach of confidentiality:

- When the student requests it

- When there is risk of harm to the student or others

- When required by a court

Connection With the Provider

Adolescents want a connection with the people they work with—in this case, the school mental health professional (Wisdom et al., 2006). Adolescents are astute observers of verbal and nonverbal cues, and report choosing to withhold information and withdraw from interaction if they are not picking up the right cues from the professional they are talking with (Wisdom et al., 2006). This means that the school counselor, nurse, psychologist, or social worker must actively listen to the student, convey concern about the student's well-being, and not be perceived as simply processing complaints. The connection is fostered by expressions of empathy and communicating an authentic understanding of the experience of depression. Engaging students with depressive symptoms requires a respect for their desire to be normal and using *their* words to describe symptoms. Acknowledging and accepting the "funk" and symptoms of depression more readily develops an alliance with the student than does imposing a diagnosis. That said, acknowledging that feelings are important to discuss and that it takes strength to seek help will facilitate the connection. School mental health professionals who develop a relationship with adolescents are more likely to engage them in treatment than those who do not (Wisdom et al., 2006).

"School mental health professionals who develop a relationship with adolescents are more likely to engage them in treatment than those who do not."

Student's Need for Information

Adolescents report wanting feedback and information about depression from the professionals they work with (Wisdom et al., 2006). It can be helpful to point out behavior that seems different from the student's usual behavior or that may indicate depression. This discussion may validate their experience and also may convey a legitimate concern. It is also important to discuss depression in the context of the personal history and experience that

the student provides—perhaps as a normal consequence of stressful or abnormal experiences. Biological and technical explanations of depression run counter to adolescents' more typical characterizations of depression as caused by external stressors and something to be solved by personal actions (Wisdom et al., 2006). They seek to understand the cognitive and behavioral mechanisms of depression that are more congruent with their characterizations. This explanatory model is a good fit with the evidence-based programs that can be offered in the school setting and are summarized earlier in this chapter.

ESSENTIALS

- Adolescents want feedback and information from professionals.

- They want professionals to collaborate with them to find solutions.

- Adolescents who are more informed about treatment options are more likely to engage in treatment.

Adolescents want professionals to work with them to find solutions (Wisdom et al., 2006). Hence, the presentation of options that are congruent with solving the problems they identify will enhance their feeling of being understood and confirm their autonomy to make decisions for themselves. In this way, there can be a balance between providing guidance and promoting the student's autonomy. Adolescents who are more informed about treatment options are more likely to engage in treatment (Wisdom et al., 2006).

KEYS TO COLLABORATION

■ Collaboration with parents and community providers is crucial for students with serious depression or who require medical services.

■ It is helpful to include adolescents in conversations with parents about depression.

■ Previewing with students what will be discussed during the parent meeting helps to clarify confidentiality issues, maintain the connection with the student, and respect the student's autonomy.

Talking With Parents

Collaboration with parents is important when working with any depressed student and meeting with parents will be crucial for students who have a more serious depression or who require a medical evaluation and perhaps community-based mental health services. Talking with parents about their adolescent's depression is best done with the student present in order to respect confidentiality and promote the adolescent's connection and autonomy.

Arranging to talk with parents will need to be discussed first with the student in order to clarify confidentiality issues, maintain the connection with the student, and respect his or her autonomy. Rehearsing a conversation for them to have with their parents about their depression will be an important step. It is helpful to have students not only describe their experience of depression and what they are doing about it, but also to articulate what they need from their parents. It is important to review with the student the goals of the

meeting and what will be discussed. Typical elements of the conversation might include: sharing the student's experience and symptoms of depression, eliciting parental observations, describing the student's perception of contributing factors, eliciting parental perceptions of contributing factors, providing an explanation of depression, identifying treatment options, sharing the student's preferences and choices, and identifying what is needed from the parents. It is also crucial to describe the role of the school mental health professionals in monitoring symptoms, providing interventions in the school setting, and optimizing the student's academic and social experience.

ACTION PLAN

■ Assess the skills of mental health professionals employed in your school. Identify strengths and gaps in these competencies.

■ Develop professional development plans to build the capacity of the school mental health team.

■ Assess the resources available within the community and the level of collaboration in place between those resources and the school mental health team.

■ Take steps to create an authentically collaborative family–school–community team to support students with depression (see Chapter 11).

RESOURCES

There are a number of excellent books available on cognitive–behavior therapy with children and adolescents. Some examples include the following:

- *Cognitive-Behavioral Interventions in Educational Settings: A Handbook for Practice (2nd ed.)* (2012) by Mennuti, Christner, and Freeman (Eds.).

- *Handbook of Cognitive–Behavior Group Therapy With Children and Adolescents* (2007) by Christner, Stewart, and Freeman (Eds.).

- *Clinical Practice of Cognitive Therapy With Children and Adolescents: The Nuts and Bolts* (2002) by Friedberg and McClure.

- *Cognitive Therapy Techniques for Children and Adolescents: Tools for Enhancing Practice* (2009) by Friedberg, McClure, and Garcia.

An important introduction to interpersonal psychotherapy is *Interpersonal Psychotherapy for Depressed Adolescents (2nd ed.)* (2004) by Mufson, Dorta, Moreau, and Weissman.
The Teens Health website (http://kidshealth.org/teen/your_mind/families/talk_depression.html) has information for adolescents to prepare for talking with their parents about their depression

The websites for Helpguide (http://www.helpguide.org/mental/depression_teen.htm) and the Palo Alto Medical Foundation (http://www.pamf.org/teen/parents/emotions/depression.html) provide information and support to parents of a depressed adolescent.

REFERENCES

Becker-Weidman, E. G., Jacobs, R. H., Reinecke, M. A., Silva, S .G., & March, J. S. (2010). Social problem-solving among adolescents treated for depression. *Behavior Research and Therapy, 48,* 11–18. doi:10.1016/j.brat.2009.08.006

Christner, R. W., Stewart, J., & Freeman, A. (Eds.). (2007). *Handbook of cognitive–behavior group therapy with children and adolescents.* New York, NY: Routledge.

Clarke, G., Lewinsohn, P., & Hops, H. (1990). Leader's manual for adolescent groups: Adolescent Coping With Depression Course. Portland, OR: Kaiser Permanente Center for Health Research. Retrieved from http://ww.kpchr.org

Friedberg, R. D., & McClure, J. M. (2002). *Clinical practice of cognitive therapy with children and adolescents: The nuts and bolts.* New York, NY: Guilford Press.

Friedberg, R. D., McClure, J. M., & Garcia, J. H. (2009). *Cognitive therapy techniques for children and adolescents: Tools for enhancing practice.* New York, NY: Guilford Press.

Gunlicks-Stoessel, M. Mufson, L., Jekal, A., & Turner, J. B. (2010). The impact of perceived interpersonal functioning on treatment for adolescent depression: IPT-A versus treatment as usual in school-based health clinics. *Journal of Counseling and Clinical Psychology, 78,* 260–267.

Hilt-Panahon, A., Kern, L., Divatia, A., & Gresham, F. (2007). School-based interventions for students with or at risk for depression: A review of the literature. *Advances in School Mental Health Promotion, 1,* 32–42.

March, J., Silva, S., Vitiello, B. & The TADS Team. (2006). The treatment for adolescents with depression study (TADS): Methods and message at 12 weeks. *Journal of the American Academy of Child and Adolescent Psychiatry, 45,* 1393–1403.

Mennuti, R. B., & Christner, R. W. (2012). *Cognitive-behavioral interventions in educational settings: a handbook for practice (2nd ed.).* New York, NY: Routledge.

Merrell, K. W. (2008). *Helping students overcome depression and anxiety: A practical guide (2nd ed.).* New York, NY: Guilford Press.

Mufson, L. (2010). Interpersonal psychotherapy for depressed adolescents (IPT-A): Extending the reach from academic to community settings. *Child and Adolescent Mental Health, 15,* 66–72.

Mufson, L., Dorta, K. P. Moreau, D., & Weissman, M. M. (2004). *Interpersonal psychotherapy for depressed adolescents (2nd ed.).* New York, NY: Guilford Press.

Rogers, A., May, C., & Oliver, D. (2001). Experiencing depression, experiencing the depressed: The separate worlds of patients and doctors. *Journal of Mental Health, 10,* 317–333.

Rohde, P., Silva, S. G., Tonev, S. T., Kennard, B. D., Vitiello, B., Kratochvil, C. J., ... March, J. S. (2008). Achievement and maintenance of sustained improvement during TADS continuation and maintenance therapy. *Archives of General Psychiatry, 65,* 447–455.

Seeley, J. R., Rohde, P., & Jones, L. B. (2010). School-based prevention and intervention for depression and suicidal behavior. In M. R. Shinn & H. M. Walker, *Interventions for achievement and behavior problems in a three-tier model including RTI.* Bethesda, MD: National Association of School Psychologists.

Stark, K. D., Brookman, C. S., & Frazeir, R. (1990). A comprehensive school-based treatment program for depressed children. *School Psychology Quarterly, 5,* 111–140.

Stark, K. D., Arora, P., & Funk, C. L. (2011). Training school psychologists to conduct evidence-based treatments for depression. *Psychology in the Schools, 48,* 272–282. doi:10.1002/pits.20551

Wisdom, J. P., & Green, C. A. (2004). 'Being in a funk': Teens' efforts to understand their depressive experiences. *Qualitative Health Research, 14,* 1227–1238.

Wisdom, J. P., Clarke, G. N., & Green, C. A. (2006). What teens want: Barriers to seeking care for depression. *Administration and Policy in Mental Health and Mental Health Services Research, 33,* 133–145. doi:10.1007/s10488-006-0036-4

CHAPTER 6

DEPRESSION CAN BE PREVENTED: EFFECTIVENESS OF PREVENTION PROGRAMS

Depression can be prevented. Evidence for this remarkable statement began accruing more than 2 decades ago and, in recent years, research has supported the conclusion that depression prevention programs are effective (Barrera, Torres, & Muñoz, 2007; Cuijpers, van Straten, Smit, Mihalopoulos, & Beekman, 2008; Muñoz, Beardslee, & Leykin, 2012; Muñoz, Cuijpers, Smit, Barreera, & Leykin, 2010; National Research Council & Institute of Medicine [NRC & IOM], 2009). Such programs are well developed, readily available, reasonable in cost, and many are designed for implementation by school personnel. Depending on the program, they can be used with entire student populations, students identified as at risk for depression, or students identified as being at high risk or as already exhibiting symptoms of depression. Although continued research is certainly needed, the National Research Council and Institute of Medicine (NRC & IOM, 2009) concluded that studies since the late 1990s have consistently demonstrated that a wide range of prevention programs, especially those that reduce risk factors or promote protective factors, are effective in contributing to the prevention of many mental health problems in students. In fact, the report cautioned that "It is no longer accurate to argue that emotional and behavioral problems cannot be prevented or that there is no evidence for the prevention of MEB [mental, emotional, and behavioral] disorders experienced during childhood, adolescence, and early adulthood" (p. 216).

Considering the human, financial, and societal costs outlined in Chapter 1, all schools should implement such programs. The fact is that these programs usually produce important benefits in addition to the prevention of depression, including improved academic, social, emotional, and behavioral outcomes for students. It is therefore hard to justify *not* offering these programs in our schools.

ESSENTIALS

■ Depression can be prevented.

■ A wide range of prevention programs are available that are effective in contributing to the prevention of many student mental health problems.

EFFECTIVENESS OF UNIVERSAL INTERVENTIONS

Universal interventions (Tier 1 of a response to intervention—RTI—framework) are those that are provided to all students, regardless of whether they have been identified as being at risk or not. These interventions include prevention programs designed to reduce negative mental health outcomes as well as mental health promotion activities that are designed to enhance students' developmental competencies, social skills, sense of mastery or control, and coping skills. Both kinds of programs tend to employ similar strategies and have similar outcomes (NRC & IOM, 2009).

Universal, school-based social–emotional learning (SEL) programs are effective across a broad range of outcomes (e.g., depressive symptoms, academic achievement, aggressive behavior, drug abuse, mental health), students, and intervention types (Durlak, Weissberg, Dymnicki, Taylor, & Schellinger, 2011; NRC & IOM, 2009). According to the Collaborative for Academic, Social, and Emotional Learning (2011), these programs focus on developing such skills as self-management (controlling one's emotions and behavior), self-awareness (recognizing one's feelings, values, strengths, and limitations), social awareness (understanding and empathizing with others), and relationship skills (developing healthy interpersonal relationships, working in teams, resolving conflict). In the specific case of suicide prevention, these universal prevention programs are the most effective (and cost-effective) approaches available (Berman, Jobes, & Silverman, 2006). Furthermore, interventions delivered school-wide seem to yield benefits for those at risk for depression without the stigma of an intervention targeted only to those identified as at risk for or already experiencing symptoms (Rivet-Duval, Heriot, & Hunt, 2011). This avoidance of stigma, combined with evidence that universal prevention strategies delivered by teachers or school mental health professionals as part of the school day are more sustainable, readily implemented, and less expensive than targeted approaches (McLaughlin, 2011), make school-wide interventions important components of a comprehensive approach to depression prevention.

ESSENTIALS

- Universal, school-based social–emotional learning programs are effective across a broad range of mental health and academic outcomes.

- Universal prevention programs may be the most effective and cost-effective approaches available for suicide prevention.

In a recent example of this line of research, Durlak and colleagues (2011) conducted a meta-analysis of 213 high-quality research studies involving 270,034 students of mixed ethnicity and socioeconomic status from both urban and non-urban schools, and provided data about the effectiveness of universal (Tier 1) SEL programs. Student outcomes in six areas were evaluated: (a) SEL skills, (b) prosocial attitudes, (c) positive social behavior, (d) conduct problems, (e) emotional distress such as depression and anxiety, and (f) academic performance (test scores and grades). The evaluation of these outcomes addressed three questions:

- Do students exposed to universal, school-based SEL programs do better in critical outcome areas than students who do not receive such programs (i.e., control groups)?

- Is there a difference in outcomes depending on whether the program is delivered by classroom teachers or by outside consultants, researchers, or other community members?

- What were the characteristics of the most effective SEL programs?

Students Who Participate in SEL Programs Have Better Outcomes

Results of this study (Durlak et al., 2011) revealed that, compared to students who do not participate in a universal school-based SEL program, students who do experience such programs have significantly better outcomes in all six areas. Follow-up studies showed that gains remained significant for a minimum of six months after the program ended. For example, students exposed to SEL programs performed 11 percentile points better on academic outcomes than students in control groups who did not participate in SEL programs. Moreover, SEL programs are successful across student groups: in elementary, middle, and high schools; in urban, suburban, and rural districts; and in schools with ethnic and socioeconomic diversity. Furthermore, there is evidence that after-school SEL programs also improve students' self-perceptions and connection to school, grades and academic performance, and behavior (Durlak, Weissberg, & Pachan, 2010).

Classroom Teachers Can Successfully Deliver SEL Programs

Durlak and colleagues (2011) also found that classroom teachers and other school personnel can successfully deliver SEL programs. SEL programs delivered by nonschool personnel produced significant outcomes in only three areas: SEL skills, prosocial attitudes, and reduced conduct problems. Programs delivered by school personnel produced significant outcomes in all six areas; indeed, "student academic performance significantly improved only when school personnel conducted the intervention" (Durlak et al., 2011, p. 413).

ESSENTIALS

- Students who participate in universal SEL programs exhibit less depression and anxiety than those who do not.

- Students who participated in universal SEL programs performed 11 percentile points better on academic outcomes than students who did not receive such a program.

- School personnel can successfully deliver SEL programs; in fact, there is evidence that student academic achievement improves only when school personnel conduct these interventions.

EFFECTIVENESS OF TARGETED INTERVENTIONS

Targeted interventions are those that are delivered (at Tier 2 of an RTI framework) to students who are at higher than average risk of developing depression or who exhibit sub-clinical levels of depressive symptoms. Interventions designed for this group have been shown to be generally effective; in fact, such programs usually have better outcomes—both immediate and long-term—than universal programs (Horowitz & Garber, 2006). Effective programs of this type typically use cognitive–behavioral strategies in a small-group format (e.g., SEL programs and group counseling) and psycho-educational family approaches.

Tier 2 Social–Emotional Learning Programs

Social–emotional learning programs have been used successfully with students at risk for social and emotional problems (e.g., depression). A meta-analysis (Payton et al., 2008) of 80 studies of SEL programming involving 11,337 students found results very similar to those found by Durlak and colleagues (2011) in the study described previously. In this case, however, the students involved were those who, while they did not have a diagnosed mental disorder and were not identified as eligible for special education, were identified as at risk for social, emotional, or behavioral problems. Similar to the outcomes found with universal SEL interventions, at-risk students had significantly better outcomes than control groups in (a) SEL skills, (b) attitudes toward self and others, (c) social behaviors, (d) conduct problems, (e) emotional distress such as anxiety and depression, and (f) academic performance. At follow-up, improvements persisted for positive attitudes, positive social behaviors, conduct problems, and emotional distress. Tier 2 SEL programs were successful for students of different ages, socioeconomic status, and settings (urban, suburban, and rural). Best results were obtained when the interventions were delivered correctly and the skills to be taught were sequenced, employed active learning, and focused specifically and for a sufficient amount of time on explicit SEL skills (see discussion of SAFE procedures below). School personnel were able to deliver these programs as effectively as researchers or community-based personnel.

The Penn Resiliency Program is an example of a program that focuses more specifically on depressive symptoms and can be delivered as either a universal or targeted intervention. In many controlled studies, students who participated in the program had significantly fewer depressive symptoms than students who did not participate in the program. These results persisted in follow-up studies ranging from 6 months to 2 years after the program ended (Muñoz, Beardsley, & Leykin, 2012).

ESSENTIALS

- Targeted interventions have been found to be effective in reducing depression.

- The best outcomes are found when interventions are combined into a comprehensive, integrated program.

Group Counseling and Psychotherapy

Group and individual cognitive–behavior therapy for depression and other mood disorders have a long history of effectiveness with children and adolescents (Huberty, 2012). This approach typically trains students in skills such as self-management training, relaxation, planning pleasant activities, problem solving, and cognitive restructuring (identifying negative thoughts and replacing them with more rational ones). Psychoeducation about the symptoms and causes of depression is often used as well. These approaches are generally practical for school application and are all evidence-based (see Vannest, Reynolds, & Kamphaus, 2008, for sample studies). However, research has shown that these strategies have the greatest effectiveness when combined in a comprehensive, integrated program (Merrell, 2008). The Penn Resiliency Program, Strong Kids/Strong Teens program, and the Adolescent Coping With Stress Class are examples of comprehensive evidence-based programs that are appropriate for school-based use (see Chapter 4).

Psychoeducational Programs for Parents

Psychoeducational programs that address the needs of depressed parents also have been shown to significantly reduce depressive symptoms among their children (Muñoz, Beardslee, & Leykin, 2012). Cuijpers and colleagues (2008) conducted a meta-analysis of 19 studies of randomized controlled trials of school- and parent-based interventions that indicated that, compared to control groups, participants who received the intervention had a 22% lower risk of developing depression.

RTI CONNECTIONS

- The recommendation for comprehensive, integrated interventions for depression fits easily within the multi-tiered problem-solving structure of RTI.

- Evidence-based interventions are available for use by school personnel at all tiers of the RTI framework.

EFFECTIVENESS OF INTENSIVE INTERVENTIONS

Intensive interventions are those delivered to students who are at very high risk of developing or are already diagnosed with a depressive disorder. Within an RTI framework, such interventions are provided to students whose problems with depression do not respond adequately to Tier 2 services. Interventions at this level are often similar to or the same as those provided at Tier 2 but delivered with greater intensity. Greater intensity typically involves more frequent sessions, combining several interventions into a comprehensive package, longer duration of service, and integration with community services.

In addition, there are some comprehensive programs that are primarily used at this tier of service. For example, studies consistently demonstrate that students who complete the Adolescent Coping With Depression Course (CWD; Clarke, Lewinsohn, & Hops, 1990) exhibit a significantly lower incidence of major depression than control students who do not take the course (Muñoz et al., 2012). Cuijpers and colleagues (2009) conducted a meta-analysis to assess the effectiveness over the past 30 years of CWD. The intervention was examined as a prevention strategy for depression in 25 randomized control trials across ages, primary care patients, and ethnic minority groups. The studies consistently showed that the intervention is effective in the prevention of new cases of depression in those that did not meet a symptom level for major depression at baseline. The chance of developing a major depressive disorder was reduced by 38% for those who participated in a preventive version of the CWD. Another study, conducted across four sites with adolescents who were at risk for depression due to parental depression or a personal history of depression, revealed that a CWD-based intervention reduced or delayed the occurrence of depression and prevented recurrence (Garber et al., 2009).

> *"The chance of developing a major depressive disorder was reduced by 38% for those that participated in a preventive version of the CWD."*

Interpersonal Psychotherapy

Interpersonal psychotherapy for adolescents (IPT-A) is an approach to individual counseling for students with depression. The program has been found to be effective in reducing depression among adolescents (for reviews, see Mufson, 2010 and Vannest et al., 2008).

ESSENTIALS

- Universal, targeted, and intensive interventions all significantly reduce student depression.

- Many studies show that targeted and intensive programs have greater effects on reducing depression than universal programs.

- Integrating universal, targeted, and intensive interventions into a comprehensive program delivered to all students is likely to yield the best outcomes.

RELATIVE EFFECTIVENESS OF UNIVERSAL, TARGETED, AND INTENSIVE INTERVENTIONS

The research on outcomes of interventions for the prevention of depression has typically shown that approaches at the universal, targeted, and intensive levels of intervention all result in significant outcomes, but that target-ed and intensive interventions have the best and most long-lasting effects (for example: Horowitz & Garber, 2006; Payton et al., 2008; Seeley, Rohde, & Jones, 2010; Stice, Shaw, Bohon, Marti, & Rohde, 2009). In one example of this line of research, Horowitz and Garber (2006) conducted a meta-analysis of research on prevention programs for depressive symptoms in children and adolescents that encompassed interventions at the universal, indicated, and intensive levels. They found that although outcomes for students who were exposed to such programs were significantly better than outcomes for students in control groups, the more intensive programs tended to produce better results than universal programs 6 months after the programs ended.

CAUTIONS REGARDING RELATIVE EFFECTIVENESS RESEARCH

Although the finding that targeted and intensive interventions for depression are more effective than universal interventions is well-established, future research and development of universal programs may modify that evaluation. Efforts at universal programming specifically designed to prevent depression and suicide have usually not been of sufficient duration and frequency, and have focused exclusively on factors that exist within the student (typically through cognitive–behavioral interventions), rather than taking a more comprehensive, ecological approach that considers the context or environment of the student as another contributor to the problem. Development of universal interventions that focus on developing protective factors and building resilience, and that are delivered with sufficient duration and intensity, will likely increase the impact of such programs in reducing depression and other mental disorders (NRC & IOM, 2009).

Moreover, results of research finding differences in the effectiveness of universal compared to targeted or intensive interventions may to some extent be due to the methodological limitations of the studies. Specifically, the incidence of major depression in the universal population is so low that very large samples are needed in order for randomized controlled trials to have adequate statistical power to detect differences between experimental and control groups (Barrera, Torres, & Muñoz, 2007). Studies of targeted or intensive interventions do not require nearly as many participants in order to discern those differences (Muñoz, Beardslee, & Leykin, 2012). In any event, comprehensive programs encompassing universal, targeted, and intensive interventions provided in a coordinated and integrated way to all students in elementary through high school grades are likely to have a synergistic effect and produce better outcomes than any individual program focusing on a single tier of intervention for a relatively brief period of time.

ESSENTIALS

- The correlation between social–emotional–behavioral performance and academic achievement is an established fact.

- Students who are given programs that teach social–emotional–behavioral skills and provide supports for mental health consistently perform significantly better on academic tasks (including grades and test scores) than their peers who are not given those programs.

EFFECTS ON ACADEMIC ACHIEVEMENT

Hundreds of studies involving hundreds of thousands of students of diverse cultural, linguistic, and socioeconomic status have confirmed the finding that social–emotional–behavioral performance is reciprocally related to academic achievement. In other words, students with better social–emotional–behavioral skills typically exhibit better academic skills and vice versa. This finding of a relationship between social–emotional–behavioral performance and academic achievement is so consistent that it is considered an established fact (Algozzine, Wang, & Violette, 2011).

Moreover, students who are exposed to programs designed to enhance social–emotional–behavioral functioning consistently perform significantly better on academic tasks than students who have not participated in such programs (NRC & IOM, 2009; New Freedom Commission on Mental Health, 2003). Durlak and associates (2011), for example, documented an improvement of 11 percentile points among students given SEL interventions compared to students not given the interventions. This kind of gain is comparable to the results of interventions that are specifically academic in nature. Other examples of studies demonstrating that students who receive mental health prevention and support services have higher academic achievement than students who do not are provided by Charvat (2012).

Not clear from the research is the mechanism behind these findings. Logically, it makes sense that the symptoms or symptomatic behavior of depressed students (e.g., impairments in thinking, memory, and attention; apathy and disengagement; fatigue and physical complaints; sadness, low self-esteem, and ruminations about deficiencies and failures) is certain to result in lower academic achievement and school performance. At the same time, teachers preoccupied with dealing with symptomatic behaviors in the classroom will not easily be able to provide an effective level of instruction to the class. Equally logical is that giving students coping strategies and relieving them of these symptoms will result in improved academic performance. Of course, a teacher relieved of having to deal with behavioral issues in the classroom will be able to more effectively provide appropriate instruction. Nonetheless, some researchers (e.g., Algozzine et al., 2011) point out that a causal relationship between social–emotional–behavioral skills and academic performance has not been demonstrated. Despite the lack of research establishing direct causation, there is a general consensus among researchers that including *both* social–emotional–behavioral and

academic skills in the curriculum for all students would yield significant improvements in both areas.

"There is general consensus among researchers that including both social– emotional–behavioral and academic skills in the curriculum for all students would yield significant improvements in both areas."

BUILDING EFFECTIVE PROGRAMS TO PREVENT DEPRESSION

Approximately a decade ago, investigators identified nine characteristics of effective prevention programs across the four areas of substance abuse, risky sexual behavior, school failure, and juvenile delinquency and violence (Nation et al., 2003). These characteristics should be just as useful to incorporate into programs for the prevention of depression. The nine characteristics of effective programs include:

- *Comprehensiveness.* Does the program include multiple components addressing domains that influence the development of the problem? For example, a school-based program to prevent depression could include peer relationships, student social competence and coping skills, and family education.

80

■ *Varied teaching methods.* Are diverse teaching methods involved? Effective programs typically use a variety of teaching approaches that focus on increasing awareness and understanding the problem behaviors, as well as acquiring or enhancing skills. Each of these—increasing awareness, understanding the problem, and skill acquisition or enhancement—can employ several strategies.

■ *Sufficient dosage.* What is the program duration, the frequency of sessions, and the nature of follow-up sessions? Sufficient dosage means that the programs provide enough of the program or intervention to achieve the desired results as well as follow-up to maintain them.

■ *Theory driven.* What is the theory that frames the understanding of depression and the design of the intervention program? Effective programs are based on accurate information and are supported by research, so there is a theoretical justification.

■ *Positive relationships.* How are positive relationships provided and modeled? The opportunity to be with adults and peers in ways that promote strong relationships and support positive outcomes should be a key component.

■ *Appropriate timing.* Does the program target developmentally appropriate assets or skills that are known to be preventive? The timing needs to be appropriate to the developmental needs of the students and early enough to be preventive. For example, enhancing social skills is much more preventive for second graders than for high school students, because the

earlier intervention prevents an accumulation of negative experiences.

■ *Socioculturally relevant.* How involved are members of the school cultural and ethnic groups in the selection of the program, modification of its features, and design of implementation in ways that consider the community and cultural norms? Programs need to be tailored to the community and cultural norms of the students and need to include the students in program planning and implementation.

■ *Outcome evaluation.* What results are reported for the program, and after what period of time? Effective programs have clear goals and objectives, and systematically document their results, not just at the end of the program but up to 3 years later or after a developmental transition (elementary to middle school, middle school to high school).

■ *Well-trained staff.* How are those that implement the intervention trained to do so? Effective programs are supported by staff (teachers, administrators, and school mental health professionals), and staff members are provided with the necessary training to implement the intervention. For example, if teachers were asked to implement a school-based intervention, they should be provided the necessary training.

The authors concluded that there was mounting evidence to support the idea that carefully designed and implemented programs can be effective in preventing many of the problems facing children and adolescents. In addition, they highlighted the importance of engaging children and their environmental context as the most likely way to produce change (Nation et al., 2003). This suggests that programs for students in their school setting are central to prevention efforts.

CHARACTERISTICS OF EFFECTIVE PREVENTION PROGRAMS

(Nation et al., 2003; Durlak, Weissman, & Pachan, 2010)

- Comprehensiveness

- Use of varied teaching and active learning methods

- Skills are sequenced and coordinated

- Program goals specifically target social, emotional, and behavioral skills

- Sufficient frequency and duration

- Based on theory

- Emphasize positive relationships

- Developmentally timed

- Socioculturally relevant

- Outcomes are evaluated

- Staff is well trained

More recently, Durlak et al. (2011) found that the best student outcomes were obtained when the interventions were monitored to ensure that they were delivered correctly and when they incorporated SAFE procedures. The acronym SAFE stands for Sequenced, Active, Focused, and Explicit as summarized below (Durlak et al., 2010).

- *Sequenced.* The program or curriculum breaks complex skills into more easily mastered steps and comprises a series of activities that are coordinated, connected to each other, and presented in a coherent sequence culminating in the learning of a specific skill.

- *Active.* The program incorporates active learning approaches (e.g., role-play) that involve the practice of specific social, emotional, or behavioral skills. Feedback on performance is built into the teaching process and mastery of one step leads to the next step in the sequence of learning.

- *Focused.* The program, in whole or in part, has a specific and significant part of the program devoted to improving social, emotional, and behavioral skills. Specific and sufficient time is allocated within the program for skills training.

- *Explicit.* The program is designed to accomplish goals related to improving specific social, emotional, or behavioral skills rather than more general skills or outcomes having to do with general development. The goals of the program are clear and explicitly identify the skills students are expected to learn.

These general characteristics of effectiveness developed by Nation et al. (2003) and Durlak et al. (2011) can serve as a guide for selecting a depression prevention program and inform program development and implementation. A discussion of how to adapt programs for culturally and linguistically diverse groups may be found in *Preventing Mental, Emotional, and Behavioral Disorders Among Young People: Progress and Possibilities* (NRC & IOM, 2009, Chapter 11).

KEYS TO COLLABORATION

■ Research suggests that the best outcomes are obtained from comprehensive, integrated prevention programs. A high degree of collaboration will be required among family members, school staff, and community providers in order to create such a program.

ACTION PLAN

All members of the collaborative mental health team must learn about and disseminate the research showing that depression (and other mental health problems) can be alleviated and student grades, test scores, and school performance significantly increased by providing programs that teach social–emotional–behavioral skills and support student mental health. School administrators are key stakeholders in this regard because they are ultimately responsible for improving outcomes in their schools. School mental health professionals are another key stakeholder group. Start with members of these groups and move toward spreading this information to parents, teachers, and community stakeholders.

■ Use this research to support your efforts at building a comprehensive, coordinated, and integrated school-wide approach to assessment, prevention, and intervention with depression and other mental health issues.

■ This research could also be used to support the use of an RTI framework for behavior, or an integrated academic–behavioral RTI approach.

RESOURCES

Charvat, J. L. (2012). *Research on the relationship between mental health and academic achievement.* Bethesda, MD: National Association of School Psychologists. Retrieved from http://www.nasponline.org/advocacy/Academic-Mental-HealthLinks.pdf

Brief summaries of research studies that demonstrate the significant correlation between mental health and academic achievement. This document could be used as a handout for administrators.

Collaborative for Academic, Social, and Emotional Learning [CASEL]. (2003). *Safe and sound: An educational leader's guide to evidence-based social and emotional learning programs.* Retrieved from http://casel.org/publications/safe-and-sound-an-educational-leaders-guide-to-evidence-based-sel-programs.

A review of SEL programs designed to be used in regular education classrooms.

Collaborative for Social, Academic, and Emotional Learning [CASEL]. (2013). *Effective social and emotional learning programs: Preschool and elementary school edition.* Chicago, IL: Author. Retrieved from http://www.casel.org/guide

An updated review of SEL programs designed to be used with preschool and elementary students.

Global Consortium for Depression Prevention (http://www.preventionofdepression.org/rcts).

A list of randomized trials of preventive interventions for depression is maintained on the website of the Global Consortium for Depression Prevention

National Research Council and Institute of Medicine [NRC & IOM]. (2009). *Preventing mental, emotional, and behavioral disorders among young people: Progress and possibilities*. Washington, DC: National Academies Press. Retrieved from http://www.nap.edu/catalog.php?record_id=12480

This report is a comprehensive review of randomized clinical trials demonstrating the effectiveness of various mental health support programs in preventing depression and other mental disorders in children and adolescents.

Payton, J., Weissberg, R. P., Durlak, J. A., Dymnicki, A. B., Taylor, R. D., Schellinger, K. B., & Pachan, M. (2008). *The positive impact of social and emotional learning for kindergarten to eighth-grade students: Findings from three scientific reviews*. Chicago, IL: Collaborative for Academic, Social, and Emotional Learning.

Available from the Collaborative for Social and Emotional Learning (http://casel.org/publications/positive-impact-of-social-and-emotional-learning-for-kindergarten-to-eighth-grade-students-findings-from-three-scientific-reviews).This report summarizes some of the research discussed in this chapter in an easy-to-understand format.

REFERENCES

Algozzine, B., Wang, C., & Violette, A. S. (2011). Reexamining the relationship between academic achievement and social behavior. *Journal of Positive Behavior Interventions, 13*(1), 3–16. doi:10.1177/1098300709359084

Barrera, A. Z., Torres, L. D., & Muñoz, R. F. (2007). Prevention of depression: The state of the science at the beginning of the 21st century. *International Review of Psychiatry, 19*(6), 655–670. doi:10.1080/09540260701797894

Berman, A. L., Jobes, D. A., & Silverman, M. M. (2006). *Adolescent suicide: Assessment and intervention (2nd ed.).* Washington, DC: American Psychological Association.

Charvat, J. L. (2012). *Research on the relationship between mental health and academic achievement.* Bethesda, MD: National Association of School Psychologists. Retrieved from http://www.nasponline.org/advocacy/Academic-MentalHealthLinks.pdf

Clarke, G., Lewinsohn, P., & Hops, H. (1990). *Coping with adolescent depression course: Leader's manual for adolescent groups.* Eugene, OR: Castalia. Available from

Collaborative for Academic, Social, and Emotional Learning [CASEL]. (2003). *Safe and sound: An educational leader's guide to evidence-based social and emotional learning programs.* Retrieved from http://casel.org/publications/safe-and-sound-an-educational-leaders-guide-to-evidence-based-sel-programs

Collaborative for Academic, Social, and Emotional Learning. (2011). *What is SEL?* Retrieved from http://casel.org/why-it-matters/what-is-sel

Cuijpers, P., van Straten, A., Smit, F., Mihalopoulos, C., & Beekman, A. (2008). Preventing the onset of depressive disorders: A meta-analytic review of psychological interventions. *American Journal of Psychiatry, 165*, 1272–1280. doi:10.1176/appi.ajp.2008.07091422. Retrieved from http://ajp.psychiatryonline.org/article.aspx?volume=165&page=1272

Durlak, J. A., Weissberg, R. P., & Pachan, M. (2010). A meta-analysis of after-school programs that seek to promote personal and social skills in children and adolescents. *American Journal of Community Psychology, 45*(3-4), 294-309. doi:10.1007/s10464-010-9300-6

Durlak, J. A., Weissberg, R. P., Dymnicki, A. B., Taylor, R. D., & Schellinger, K. B. (2011). The impact of enhancing students' social and emotional learning: A meta-analysis of school-based universal interventions. *Child Development, 82*(1), 405–432.

Durlak, J. A., Weissberg, R. P., & Pachan, M. (2010). A meta-analysis of after-school programs that seek to promote personal and social skills in children and adolescents. *American Journal of Community Psychology, 45*, 294–309.

Garber, J., Clarke, G. N., Weersing, V. R., Beardsley, W. R., Brent, D. A., Gladstone, T. R. G., … Iyengar, S. (2009). Prevention of depression in at-risk adolescents: A randomized controlled trial. *Journal of the American Medical Association, 301*(21), 2215–2224. doi:10.1001/jama.2009.788

Horowitz, J. L., & Garber, J. (2006). The prevention of depressive symptoms in children and adolescents: A meta-analytic review. *Journal of Consulting and Clinical Psychology, 74*, 401–415.

Huberty, T. J. (2012). *Anxiety and depression in children and adolescents: Assessment, intervention, and prevention.* New York, NY: Springer.

McLaughlin, K. A. (2011). The public health impact of major depression: A call for interdisciplinary prevention efforts. *Prevention Science, 12*(4), 361–371. doi:10.1007/s11121-011-0231-8

Merrell, K. W. (2008). *Helping students overcome depression and anxiety: A practical guide (2nd ed.).* New York, NY: Guilford Press.

Mufson, L. (2010). Interpersonal psychotherapy for depressed adolescents (IPT-A): Extending the reach from academic to community settings. *Child and Adolescent Mental Health, 15,* 66–72.

Muñoz, R. F., Beardslee, W. R., & Leykin, Y. (2012). Major depression can be prevented. *American Psychologist, 67*(4), 285–295.

Muñoz, R. F., Cuijpers, P., Smit, F. Barrera, A., & Leykin, Y. (2010). Prevention of major depression. *Annual Review of Clinical Psychology, 6,* 181–212. doi:10.1146/annurev-clinpsy-033109-132040

Nation, M., Crusto, C., Wandersman, A., Kumpfer, K. L., Seybolt, D., Morrissey-Kane, E., & Davino, K. (2003). What works in prevention: Principles of effective prevention programs. *American Psychologist, 58,* 449–456.

National Research Council and Institute of Medicine. (2009). *Preventing mental, emotional, and behavioral disorders among young people: Progress and possibilities.* Washington, DC: National Academies Press. Retrieved from http://www.nap.edu/catalog.php?record_id=12480

New Freedom Commission on Mental Health. (2003). *Achieving the promise: Transforming mental health care in America.* DHHS Pub. No. SMA-03-3832. Rockville, MD: U.S. Department of Health and Human Services.

Payton, J., Weissberg, R. P., Durlak, J. A., Dymnicki, A. B., Taylor, R. D., Schellinger, K. B., & Pachan, M. (2008). *The positive impact of social and emotional learning for kindergarten to eighth-grade students: Findings from three scientific reviews.* Chicago, IL: Collaborative for Academic, Social, and Emotional Learning.

Rivet-Duval, E., Heriot, S., & Hunt, C. (2011). Preventing adolescent depression in Maruitius: A univerisal school-based program. *Child and Adolescent Mental Health, 16*(2), 86–91. doi:10.1111/j.1475-3588.2010.00584.x

Seeley, J. R., Rohde, P., & Jones, L. B. (2010). School-based prevention and intervention for depression and suicidal behavior. In M. R. Shinn & H. M. Walker (Eds.), *Interventions for achievement and behavior problems in a three-tier model including RTI* (pp. 363–396). Bethesda, MD: National Association of School Psychologists.

Stice, E., Shaw, H., Bohon, C., Marti, D.N., & Rohde, P. (2009). A meta-analytic review of depression prevention programs for children and adolescents: Factors that predict magnitude of intervention effects. *Journal of Consulting and Clinical Psychology, 77,* 486–503.

Vannest, K. J., Reynolds, C. R., & Kamphaus, R. W. (2008). *BASC-2 intervention guide for behavioral and emotional issues.* Minneapolis, MN: Pearson.

CHAPTER 7

Protective Factors

Protective factors are defined as characteristics of an individual student or that student's environment that are associated with a lower likelihood of problem outcomes (e.g., depression). Protective factors (and risk factors) arise from the individual student as well as the environment in which the student lives. Individual protective factors are strengths, developmental competencies, or resilient characteristics that enhance adaptation and coping with life challenges. Environmental protective factors are those aspects of the student's environment (family, school, and community) that support and nurture adaptation and developmental competencies. Examples of protective factors are provided in Table 1. The continuum of successful to less successful developmental outcomes may be thought of as reflecting an interactive process between the context and factors that induce harm (risk or vulnerability factors) and those that minimize harm (protective factors). The value of protective factors for children and adolescents rests in their relationship to optimal developmental outcomes and to the ability to function optimally in life.

Strategies designed to increase the prevalence of protective factors can be used to prevent the occurrence of depression and other behavioral or mental health problems. Most protective factors are connected to a broad range of social, emotional, and behavioral outcomes, including (but not exclusively) depression. The main implication of this concept is that we do not need to target specific disorders such as depression in developing prevention programs for that disorder (NRC & IOM,

2009). Strategies for universally enhancing these broad protective factors may be equally effective, easier to implement, and helpful to a wider variety of students.

WHAT IS RESILIENCE?

Resilience is the process of coping with stressors, adversity, or change so that positive developmental outcomes (the presence of positive adjustment as well as the absence of depression and other mental health problems) are achieved. Over the past 30 years, researchers have sought to understand why some children are more resilient than others in the face of adversity and disadvantages, such as substance-abusing families, abusive or violent homes or neighborhoods, families with mental illness, and poverty. Why do some children seem to better weather the challenges of peer relationships, classroom learning, and the school environment—even in the face of other vulnerabilities? Research in this area has examined why some students who experience extremely adverse circumstances or severe disadvantages appear to live healthy and productive lives whereas others faced with relatively few challenges struggle to overcome adversities experienced in early life. As risk factors have become better understood, the focus among researchers has shifted to understanding the protective factors that counterbalance the vulnerabilities to yield resilience. The contemporary understanding of resilience is that it is a developmental outcome of the combined effects of protective and risk factors on the child (Edwall, 2012).

Table 1. Examples of Protective Factors

Context	Characteristics	
Individual ■ Intelligence ■ Easy temperament ■ Regulation of emotions ■ Positive self-esteem	■ Problem-solving skills ■ Verbal skills ■ Conflict resolution skills ■ Social skills ■ Adaptability	■ Willing to ask for assistance ■ Emotional regulation ■ Positive self-esteem ■ Connectedness to school
Family ■ Positive parenting ■ Positive parent–child relationship ■ Marital quality	■ Warmth & responsiveness ■ Positive expectations ■ Consistent structure ■ Nurturing	■ Positive relationship model ■ Predictable, safe, and stable home environment
School ■ Positive classroom management ■ Smaller schools ■ Investment of resources	■ Positive relationship with at least one caring adult ■ Positive instructional climate ■ Positive behavioral climate ■ Positive relationships with peers	■ Opportunities to participate, contribute, and be recognized ■ Extracurricular activities ■ Learning resources
Community ■ Facilities ■ Programs ■ Services ■ Vocational opportunities	■ Safe neighborhoods ■ Parks, libraries, youth centers ■ Good schools and child care ■ Health care services	■ Recreational programs ■ Employment and job training opportunities ■ Norms favoring pro-social behavior

"The contemporary understanding of resilience is that it is a developmental outcome of the combined effects of protective and risk factors on the child."

INDIVIDUAL PROTECTIVE FACTORS

Child intelligence is one of the most widely researched and validated protective factors for children and adolescents. It is thought that children with higher intelligence are able to more effectively process information and have better problem-solving skills. These abilities in turn help them to more effectively respond to stressors and challenges. The well-developed verbal cognitive abilities and verbal skills that are linked to higher intelligence likely make it possible to manage conflict and lead to a wider range of coping abilities. Intelligence is also associated with the fluid adoption of social norms that facilitate peer acceptance (Vanderbilt-Adriance & Shaw, 2008). Although intelligence may not be amenable to change in school-age children, the skills of verbal communication, social interaction, problem solving, and conflict resolution can be taught in the school setting.

Easy temperament (adaptable, approachable, positive mood, low reactivity) is also thought to be a protective factor. Children with easy temperaments are less reactive to stressors and challenges. Furthermore, when faced with challenges, those with an easy temperament are not only more adaptable in general but also are more likely to use active and flexible coping strategies (Compas, Connor-Smith, & Jaser, 2004). Although temperament is biologically rooted and not easily altered, the coping strategies that come readily to those with an easy temperament can be taught to students with more difficult temperament who would benefit from learning them. In particular, allowing students the time required to transition when stressed, or to transition into or from a challenging situation, and to talk those through, can facilitate adaptability and lower reactivity.

Regulation of emotions is another feature of an easy temperament that is, in general, a protective factor. Emotional regulation refers to the processes that monitor, evaluate, or modify the intensity and duration of emotional reactions. Not only is better regulation of sadness and anger a particular advantage (Olson, Bates, Sandy, & Schilling, 2002), but children and adolescents who are adept at managing their emotions also are able to modulate their negative moods and emotional expression and thereby function better at school and in social relationships. Recognizing and labeling feelings, as well as appropriate expression of feelings, can be taught in the earliest years of school. To the extent that attention is given to emotional regulation, instructional time is not lost because classroom learning can be more effective for all students as a result.

ESSENTIALS

Individual protective factors include:

■ Intelligence

■ Easy temperament

■ Emotional regulation

■ Self-esteem

■ Connectedness to school

Self-esteem and self-concept refer to the sum of feelings and beliefs about one's self or personality. Self-esteem may be generally thought of as an affective component of the self; that is, the positive feeling one holds about one's self. Self-concept is a cognitive component of the self and refers to the beliefs one has about one's competencies in various activities and performance. These terms are often used interchangeably and broadly refer to feelings of self-worth, self-confidence, and self-respect. The research literature reveals strong associations between low self-esteem and depression among children and adolescents, not only in clinical and at-risk groups but among healthy children and adolescents as well. In fact, for school-age children, lower self-esteem has a more powerful influence on the development of depression over time than depression has on the development of self-esteem (Kim & Cicchetti, 2009), and low self esteem in

15-year-olds predicts depression subsequently in adolescence and young adulthood (Orth, Robins, & Roberts, 2008).

Positive self-esteem has been one of the strengths or factors found to protect children from depression and other negative outcomes in the face of challenges (Abela & Taylor, 2003). Unlike depression, self-esteem can be rather stable over time. Given that stability, it is not surprising that a review of the evidence for school-based interventions revealed that the greatest effect on the promotion of self-esteem and coping outcomes resulted from a sustained focus on the broader school climate (Green, Howes, Waters, Maher, & Oberklaid, 2005).

Connectedness to school is an individual protective factor that refers to the degree that a student feels cared for by people at school and feels like a part of the school. Students who feel connected to school in this way report higher levels of emotional well-being; they have fewer behavior problems or problems with anxiety, depression, and suicidality, and as adolescents are less likely to engage in high-risk behaviors (Resnick et al., 1997; Sulkowski, Demaray, & Lazarus, 2012). Connected students also have greater access to school resources, such as extracurricular activities, teacher investment, and opportunities with peers. Of interest is research that revealed that elementary school children who participated in team sports (not individual sports) had higher self-esteem, and this result did not vary across gender, ability in the sport, or peer acceptance (Slutzky & Simpkins, 2009). Alternatively, school connectedness is thought to operate as a form of social capital that allows students to make use of the school resources (Blum, McNeely, & Nonnemaker, 2002) and is largely determined by the school environment. In other words, self-esteem may make it possible to participate in sports, but the sports program has to be available.

ENVIRONMENTAL PROTECTIVE FACTORS

Most research in the area of protective and risk factors has focused on individual factors within the student. The student's family is an environmental factor that has traditionally also received a lot of attention. In recent years, environmental protective and risk factors related to schools and communities have received a great deal of study.

Family Protective Factors

Positive parenting has rather consistently been identified as a protective factor for optimal child development. Parental warmth, emotional availability, and responsiveness are central features of positive parenting. In addition, positive expectations, consistent structure, and monitoring of the student's behavior are important components. Parental approaches to discipline that emphasize teaching the child appropriate behavior, rather than simply controlling child behavior, facilitate the development of self-regulation abilities. Overall, nurturing and positive parenting are associated with higher self-esteem, lower levels of behavior problems, and more adaptive social competence.

These positive parenting practices further contribute to a *quality relationship* between parents and their children. A positive relationship with one's parent or guardian contributes to a child's positive self-esteem and self-efficacy, both protective factors against depression. A positive parent–child relationship also provides a model for peer relationships and prepares the student to engage in healthy and productive friendships. The ability to engage in healthy and productive social relationships is a protective factor that facilitates students' interaction with the school, school activities, and other social contexts that offer additional protective factors.

ESSENTIALS

Family protective factors include:

- Positive parenting

- A quality relationship between parents and their children

- Parents' marital quality

Much research has focused on how the *quality of the marriage* affects parenting and the parent–child relationship. Marital quality is a protective factor that has been found to increase parents' psychosocial resources, enabling them to provide the warmth, emotional availability, and responsiveness necessary to their children's development. Marital quality enhances the ability to provide consistency in expectations, structure, monitoring, and discipline. Low conflict and marital stability provide an environment of security, but there are additional benefits to constructive problem-solving that serve the child's learning of conflict resolution and social problem-solving skills that enhance social competence.

School Protective Factors

School is an important social and learning environment, with an impact on academic achievement, health, and wellbeing. The quality of relationships with peers and school staff members has been found to be important to engagement in learning and connectedness to school. Several interrelated factors determine school connectedness and although school connectedness is a protective factor that ultimately resides in the individual student, it is determined in large part by factors in the school environment.

A *positive classroom climate* contributes to students feeling more connected to school. The teachers' ability to manage both the instructional and behavioral climates of the classroom enhances the educational adjustment of students in the current classroom as well as in the following years (Farmer et al., 2011). Class size itself, however, is not necessarily associated with school connectedness, and the research on class size and student outcomes has been ambiguous. Class size may matter more for some students than others, such as those with less ability or those who are less socially engaged. Nonetheless, sustaining warm, positive involvement with all students is critical to student motivation and learning (Farmer et al., 2011).

ESSENTIALS

Protective factors in the classroom include:

- Supportive student–teacher relationships
- Positive instructional climate
- High expectations for success of all students
- Climate that encourages pro-social behavior
- Student connection to peers, teachers, and school
- Norms and policies against bullying, discrimination, and violence
- Low levels of aggressive behavior

Even though class size is not so important, the *size of the school* is important to students' sense of connectedness. Essentially, students in smaller schools feel more attached to the school than those in larger schools, with considerable evidence supporting the finding that large schools are detrimental to students (McNeely et al., 2002). In part, it may be that larger schools present challenges to teachers' ability to maintain warm, positive relationships with all students.

Although much emphasis tends to be placed on discipline policies, these seem to have limited association with students' sense of school connectedness (Resnick et al., 1997) or even a contrary impact, with harsher policies linked to decreased connectedness (McNeely et al., 2002). Instead of focusing primarily on disciplinary issues, *policy efforts need to be designed to strengthen the protective factors* in the lives of students.

RTI CONNECTIONS

- Tier 1: Enhancing protective factors is part of building capacity within the general education program.

- Tier 1 and 2: Assessment of protective and risk factors may be part of a screening for depression.

- Tier 2 and 3: Groups or individual programs designed to enhance protective factors (e.g., social skills) are provided to students identified through screening.

- Student response to interventions is systematically monitored.

Attainment of good grades and participation in extracurricular activities and other *resources that support learning* contribute to connectedness to school. Thus, the availability of these resources allows students not only to participate but to experience a sense of investment as well. Furthermore, these activities provide opportunities for supportive relationships with teachers and peers. Elementary students who perceive support from teachers and school peers have higher resiliency, self-esteem, and additional individual protective characteristics (Stewart & Sun, 2004).

Community Protective Factors

Where a student lives, and whether that community can be characterized as advantaged or disadvantaged, is associated with a wide range of protective and risk factors in that child's or adolescent's life. Family and community poverty itself is a cause of many mental, emotional, and behavioral problems in young people (Yoshikawa, Aber, & Beardslee, 2012). Strong institutions (schools, churches, youth centers), quality health services, adequate housing, op-

portunities for employment, and norms against violence, gang activity, and drug abuse are just some of the protective factors that contribute to creating resilient young people.

COLLABORATION TIPS

- Promoting protective factors among children and adolescents can take place in school, at home, and in the community.

- Changing environments is not easy and key stakeholders from each setting will need to collaborate in order to make a significant impact.

ACTION PLAN

- Educate school personnel, parents, students, and community leaders about the role of protective factors in counteracting risk factors, building resilience against depression and other mental health problems, and promoting important positive life outcomes for students.

- Use a collaborative family–school–community problem-solving team to assess protective and risk factors for your students, determine which ones you can impact, and implement a plan to do so. In particular, make sure that every student has a relationship with at least one caring adult in the school.

- Advocate for the creation of nurturing environments for children and adolescents through increasing protective factors and decreasing risk factors in family, school, and community environments.

RESOURCES

Preventing Mental, Emotional, and Behavioral Disorders Among Young People: Progress and Possibilities, a book published by the National Research Council and Institute of Medicine (2009), is freely available online and is an outstanding source of information about the prevention of depression and other mental health problems. A chapter is devoted to protective and risk factors.

REFERENCES

Abela, J. R. Z., & Taylor, A. V. L. (2003). A test of the integration of the hopelessness and self-esteem theories of depression in schoolchildren. *Cognitive Therapy and Research, 27*(5), 519-535. doi:10.1023/A:1026303020478

Berman, A. L., Jobes, D. A., & Silverman, M. M. (2006). *Tangled up in blues: Adolescent suicide* (2nd ed.). Washington, DC.: American Psychological Association.

Blum, R. W., McNeely, C. A., & Nonnemaker, J. (2002). Vulnerability, risk, and protection. *Journal of Adolescent Health, 31S*(1), 28-29. doi:10.1016/S1054-139X(02)00411-1

Bond, L., Butler, H., Thomas, L., Carlin, J., Glover, S., Bowes, G., & Patton, G. (2007). Social and school connectedness in early secondary school as predictors of late teenage substance use, mental health, and academic outcomes. *Journal of Adolescent Health, 40*(4), 357.e9-357.e18. doi:10.1016/j.jadohealth.2006.10.013

Collaborative for Academic, Social, and Emotional Learning. (2011). Collaborative for academic, social, and emotional learning. Retrieved from http://casel.org

Compas, B. E., Connor-Smith, J., & Jaser, S. S. (2004). Temperament, stress reactivity, and coping: Implications for depression in childhood and adolescence. *Journal of Clinical Child and Adolescent Psychology, 33*(1), 21-31. doi:10.1207/S15374424JCCP3301_3

Durlak, J. A., Weissberg, R. P., & Pachan, M. (2010). A meta-analysis of after-school programs that seek to promote personal and social skills in children and adolescents. *American Journal of Community Psychology, 45*(3-4), 294-309. doi:10.1007/s10464-010-9300-6

Durlak, J. A., Weissberg, R. P., Dymnicki, A. B., Taylor, R. D., & Schellinger, K. B. (2011). The impact of enhancing students' social and emotional learning: A meta-analysis of school-based universal interventions. *Child Development, 82*(1), 405-432. doi:10.1111/j.1467-8624.2010.01564.x

Edwall, G. E. (2012, Spring). Intervening during childhood and adolescence to prevent mental, emotional, and behavioral disorders. *The Register Report, 38,* 8–15.

Farmer, T. W., Lines, M. M., & Hamm, J. V. (2011). Revealing the invisible hand: The role of teachers in children's peer experiences. *Journal of Applied Developmental Psychology, 32*(5), 247-256. doi:10.1016/j.appdev.2011.04.006

Green, J., Howes, F., Waters, E., Maher, E., & Oberklaid, F. (2005). Promoting the social and emotional health of primary school aged children: Reviewing the evidence base for school based interventions. *International Journal of Mental Health Promotion, 7*(3), 30-36. doi: 10.1080/14623730.2005.9721872

Kim, J., & Cicchetti, D. (2009). Longitudinal pathways linking child maltreatment, emotion regulation, peer relations, and psychopathology. *Journal of Child Psychology and Psychiatry, 51*(6), 706-710. doi:10.1111/j.1469-7610.2009.02202.x

McNeely, C. A., Nonnemaker, J. M., & Blum, R. W. (2002). Promoting school connectedness: Evidence from the National Longitudinal Study of Adolescent Health. *Journal of School Health, 72*(4), 138-146. doi:10.1111/j.1746-1561.2002.tb06533.x

National Institute of Mental Health. (2011). Statistics. Retrieved from http://www.nimh.nih.gov/statistics/index.shtml

National Research Council and Institute of Medicine. (2009). *Preventing mental, emotional, and behavioral disorders among young people: Progress and possibilities.* Washington, DC: National Academies Press. Retrieved from http://www.nap.edu/openbook.php?record_id=12480&page=R1

Olson, S. L., Bates, J. E., Sandy, J. M., & Schilling, E. M. (2002). Early developmental precursors of impulsive and inattentive behavior: From infancy to middle childhood. Journal of child psychology and psychiatry, 43(4), 435-447. doi: 10.1111/1469-7610.00035

Orth, U., Robins, R. W., & Roberts, B. W. (2008). Low self-esteem prospectively predicts depression in adolescence and young adulthood. *Journal of personality and social psychology, 95*(3), 695-708. doi: 10.1037/0022-3514.95.3.695

Resnick, M. D., Bearman, P. S., Blum, R. W., Bauman, K. E., Harris, K. H., Jones, J., Tabor, J., Beuhring, T., Sieving, R. E., Shew, M., Ireland, M., Bearinger, L. H., & Udry, J. R. (1997). Protecting adolescents from harm. Findings from the National Longitudinal Study on Adolescent Health. *Journal of the American Medical Association, 278*(10), 823-832. doi: 10.1001/jama.1997.03550100049038

Slutzky, C. B., & Simpkins, S. D. (2009). The link between children's sport participation and self-esteem: Exploring the mediating role of sport self-concept. *Psychology of sport and exercise, 10*(3), 381-389. doi:10.1016/j.psychsport.2008.09.006

Stewart, D., & Sun, J. (2004). How can we build resilience in primary school aged children? The importance of social support from adults and peers in family, school and community. *Asia-Pacific Journal of Public Health, 16*(Suppl), S37-S41.

Sulkowski, M. L., Demaray, M. K., & Lazarus, P. J. (2012). Connecting students to schools to support their emotional well-being and academic success. *NASP Communiqué, 40*(7), 1, 20–22.

Vanderbilt-Adriance, E., & Shaw, D. S. (2008). Protective factors and the development of resilience in the context of neighborhood disadvantage. *Journal of Abnormal Child Psychology, 36*(6), 887-901. doi: 10.1007/s10802-008-9220-1

Yoshikawa, H., Aber, J. L., & Beardslee, W. R. (2012). The effects of poverty on the mental, emotional, and behavioral health of children and youth. *American Psychologist, 67*(4), 272–284.

CHAPTER 8

VULNERABILITIES AND RISK FACTORS

A risk factor for depression is a characteristic within the student or in the student's environment that is associated with the later development of depression. Risk factors (and protective factors) arise within the individual student as well as within the environment in which the student lives. Individual risk factors include biological influences, difficult or slow-to-warm-up temperament, previous history of depression or anxiety, poor interpersonal relationships, and a negative explanatory style of thinking. Environmental risk factors include such things as parental depression, poor parenting, stressful life events such as bereavement, and maltreatment (NRC & IOM, 2009). Table 1 provides examples of risk factors for depression.

Some risk factors are specifically for depression (e.g., previous history of depressed behavior). Others are more general risk factors (e.g., sexual abuse) for a broad range of negative mental health outcomes, including depression. Reducing specific or non-specific risk factors within a family, school, or community can, therefore, contribute to the prevention of depression or a decrease in depressive symptoms. In planning prevention programs in schools, therefore, it is not always critical to design programs around specific risk factors for depression; broader strategies of reducing non-specific factors may also be effective. At the same time, assessment of risk factors can help identify specific groups of students who might benefit from preventive interventions.

As noted, the interventions do not necessarily have to target depressive symptoms specifically; they may target identified non-specific risk factors (e.g., in a group for children of divorce) that are associated with depression. Approaches that target both specific and non-specific risk factors for depression are apt to be the most effective (NRC & IOM, 2009).

ESSENTIALS

■ Risk factors are individual or environmental factors that are associated with the development of depression.

■ Some risk factors are specifically for depression and others are associated with a variety of mental health problems in addition to depression.

■ Assessment of risk factors can be used to identify students for intervention.

■ Interventions targeting either specific or non-specific risk factors can help to prevent depression.

Table 1. Examples of Negative Risk Factors

Context	Characteristics
Individual ■ Biological ■ Difficult or slow-to-warm up temperament ■ Prior history of mental health problems	■ Poor nutrition ■ Exposure to toxins, infection, injury ■ Personal or family history of depression or other mental health problems; Shyness
Family ■ Parental depression ■ Poor parenting ■ Maltreatment ■ Loss and bereavement ■ Poverty	■ Withdrawn, less responsive parenting ■ Lack of parental monitoring ■ Inconsistent or authoritarian discipline ■ Chronic family stress ■ Family conflict and divorce ■ Death of family member ■ Maltreatment, neglect, abuse ■ Financial hardship
School ■ Poor student–teacher relationships ■ Lack of positive peer connections	■ Conflicted student–teacher interactions ■ Mismatch between student temperament and classroom environment ■ Disengaged peer group ■ Troubled peer relationships or rejection
Community ■ Violence	■ Unsafe neighborhoods and exposure to violence, drug abuse

RECOGNIZING RISK FACTORS FOR DEPRESSION IN CHILDREN AND ADOLESCENTS

Early experiences in children and adolescents can create vulnerability for current or later depression. In a review of the literature, Kovacs and Lopez-Duran (2010) concluded that children and adolescents who experience as few as two depressive symptoms for at least a week are very likely to have an eventual first episode of major depression. This finding highlights the role of previous depressive symptoms as risk factors for depression and the need to intervene with these early symptoms in order to prevent more serious depression later.

The risk for depression increases with the age of the child. The prevalence of major depressive disorder in adolescents is three to four times higher than in elementary school children (Mazza, Fleming, Abbott, Haggerty, &

Catalano, 2010), and for people between the ages of 15 and 44 years, major depressive disorder is the leading cause of disability (NIMH, 2011). With an age-related trajectory and the disability outcome, understanding the risk factors that indicate vulnerability for depression—especially during elementary school—is crucial for prevention and early intervention.

"Understanding the risk factors that indicate vulnerability for depression—especially during elementary school—is crucial for prevention and early intervention."

Vulnerability to Depression

It is now well understood that both biological factors and adverse psychosocial experiences during childhood influence mental disorders such as depression. Whereas the biological factors are largely individual to the child, the adverse experiences occur in the home (parental and familial), at school, or in the larger community. Individual vulnerabilities may include prenatal exposures, low birth weight, temperament, and inherited predispositions. In the home, parental mental health disorder, poor parent–child or family relationships, financial hardship, abuse and neglect, exposure to trauma, and loss (bereavement) are factors that make the student vulnerable to depression. In the school or larger community, vul-nerabilities stem from classroom climate, educational and/or extracurricular opportunities that affect connectedness, exposure to trauma and poverty, and availability of community resources. A recent study in adolescents found that health risk behaviors were predicted by the contextual factors of deviant peers, limited caregiver monitoring, and poor school engagement (Leslie et al., 2010). In considering the potential effects of various risk factors, it is important to note that risk factors may have little or no impact or a profound impact depending on the age they occur, whether they occur alone or in combination with other vulnerabilities, and whether they are offset by protective factors in the social environment.

INDIVIDUAL RISK FACTORS

Individual risk factors are those that exist primarily within the student. These can include biological and temperamental influences, thinking styles, and personal history (e.g., previous mental health problems). This section discusses various biological and temperamental influences as risk factors for depression.

ESSENTIALS

■ Depression results from a combination of biological, psychological, and social influences.

■ The effect of risk factors depends on the age at which they occur, whether they occur alone or with other risks, and whether they are offset by protective factors.

INDIVIDUAL RISK FACTORS FOR DEPRESSION

■ Difficult or slow-to-warm-up temperament

■ Extreme need for approval or social support

■ Family history of depression or anxiety

■ Prior history of sub-clinical depressed behavior

■ Poor nutrition, toxin exposure, infection, injury

■ Insecure attachment

■ Negative thoughts about self

■ Negative explanatory thinking style

■ Feelings of low self-worth or incompetence

■ Disengagement

■ Poor social, communication, and problem-solving

Sources: NRC & IOM (2009), among others.

Biological Influences

Considerable research conducted by the National Institute of Mental Health (NIMH) has documented multi-generational depression—depression that runs in families—and changes in the brain's structure and function that precede symptoms of depression. To what extent the relative contributions from families can be attributed to biological influences versus environmental influences is nearly impossible to ascertain, but most agree that these factors interact. What we do know is that a family history of depression exists for 20% to 50% of depressed children and adolescents (Kovacs, Devlin, Pollock, Richards, & Muk-

erji, 1997; Weissman, Warner, Wickramaratne, Moreau, & Olfson, 1997). Thus, while depression results from a combination of biological, psychological, and social influences, biological factors are involved for at least some students, making a family history of depression a biological vulnerability.

Biological influences for depression, however, are not only genetically based or inherited. Poor nutrition, exposure to toxins, infection, or injury can contribute to depression. School personnel must be aware of students experiencing these biological conditions, even though they may not be easily observed.

An awareness of certain environmental conditions students face may help in the detection of these biological problems. Some conditions require an understanding of the community that the school serves in order to be alert to the conditions that emerge, for example, from not having enough food or living in neighborhoods with homes that are likely to have lead paint or molds. When students are identified as suffering from an infection or having an injury that limits mobility or impacts other functioning, it is again important to be alert to the student's mood and vulnerability to depressive symptoms.

"A family history of depression exists for 20% to 50% of depressed children and adolescents."

Certain other mental disorders are thought to have a genetic component as well, such as attention deficit hyperactivity disorder (ADHD), bipolar disorder, or schizophrenia, and these often co-occur with depression. Diagnosis of any one of these disorders represents vulnerability and should alert school personnel to the potential for depression as well. Even if ADHD is not formally diagnosed, attention problems in early grade school—as early as second grade—are predictive of later depressive symptoms (Mazza et al., 2010).

Influences of Temperament

Temperament is considered to be a biologically based coping style, and is a potential biologically based vulnerability for children. First evident in early infancy, the characteristics of temperament can be observed in children by the time they reach school age. Temperament is manifested by activity level, prevailing mood, threshold and intensity of response, persistence, approach or withdrawal in response to new stimuli, adaptability to new experiences, distractibility, ease of soothing, and regularity of biological functions (Thomas & Chess, 1977). Temperament is relatively stable by 3 years of age (Houck, 1999) and, therefore, persists through school age and adolescence. Characteristic patterns of these behaviors are classified as three basic temperament types: easy, difficult, and slow-to-warm-up.

Children classified having an easy temperament typically have a positive mood, mild reactivity and intensity, low to moderate activity level, moderate persistence, and high tolerance level. They are usually adapt-able, sociable, outgoing, and mellow. These characteristics act as protective factors for these children. In contrast, having a difficult or slow-to-warm up temperament can be a risk factor for depression (see Table 1).

> *"Temperament is considered to be a biologically based coping style, and is a potential biologically based vulnerability for children."*

Difficult Temperament

Students classified as having difficult temperament tend to have a more negative mood, high activity level, and irregular or unpredictable biorhythms. They are typically not readily adaptable, tend to be reactive to new situations, and react with high intensity. In other words, children with a difficult temperament are considered difficult to interact with, which constitutes the basis of their typically poor social adjustment.

Students with difficult temperament are particularly vulnerable to having social skills deficits and poor relationships that are predictors for later depression. They tend to be easily frustrated, with difficulty recognizing their needs and appropriately expressing them.

Table 1. Comparison of Temperament

Characteristics	Easy	Difficult	Slow to Warm up
Activity level (how active the child is)	Relaxing approach, easily entertained	High, often impulsive activity level	Judicious, rather than fearful
Regularity (predictability of physical functions)	Predictable biological rhythms, such as eating and sleeping cycles	Irregular biological rhythms, such as hunger/sleep cycles	Can vary from predictable to irregular
Approach or withdrawal (how the child handles new situations)	Positive approach response to new situations and experiences	Overwhelmed by change in routines and new experiences	Initially withdraws, but given time, gradually adjusts to new situations and routines
Threshold of responsiveness (how sensitive to physical sensations)	Responds to environment in an easy manner	Intense, inflexible reactions	More prone to becoming overwhelmed by loud noises, new textures, extreme temperatures, pain and environments that are crowded, chaotic, or disorganized
Intensity (how the child reacts)	Responds in a calm and quiet manner	Reacts intensely with ability to get needs met	Very sensitive to emotions and to external stimuli
Quality of mood (how the child reacts either positively or negatively)	Has a happy easy going mood most of the time; smiles often	Rapid, intense mood swings leading to acting out or withdrawing	Cautious nature and wait and see attitude
Distractibility (the degree of concentration)	Focuses and completes task	Easily distracted or incredibly focused	Varies from easily distracted to incredibly focused
Attention span and persistence (the inability to give up)	Accepts frustration with little fuss	Won't stop doing an activity when asked, wants to complete the task	Needs more time to pause and check out options
Adaptability (how well the child responds to new situations)	Adapt to change quickly	Adapts slowly to change	Less flexible adjusting to new encounters or routines

They typically need to learn patience, to use their words to deal with anger and frustration, and to control their temper. Stimulation for these children must be modulated, especially when faced with new students, crowds, excitement, and new situations. Transitions are best tolerated when managed slowly, and students with a high activity level need physical outlets on the playground or through athletic or other physical activities. Thus, children experiencing problems who actually have a difficult temperament can be reframed as such, and their experiences can be reframed as learning opportunities. If this is not done, the negative attitudes, expectancies, and values held about the attributes of difficult temperament can seriously impact teacher–student interaction, perhaps exacerbating the consequences of negative parent–child interaction and thereby impacting psychosocial functioning. The criticism, irritability, and conflicted or coercive interactions to which these students are vulnerable have been linked to behavior problems and depression from preschool through young adulthood.

ESSENTIALS

■ Students with difficult or slow-to-warm up temperaments are particularly vulnerable to having social skills deficits and poor relationships that are predictors for later depression.

■ A lack of fit between a student's temperament and the climate of the classroom can add to a student's risk for depression.

Slow-to-Warm-Up Temperament

Children classified as slow to warm up are notable for an initial quiet alertness and being emotionally subdued in the face of new situations and stimulation; they are slow to approach people, tend to observe others, and are socially reticent. Once they warm up, however, their behavior gives way to features of an easy or difficult temperament. These children can be considered "too much work to interact with," at least initially, and may be ignored by peers or become socially withdrawn.

Students with a slow-to-warm-up temperament are also vulnerable to having social skills deficits and poor relationships with peers or even social isolation, with consequent depression in childhood (Jaffee, Moffitt, Caspi, Fombonne, Poulton, & Martin, 2002) and early adolescence (Karevold, Roysamb, Ystrom, & Mathiesen, 2009). These students are often considered shy and tend to withdraw from social demands and new situations, especially new social situations. In a recent nationally representative survey of more than 10,000 adolescents, about half identified themselves as shy (Burstein, Ameli-Grillon, & Merikangas, 2011). Of those, about a fourth had an anxiety disorder and another 10% were depressed (Burstein et al., 2011). Thus, the vulnerability to problems underlying shyness or slow-to-warm-up temperament is considerable. Rather than pushing them toward sociability, these students need verbal or in vivo preparation for new situations and time to observe others and engage with them at their own pace. They may additionally benefit from working with an adult who can facilitate their expression of needs so that they are not ignored. Opportunities to have responsibility for a younger student may also help such students experience social leadership. In the absence of such efforts, particularly if the student also experiences parental criticism, impatience, and pressure for sociability, the slow-to-warm-up student is at risk for low self-esteem, social withdrawal or isolation, and subsequent depression.

Matching Classrooms to Student Temperament

In relation to temperament, the central issue for the student's success is the fit of his or her behavioral style with the classroom setting and the school social environment. The crux of difficult temperament is twofold: (a) the

impact the behavioral style has on the learning context and the student's cognitive or academic competence, and (b) the impact of the style on social relations in terms of aggressive or antisocial behavior and the student's rejection by peers. Students with slow-to-warm-up temperament likely suffer few consequences with respect to learning and cognitive competence other than their social reticence potentially impeding their ability to assert their academic needs. Rather, the consequences for students that are slow-to-warm-up rest in the impact of this behavioral style on the social environment. Lack of assertiveness, although not strongly associated with depression by

Table 2. Profiles of Risk Factors for Depression in Young Children

Profile	Characteristics	Outcomes
Well-Adjusted Profile	■ Doing well academically ■ Accepted by peers ■ Low levels of depressive symptoms ■ Low levels of aggressive behavior	■ 6% met criteria for major depressive disorder in adolescence ■ 5% met criteria for conduct disorder
Behavior–Academic–Peer Risk Profile	■ Below average academic achievement ■ Below average peer acceptance ■ Average level of depressive symptoms ■ Above average level of aggressive behavior	■ 7% met criteria for major depressive disorder in adolescence ■ 35% met criteria for conduct disorder (10 times more likely than well-adjusted profile) ■ Low academic performance in later school years
Academic–Peer Risk Profile	■ Below average academic achievement ■ Below average peer acceptance ■ Above average level of depressive symptoms ■ Slightly below average level of aggressive behavior	■ 15% met criterion for major depressive disorder in adolescence (3 times more likely than other profiles) ■ 25% met criteria for conduct disorder (6 times more likely than well-adjusted profile) ■ Low academic performance

itself, has been found to be more strongly related to depression in the face of peer victimization (Keenan, Hipwell, Feng, Rischall, Henneberger, & Klosterman, 2010). In other words, the lack of assertiveness exacerbates negative experiences with peers and vulnerability for depression. Alternatively, there is a greater likelihood of social withdrawal and being ignored by peers, leading to social isolation for some of these students. These problems with behavior, anxiety, and social competence as early as second grade are linked to later depressive symptoms (Mazza et al., 2010), making students with difficult and slow-to-warmup temperaments vulnerable.

Risk Factors in Young Children

A recent study identified patterns of risk among first graders and their mental health outcomes in adolescence (Valdez, Lambert, & Ialongo, 2011). In this study, three profiles, including two risk profiles, were identified among first graders and were linked to adolescent outcomes. Characteristics of the three profiles, along with a description of their associated outcomes, are described in Table 2. Multiple risk factors, rather than the specific type of risk factors, predict later outcomes, suggesting that risk for depression is cumulative (Valdez et al., 2011).

ENVIRONMENTAL RISK FACTORS

Environmental risk factors are those that arise primarily from the broader context in which the child lives. These include risk factors associated with the student's parents or guardians, family conditions, school, and community.

Parental Depression and Parenting

Separate from the biological link for depression, there are effects of depression in a parent that influence the quality of parenting and the psychosocial environment of the family. This is especially so for depressed mothers given that, in our society, mothers continue to serve as the primary caregivers for their children. Depressed mothers have been found to be more withdrawn or less engaged, express little warmth, and be less sensitive and responsive to their child's needs and cues. In terms of limit setting and other aspects of family structure, depressed parents may be more irritable and therefore more critical, demanding, and authoritarian without reasoning or explaining (Palaez, Field, Pickens, & Hart, 2008). Controlling behavior may be more severe if the parent is additionally experiencing anxiety or an anxiety disorder. Alternatively, the parents may be more withdrawn and low-energy, characteristics that can result in the neglect of structure and routines, and inadequate supervision of the child.

The consequences of maternal depression vary with the child's age and developmental phase. In the first few months of life—even in the newborn period—infants have sensitivity to negative or flat maternal affect, and in turn engage in withdrawal, aversion, or distressed behavior. The parenting behaviors described above, as manifestations of depressive symptoms, impact the child variously according to development and contribute to whether or not the child attains the appropriate cognitive and social competencies. Unfortunately, the effects of parenting tend to be most profound and ultimately predictive before the age of 5 years, before children are in the school setting (Karevold et al., 2009). In these early years, parenting is most intense and parents tend to be the primary participants in the child's social environment, surpassing the day care setting in terms of influence.

"The adverse experiences of marital and family conflict, separation and divorce, and limited social support should be indicators for the vulnerability to depression in elementary, middle school, and high school students."

Nonetheless, parental depression is a form of parental distress, and maternal distress, regardless of the mental health problem, has been found to trigger other adverse contextual factors. These include more chronic stress in the family, limited social support, marital and family conflict, and divorce. Such family adversity, experienced when children were 8 to 9 years of age, has predicted depression and led to the conclusion that maternal depression represents a genetic liability in children that leads to an increased sensitivity to the very life events that accompany maternal depression (Karevold et al., 2009). Given the negative impact of maternal depression and distress on family life, the adverse experiences of marital and family conflict, separation and divorce, and limited social support should be indicators for the vulnerability to depression in elementary, middle school, and high school students.

FAMILY RISK FACTORS FOR DEPRESSION

- Parental depression
- Marital conflict or divorce
- Poor parenting or parent–child conflict
- Child abuse or maltreatment
- Loss and bereavement
- Financial hardship and poverty

Sources: NRC & IOM (2009), among others

Loss and Bereavement

The sad and lonely state that comes with loss or the death of a family member—parent, sibling, grandparent, aunt or uncle, cousin, or pet—is often called bereavement. Grief is the result, and involves feelings of distress, sorrow, and perhaps even painful regret. The loss of a loved one puts the psychological process of mourning into motion. The death of someone important to a child or adolescent is one of the single most stressful events experienced (American Academy of Pediatrics, 2000), and the death of a parent or sibling is the most disturbing serious loss.

"It is critical for students who experience a death to have a relationship with an adult in the school setting who can be an effective source of support and involvement. "

A student may exhibit signs of depression following loss and may require intervention for relief of symptoms if it continues for a long time or becomes more severe. Children and adolescents are vulnerable to pathological bereavement or depression if they have a previous history of individual or family problems or if they have a history of several family losses. In addition, if they are not allowed to participate in the rituals around death (as developmentally appropriate), they are more vulnerable to depression since services and rituals provide an important way to grieve, especially if such involvement includes supportive family gatherings. Children's understanding is limited to their level of cognitive development, so they need help to understand the facts of death and to correct misunderstandings. The expressions of feelings and memories are normal, and a lack of adult sensitivity to these expressions and sharing memories will increase the vulnerability to unresolved grief and depression. It is critical for students who experience a death to have a relationship with an adult in the school setting who can be an effective source of support and involvement (AAP, 2000). School personnel can be especially important in this role when loss and bereavement present vulnerability for depression.

Maltreatment

Most states recognize four types of maltreatment: neglect, physical abuse, psychological maltreatment, and sexual abuse. The Child Abuse Prevention and Treatment Act (CAPTS) defines maltreatment as including any recent act or failure to act on the part of a parent or caretaker, including actions that present imminent harm. In 2010, there were more than 3 million referrals received by Child Protective Services (CPS) agencies that alleged maltreatment of nearly 6 million children, and nearly 2 million reports were screened positive for investigation. Of those reports investigated, one fifth was substantiated (NCANDS, 2010). These statistics reflect an alarming number of children and adolescents exposed to abusive parenting practices that warranted a report to a CPS agency, whether or not the reports were substantiated. Further, from a third to a half of these are reported more than once (Thompson & Wiley, 2009).

ESSENTIALS

■ Large numbers of children and adolescents are maltreated, usually by family members.

■ Most reports of maltreatment are made by professionals in the schools and community.

■ Maltreated students manifest the consequences through social withdrawal, depression, and anxiety, as well as aggression, delinquency, criminal behavior, and posttraumatic stress symptoms.

More than 80% of the perpetrators of abuse are parents and of those parents, 80% are the biological parent. Sibling aggression and abuse is well hidden and dismissed as sibling rivalry and fighting. Maltreatment is a serious vulnerability residing in the family. The greatest percentage of children are neglected (75%), 15% are physically abused, and 10% are sexually abused (NCANDS, 2010). It is not surprising, then, that it is up to those outside the family in the systems in which children are involved

107

to detect and report maltreatment. In fact, three fifths of the reports of alleged maltreatment were made by professionals including teachers and other school personnel, health care providers, social services staff, and police officers (NCANDS, 2010). The importance of school professionals to be proactive about identifying and reporting neglect and abuse is clear, especially given the consequences for developing children and adolescents.

Maltreatment creates vulnerability to depression and other negative outcomes.

Maltreatment, neglect, and abuse create vulnerability to depression and other negative outcomes. Numerous studies have found that children who experience chronic maltreatment manifest the consequences in various ways, including internalizing behavior problems with social withdrawal, depression, and anxiety, as well as externalizing behavior, aggression, delinquency, and criminal behavior. Posttraumatic stress symptoms are not uncommon, and maltreated children additionally have poorer cognitive abilities and school performance. Children who are neglected and/or abused across developmental periods have more negative social and cognitive outcomes compared to those who are maltreated during a single developmental period, whereas the developmental timing of the maltreatment does not seem to have a unique impact on behavioral or cognitive competence (see Jaffee & Maikovich-Fong, 2011).

A recent report from a prospective study of low-income families, followed for more than 10 years, identified five factors that predict child maltreatment (Dubowitz, Kim, Black, Weisbart, Semiatin, & Magder, 2011):

1. *Students with developmental problems and those who are not delayed but function at a below-average level* are at greatest risk for maltreatment.
2. *Families with low income* and with *mothers who have low education* also increase the risk of maltreatment, perhaps due to poorer problem-solving skills and fewer financial or community resources to assist with childrearing.
3. *Parental depression* increases the risk of child maltreatment and depression.
4. *Parental substance use* increases the risk for maltreatment. Depression has been linked to inattention to parenting, and substance use renders parents unavailable emotionally to their children or to active parenting.
5. *Large families and multiple children* are risk factors as well. These risks are exacerbated when mothers are single parents, without a partner to offset these vulnerabilities.

In summary, a brief screen for five factors can identify students vulnerable to maltreatment so that preventive services can be facilitated: child below average development or having developmental delay, low maternal education/low income, maternal depression, maternal substance use, and multiple children in the family.

ESSENTIALS

Risk factors for child maltreatment:

- Below-average development or developmental delay

- Low parental education/income

- Parental depression

- Parental substance abuse

- Multiple children in the family

School and Peer Influences

The influence of the school context is largely through the teacher in the classroom. In the classroom, teachers operate as an authority to impart information, reinforce socially appropriate behavior and expectations for conduct in the classroom, and provide guidance for classroom and school norms. In addition, teachers have the role of facilitator of students' social interactions, opportunities, and general peer dynamics (Farmer, Lines, & Hamm, 2011). Collectively, research reviews suggest that students with behavior problems are likely to develop conflicted relationships with teachers that, in turn, further support students' social and emotional problems. In addition to establishing the overall classroom climate and a relationship with the students as a group, the distinct relationships teachers have with individual students are also important. There is evidence that the interactions become synchronized in ways that sustain or support students' problem behavior. Poor student–teacher relationships, then, present a vulnerability for behavior problems and, hence, depression.

Poor student–teacher relationships present vulnerability for behavior problems and depression.

Although peer group process is not an explicit focus of classroom instruction, there is evidence that peer relations influence engagement in learning and academic achievement (Kindermann, 2007; Kindermann & Skinner, 2009; Skinner, Furrer, Marchand, & Kindermann, 2008). Notably, student peer groups are homogeneous in their members' levels of classroom engagement, and this influence extends across the academic year and exists over and above contributions from parents and teachers (Kindermann, 2007). It seems that peer engagement makes a direct contribution to the individual's engagement (Kindermann & Skinner, 2009) and may make a contribution to students' learning and success through the supports or distractions the peer group offers. For example, peers highly engaged in learning are more likely to teach or tutor one another, help keep track of assignments, or study together whereas those not so highly engaged provide alternative, distracting activities that compete with learning and academic work. Furthermore, students who are engaged are more likely to secure a teacher's involvement, whereas those who are disaffected or disengaged from learning are likely to experience teachers becoming more controlling, punitive, and withdrawn from involvement with them (Skinner, Furrer, Marchand, & Kindermann, 2008). It is, therefore, not surprising that teachers' ability to manage both the instructional and behavioral climates of the classroom has been linked to the concurrent and subsequent educational adjustment of students (Farmer et al., 2011). Creating a mix of engaged and less-engaged students, as well as sustaining involvement with all students, becomes crucial to student motivation and learning.

"Troubled peer relationships present vulnerability for depression and, in turn, may directly contribute to depressive symptoms."

Peer groups and social acceptance also have enormous implications for student emotional adjustment. The acceptance or rejection of students by their peers is an important factor for mental health and social and academic adjustment. Students that are aggressive tend to be rejected and those that are socially inhibited or wary tend to be ignored or neglected. Those who are less liked by their peers are prone to more depressive symptoms and, in turn, are likely to be rejected. The consistency of such findings has led to the development of interventions to promote positive peer relationships in order to reduce socio-emotional problems (Zimmer-Gembeck, Waters, & Kindermann, 2009). Therefore, troubled peer relationships present vulnerability for depression and, in turn, may directly contribute to depressive symptoms.

KEYS TO COLLABORATION

■ Decreasing risk factors for depression in school, at home, and in the community will require that key stakeholders from each setting collaborate in order to make a significant impact.

Community Risk Factors

According to statistics provided by the National Center for Children Exposed to Violence, 30% to 90% of children and adolescents witness family and community violence in a given year. Exposure to family or community violence has been linked to anxiety and other internalizing symptoms that typically co-occur with depression (Mian, Wainwright, Briggs-Gowan, & Carter, 2011). However, witnessing violence in the community has not been linked directly to depression. It is thought that community violence, poverty, and other disadvantages influence parents and their mental health, and thereby their attention to parenting, factors that directly create vulnerability for depression in children and adolescents. Thus, community and neighborhood disadvantages influence the family in ways that contribute to depression in students and could be more distal risk factors to which school personnel should be alert. However, it is crucial to recognize victims of violence in this context. As with maltreatment, victims of violence experience more than the wounds inflicted, including depression, anxiety, fear, and posttraumatic stress syndrome (Connor, Fletcher, & Sokol, 2011).

```
┌─────────────────────────────────────┐
│      COMMUNITY RISK FACTORS          │
│          FOR DEPRESSION              │
│                                      │
│   ■ Poverty                          │
│                                      │
│   ■ Violence                         │
│                                      │
│   ■ Unsafe neighborhoods             │
│                                      │
│   Sources: NRC & IOM (2009),         │
│   among others.                      │
└─────────────────────────────────────┘
```

```
┌─────────────────────────────────────┐
│           RTI CONNECTIONS            │
│                                      │
│  ■ Tier 1: Reducing environmental    │
│    risk factors is part of the       │
│    effort to increase the ca-        │
│    pacity to serve students within   │
│    the    gen-                       │
│    eral education program.           │
│                                      │
│  ■ Tier 1 and 2: Assessment of       │
│    protective and risk factors may   │
│    be part of screening efforts.     │
│                                      │
│  ■ Tier 2 and 3: Groups or           │
│    individual programs designed to   │
│    address individual risk factors   │
│    (e.g., cognitive therapy to       │
│    counter negative thinking         │
│    styles) or environmental risk     │
│    factors (e.g., peer rejection)    │
│    identified through screening      │
│    may be provided.                  │
└─────────────────────────────────────┘
```

NURTURING ENVIRONMENTS

Noting that the 2009 Institute of Medicine report on prevention of mental, emotional, and behavioral disorders (NRC & IOM, 2009) found that most mental health problems, including depression, develop from the same environmental conditions, Biglan and colleagues proposed a general strategy of increasing the prevalence of *nurturing environments* as a way to prevent mental health problems (Biglan, Flay, Embry, & Sandler, 2012). Synthesizing data on protective and risk factors, they define nurturing environments as those that enhance successful development and prevent psychological problems. There are four main characteristics of these environments:

- They minimize biological and psychologically toxic conditions.

- They teach and reinforce pro-social behavior.

- They monitor and limit opportunities for problem behavior.

- They promote psychological flexibility.

Biglan and colleagues (2012) noted, "If we want to prevent multiple problems and increase the prevalence of young people who develop successfully, we must increase the prevalence of nurturing environments" (p. 258). They concluded with a call for a widespread public health movement dedicated to increasing the prevalence of nurturing environments and suggest a number of steps for bringing such a movement about.

ACTION PLAN

- Educate school personnel, parents, students, and community leaders about the influence of various risk factors that can cause depression and other mental health problems.

- Assess risk factors for depression among the students in your school. Choose important and modifiable ones and work on reducing them. Collaborative family–school–community teams can help with this.

■ Advocate for the creation of nurturing environments for children and adolescents through increasing protective factors and decreasing risk factors in family, school, and community environments.

RESOURCES

The 2009 report from the National Research Council and Institute of Medicine (NRC & IOM) entitled *Preventing Mental, Emotional, And Behavioral Disorders Among Young People: Progress and Possibilities* has an excellent chapter on risk and protective factors. It also provides a chart (pp. 522–525) listing risk factors related *specifically* to the development of depression by age range in the four areas of individual, family, school and peers, and neighborhood and family. The entire report is available free of charge for reading online (http://www.nap.edu/openbook.php?record_id=12480&page=R1).

REFERENCES

American Academy of Pediatrics. (2000). The pediatrician and childhood bereavement. *Pediatrics, 105*(2), 445-447. doi: 10.1542/peds.105.2.445

Biglan, A., Flay, B. R., Embry, D. D., & Sandler, I. N. (2012). The critical role of nurturing environments for promoting human well-being. *American Psychologist, 67*(4), 257–271.

Burstein, M., Ameli-Grillon, L., & Merikangas, K. R. (2011). Shyness versus social phobia in US youth. *Pediatrics, 128*(5), 917-925. Doi:10.1542/peds.2011-1434

Committee on Psychosocial Aspects of Child and Family. (2002). The pediatrician and childhood bereavement. *Pediatrics, 105*(2), 445-447. doi:10.1542/peds.105.2.445

Dubowitz, H., Kim, J., Black, M. M., Weisbart, C., Semiatin, J., & Magder, L. S. (2011). Identifying children at high risk for a child maltreatment report. *Child Abuse & Neglect, 35*(2), 96-104. doi:10.1016/j.chiabu.2010.09.003

Farmer, T. W., Lines, M. M., & Hamm, J. J. (2011). Revealing the invisible hand: The role of teachers in children's peer experiences. *Journal of Applied Developmental Psychology, 32*(5), 247-256. doi:10.1016/j.appdev.2011.04.006

Houck, G. M. (1999). The measurement of child characteristics from infancy to toddlerhood: Temperament, developmental competence, self-concept, and social competence. *Issues in Comprehensive Pediatric Nursing, 22*(2-3), 107-127. doi:0.1080/014608699265329

Insel, T. R., & Scolnick, E. M. (2006). Cure therapeutics and strategic prevention: Raising the bar for mental health research. *Molecular Psychiatry, 11*(1), 11-17. Retrieved from: http://www.nimh.nih.gov/about/director/publications/cure-therapeutics-and-strategic-prevention-raising-the-bar-for-mental-health-research.shtml doi: 10.1038/sj.mp.4001777

Jaffee, S. R., & Maikovich-Fong, A. K. (2011). Effects of chronic maltreatment and maltreatment timing on children's behavior and cognitive abilities. *Journal of Child Psychology and Psychiatry, 52*(2), 184-194. doi: 0.1111/j.1469-7610.2010.02304.x

Jaffee, S. R., Moffitt, T. E., Caspi, A., Fombonne, E., Poulton, R., & Martin, J. (2002). Differences in early childhood risk factors for juvenile-onset and adult-onset depression. *Archives of General Psychiatry, 59*(3), 215-222. doi:10.1001/archpsyc.59.3.215

Karevold, E., Roysamb, E., Ystrom, E., & Mathiesen, K. S. (2009). Predictors and pathways from infancy to symptoms of anxiety and depression in early adolescence. *Developmental Psychology, 45*(4), 1051-1060. doi:10.1037/a0016123

Keenan, K., Hipwell, A., Feng, X., Rischall, M., Henneberger, A., & Klosterman, S. (2010). Lack of assertion, peer victimization, and risk for depression in girls: Testing a diathesis-stress model. *Journal of Adolescent Health, 47*(5), 526-528. doi:10.1016/j.jadohealth.2010.03.016

Kindermann, T. A. (2007). Effects of naturally existing peer groups on changes in academic engagement in a cohort of sixth graders. *Child Development, 78*(4), 1186-1203. doi: 10.1111/j.1467-8624.2007.01060.x

Kindermann, T. A., & Skinner, E. A. (2009). How do naturally existing peer groups shape children's academic development during sixth grade? *European Journal of Psychological Science, 3*(1), 31-43.

Kovacs, M., Devlin, B., Pollack, M., Richards, C., & Mukerji, P. (1997). A controlled family history study of childhood-onset depressive disorders. *Archives of General Psychiatry, 54*(7), 613-623. doi:10.1001/archpsyc.1997.01830190033004

Leslie, L. K., James, S., Monn, A. R., Kauten, M. C., Zhang, J. J., & Aarons, G. A. (2010). Health-risk behaviors in young adolescents in the child welfare system. *Journal of Adolescent Health, 47*(1), 26-34. doi:10.1016/j.jadohealth.2009.12.032

Mazza, j. J., Fleming, C. B., Abbott, R. D., Haggerty, K. P., & Catalano, R. F. (2010). Identifying trajectories of adolescents' depressive phenomena: An examination of early risk factors. *Journal of Youth and Adolescence, 39*(6), 579-593. doi:10.1007/s10964-009-9406-z

Mian, N. D., Wainwright, L., Briggs-Gowan, M. J., & Carter, A. S. (2011). An ecological risk model for early childhood anxiety: The importance of early child symptoms and temperament. *Journal of Abnormal Child Psychology, 39*(4), 501-512. doi:10.1007/s10802-010-9476-0

National Research Council and Institute of Medicine. (2009). *Preventing mental, emotional, and behavioral disorders among young people: Progress and possibilities.* Washington, DC: National Academies Press. Retrieved from http://www.nap.edu/openbook.php?record_id=12480&page=R1

Pelaez, M., Field, T., Pickens, J. N., & Hart, S. (2008). Disengaged and authoritarian parenting behavior of depressed mothers with their toddlers. *Infant Behavior and Development, 31*(1), 145-148. doi:10.1016/j.infbeh.2007.06.002

Skinner, E., Furrer, C., Marchand, G., & Kindermann, T. (2008). Engagement and disaffection in the classroom: Part of a larger motivational dynamic? *Journal of Educational Psychology, 100*(4), 765-781. doi:10.1037/a0012840

Thomas, A., & Chess, S. (1977). *Temperament and development.* Oxford, England: Brunner/Mazel.

Thompson, R., & Wiley, T. R. (2009). Predictors of re-referral to child protective services: A longitudinal follow-up of an urban cohort maltreated as infants. *Child Maltreatment, 14*(1), 89-99. doi:10.1177/1077559508325317

U.S. Department of Health & Human Services, Administration for Children and Families, Administration on Children, Youth, and Families, and Children's Bureau. (2010). *Child Maltreatment 2010.* Washington D.C.: Children's Bureau. Retrieved from http://www.acf.hhs.gov/programs/cb/stats_research/index.htm#can.

Weissman, M. M., Warner, V., Wickramaratne, P., Moreau, d., & Olfson, M. (1997). Offspring of depressed parents: 10 years later. *Archives of General Psychiatry, 54*(10), 932-940. doi:10.1001/archpsyc.1997.01830220054009

Zimmer-Gembeck, M. J., Waters, A. M., & Kindermann, T. (2010). A social relations analysis of liking for and by peers: Associations with gender, depression, peer perception, and worry. *Journal of Adolescence, 33*(1), 69-81. doi:10.1016/j.adolescence.2009.05.005

CHAPTER 9

RECOGNIZING STUDENTS WITH DEPRESSION: SCREENING FOR PREVENTION

Screening is a way of assessing large groups of students (classrooms, schools, districts) to identify those who might have or be at risk for having a disorder or disability. For example, in schools, we screen all students for math problems by administering benchmarking tests several times per year. Some schools also use office discipline referrals, absences, and other similar data to screen for students at risk for academic, behavioral, or mental health problems. The results in all cases are used to develop programs and interventions to identify at-risk students early and provide them with interventions designed to prevent their problems from getting worse. Depression is treatable; it is also preventable if discovered early. Screening is an important component of a comprehensive, coordinated approach to preventing depression.

MENTAL HEALTH SCREENING IN SCHOOLS

An increasingly large number of medical and mental health associations, state and federal agencies, and advocacy groups support mental health screening for youth in one form or another (for a list, see National Center for Mental Health Checkups, 2003). Within the school mental health literature, universal screening for depression and other behavioral health problems is considered best practice. For ex-

ample, the President's New Freedom Commission on Mental Health (2003) and the National Association of School Psychologists (NASP, 2009) support universal social, emotional, and behavioral screening in schools to identify students at risk for social and emotional difficulties. Research indicates that (a) students are generally unlikely to seek professional help on their own for depression and suicide, (b) a screening process is likely to identify students that otherwise might not be found, and (c) identified students are then more likely to accept professional treatment and reduce their level of risk (Robinson et al., 2011).

ESSENTIALS

- Students are generally unlikely to seek professional help on their own for depression and suicide.

- A screening process is likely to identify students that otherwise might not be found.

- Identified students are then more likely to accept professional treatment and reduce their level of risk.

Unfortunately, only a very small percentage of schools implement systematic, universal screening for mental disorders. Many still rely to a great extent on teacher referrals, a practice derided as a "wait to fail" approach when used for academic problems. The opportunity to detect depression or other mental health issues at an early stage, when interventions aimed at prevention have the best chance of working, is typically not realized (Levitt & Merrell 2009). However, an ever-increasing number of schools are implementing a systematic, universal process for identifying *academic* problems—within a response-to-intervention (RTI) framework. This framework, and the mindset it engenders, offers a good context within which to start moving schools to a more prevention and early intervention approach to students' behavioral and mental health needs. Universal screening is an important tool in such a process.

> *"Within the school mental health literature, universal screening for depression and other behavioral health problems is considered best practice."*

TYPES OF SCREENING APPROACHES

Referral-Based Screening

In a referral-based system, a student's depressive symptoms have to be significant enough to catch the teacher's attention and prompt him or her to make the appropriate referral. Problems with this approach are well known: (a) lack of knowledge about the symptoms of depression, (b) varying thresholds for referring students, (c) the nature of internalizing disorders, and (d) other classroom problems

seen as higher priorities for referral. Teachers are often unfamiliar with the signs or symptoms of mental disorders and have different levels of tolerance and competence for working with students with emotional or behavioral problems, and therefore refer at different rates. That is, the same student, showing exactly the same behavior, might be referred if he happened to have one teacher and not referred if he happened to have another. These problems are exacerbated when working with internalizing disorders because the behaviors in question are frequently invisible; that is, they consist of thoughts and emotions that are internal to the student. Even when teachers are knowledgeable about internalizing disorders, students with externalizing disorders are often first on the list for referral to mental health services because of their disruptive effect on the classroom environment. As a result, teachers are generally better at identifying students with externalizing than internalizing problems.

ESSENTIALS

Teacher referrals can be unreliable because of:

- Lack of knowledge about depression

- Varying thresholds for referring the student

- The often invisible nature of depression

- Other classroom problems seen as higher priorities

One way some schools attempt to improve somewhat on this approach is to ask teachers to identify all students in their class about whom they have concerns in various social, emotional, or behavioral areas (Burns, Deno, & Jimerson, 2007). The list would then be further screened by a school mental health professional in order to identify students who need further assessment or intervention (a form of multi-stage screening; see below). This approach can also be improved by professional development for teachers on how to identify students with depression and other internalizing problems.

Nevertheless, relying on teacher referral as a screening method for mental health issues typically results in a large number of false-negative errors (i.e., under-identification of truly depressed students), and epidemiological studies generally show that referral-based methods are inadequate for internalizing disorders. What is needed is a more systematic method of universal screening for emotional and behavioral problems that is specifically sensitive to internalizing disorders such as anxiety and depression.

"Epidemiological studies generally show that referral-based methods are inadequate for internalizing disorders."

> **ESSENTIALS**
>
> ■ Assessing protective factors is much easier than assessing risk factors in the school environment.
>
> ■ Assessment of strengths and developmental assets forms the basis for building students' resilience.

Assessing Risk Factors

Some schools screen for social, emotional, and behavioral problems by screening all students for the presence of risk indicators (e.g., office discipline referrals, visits to school mental health professionals, absences). In these kinds of approaches, students who exhibit a criterion level for number of indicators are identified as at risk and provided with further assessment. This approach can be effective but, as typically implemented, it is much more likely to identify students with externalizing than internalizing behaviors. The approach can be improved, however, by including screeners for risk factors associated specifically with depression (e.g., divorce, difficult or slow-to-warm-up temperament, poor peer relationships), or for risk factors that are not specific to depression but associated more broadly with behavioral or mental health problems in general. Some school-wide intervention programs include such screening instruments as part of their curricular materials.

"When implemented with appropriate family, school, and community involvement, mental health screening in schools has the potential to be a cornerstone of a transformed mental health system that identifies youth in need, links them to effective services, and contributes to positive health and educational outcomes valued by families, schools, and communities." (Weist, Rubin, Moore, Adelsheim, & Wrobel, 2007, p. 57)

Assessment of some risk factors can be very difficult in a school environment (e.g., parental depression; Baker, 2008). Assessment of protective factors is seldom difficult, and the results can be used to design interventions that build resilience and protect against risk factors. Efforts to strengthen the protective factors in the lives of students are central to building resilience and enhancing the process of coping with stressors, adversity, or change so that positive developmental outcomes are achieved. Foundational to building resilience is the assessment of assets or strengths. Strength-based assessment is rooted in positive psychology, an umbrella term for the study of positive emotions and character strengths, and the institutions that sup-

Table 1. Examples of Resources for Screening Protective Factors

Name	Description	Access
Search Institute	Grades 4–12; surveys of 40 developmental assets.	http://www.search-institute.org
Collaborative for Academic, Social, and Emotional Learning (CASEL)	Grades K–12; measures for student school climate and student outcomes; many other tools for SEL programs and assessment. See "Compendium of SEL Assessment Tools" (http://casel.org/publications/compendium-of-sel-assessment-tools)	http://casel.org/in-schools/assessment
Psycho-Social Environment Profile	Survey completed by school staff to assess various contextual protective factors in a school	World Health Organization: *Creating an Environment of Emotional and Social Wellbeing* (http://www.who.int/school_youth_health/media/en/sch_childfriendly_03_v2.pdf)

port them (Seligman, Steen, Park, & Peterson, 2005). The overall aim of positive psychology and its interventions is to increase individual happiness or well-being through three distinct routes: positive emotion and pleasure, engagement, and meaning. Consistent with this perspective, strength-based assessment focuses on identifying strengths and assets that support positive growth and, accordingly, providing intervention that emphasizes promoting mental health and well-being even in the face of adverse experiences (Beaver, 2008; Felver-Gant & Merrell, 2009). Baker (2008) reviewed a number of instruments designed to assess individual and contextual protective factors. A sampling of these is summarized in Table 1.

One of the few practical assessment tools designed to evaluate protective factors that promote resilience in children and adolescents is the Social–Emotional Assets and Resilience Scales (SEARS; Merrell, 2008). The SEARS is a strength-based assessment for assessing positive social-emotional characteristics of children and adolescents that cluster around four social–emotional assets:

- *Self-Regulation*: self-awareness, meta cognition, intrapersonal insight, self-management, and self-direction

- *Social Competence*: the ability to make and maintain friendships, verbal effectiveness, and comfort around groups of peers

- *Empathy*: the ability to empathize with the feelings and situations of others

- *Responsibility*: acceptance of responsibility, conscientiousness, and reflective thinking

> *"Efforts to strengthen the protective factors in the lives of students are central to building resilience and enhancing the process of coping with stressors, adversity, or change so that positive developmental outcomes are achieved"*

The SEARS assessments were designed for screening, assessment, intervention planning, monitoring, and evaluation from a strength-based perspective. There are four different measures: a teacher rating scale, parent rating scale, student self-report for students in grades 3–6 and 7–9. The items are worded as positive and desirable characteristics with higher ratings/scores reflecting more of that characteristic. The scales are estimated to take about 20 minutes to administer and 20 minutes to score. There are also short forms available, with just 12 items each, for children, adolescents, parents, and teachers. The total score on these short forms reflect the more global social resilience score assessed by the full scales, and seem to be fairly reliable. The measures have been found to be strongly correlated with measures of emotional problems and to have adequate internal consistency.

More information about the SEARS assessment system and its development may be found at http://strongkids.uoregon.edu/SEARS, where examples of the items for the student self-report assessments may be reviewed. The scales themselves are available for purchase through www.parinc.com.

One caution regarding screening for risk and protective factors is that the instruments used frequently lack standardization of procedures or national normative samples against which to judge students' behavior. The use of more psychometrically sophisticated behavioral rating scales and self-report instruments can help overcome these limitations. In any event, the powerful role of nurturing environments in preventing most mental, emotional, and behavioral disorders (Biglan, Flay, Embry, & Sandler, 2012) suggests that risk and protective factors, both individual (within the student) and contextual (within the family–school–community environment) should be routinely assessed. The results of these assessments should then be used in two ways: (a) to design interventions for individual students who are at risk for depression and other mental health problems and (b) to intervene school-wide in areas where protective factors are weak and risk factors are high.

Teacher Rating Scales and Student Self-Report Measures

The use of teacher rating scales and, especially, student self-report measures can help to increase the accuracy of a screening process, especially in the case of internalizing disorders (because the students have access to their inner thoughts and feelings). As an example, Levitt and Merrell (2009) suggest a general ap-

proach to screening for internalizing disorders that involves two parts: student self-reports and teacher rating scales. They suggest using subscales of internalizing behavior taken from a comprehensive behavior rating instrument and identifying for further assessment students scoring at or above the 75th percentile on both teacher and student ratings.

ESSENTIALS

■ Risk and protective factors should be routinely assessed in schools.

■ School risk indicators (e.g. discipline referrals, absences) are more likely to reflect externalizing than internalizing behaviors.

■ Student self-reports and teacher rating scales can increase screening accuracy, particularly when used together.

■ Screening results may be used to design interventions for individual students and suggest programmatic changes in the school or district.

Multi-Stage Screening

Multi-gate or multi-stage screening (e.g., using a self-report measure followed by interviews or teacher/parent rating scales with flagged students) is one way to improve the accuracy of screening. These approaches are characterized by successive stages (or gates) of screening through which students must pass in order to be identified. A good example of this kind of approach is the Systematic Screening for Behavior Disorders (SSBD; Walker & Severson, 1992), which utilizes teacher rankings of students on evidence of internalizing and externalizing disorders as the first screening stage. Students flagged at this stage are further screened at stage two with behavioral check-

ESSENTIALS

- A multi-stage screening process integrates progressively in-depth assessments of students deemed at risk.

- Three stages include initial teacher referral, behavioral checklists, and direct observation by a mental health professional.

lists. Stage three involves direct observation of students flagged at stage two. Students identified at the observation stage are considered for further assessment or targeted (RTI tier 2) intervention. Another good example of an instrument that may be used alone or as part of a multi-stage screening process is the BASC-2 Behavioral and Emotional Screening System (BESS; Kamphaus & Reynolds, 2007). Commonly used screening measures that focus on suicide behavior among secondary school students are the Columbia TeenScreen program and Signs of Suicide prevention program.

Screening to Determine Appropriate Interventions

A potential limitation of procedures that screen for broad categories of problems becomes evident when teams begin to use the results of those screening instruments to design targeted interventions at tier 2 of their RTI framework. The categories identified are sometimes too broad to allow accurate assignment of students to appropriate interventions. For example, a screening procedure that identifies students as having either internalizing or externalizing problems gives some guidance as to programming (we probably will at least have separate groups for students showing internalizing and externalizing behavior). But

within those broad categories are students with possibly different needs. For example, within the internalizing group, students with depression may not need the same interventions as those with withdrawn, anxious, or somatic behavior. The closer a targeted intervention is related to the specific problems exhibited by students, the more effective it will be.

Screenings are not used for diagnosis, but to identify at-risk students and assist in determining appropriate interventions. Sometimes, however, a more in-depth screening can improve the chances of developing an intervention that will be successful. For example, a more comprehensive behavioral rating scale may be used (with parent permission and not for diagnosis or classification) for this purpose. Advantages of a more in-depth screening include the following:

- Because other social, emotional, and behavioral problems often co-occur with depression, comprehensive screening of this type helps to identify those problems and, more importantly, provides information that could be very helpful in intervention planning.

- In addition to greatly enhancing the screening process for internalizing disorders, comprehensive screening approaches also supplement and enhance a school's screening procedures (e.g., ODRS, attendance) for externalizing disorders.

- Some students may not attain a clinically significant score on any single scale but may, when given a broadband screening instrument, show subclinical elevations on a number of scales which, when taken together, may indicate a child or adolescent at significant risk. A more narrowband screening approach would probably not identify such a student.

■ Many broadband screening instruments include scales for adaptive skills that provide information important to intervention planning. Including adaptive skills in a screening process has also been shown to increase its acceptability to teachers (DiStefano et al., 2003).

■ Computerized administration and scoring of comprehensive screening instruments (e.g., AIMSweb Behavior) make this approach efficient and ultimately also useful for progress monitoring.

See Table 2 for information about sample screening instruments. The National Assembly on School-Based Health Care also offers a list of screening and assessment tools for mental health problems on its website (http://www.nasbhc.org/site/c.ckLQKbOVLkK6E/b.7697107/apps/s/content.asp?ct=11072845).

Table 2. Examples of Screening Instruments

Name	Description	Access
AIMSweb Behavior	Grades K–12 web-based screening, progress monitoring, data management with intervention resources	http://www.aimsweb.com/behavior
BASC-2/Behavior and Emotional Screening Scale (BESS)	Grades K–12 screens internalizing, externalizing, and adaptive skills	Kamphaus & Reynolds, (2007)
SOS Signs of Suicide Prevention Program	Grades 5–12 universal depression and suicide screening and training for students	http://www.mentalhealthscreening.org/programs/youth-prevention-programs/sos
Systematic Screening for Behavior Disorders (SSBD)	Grades K–6 multiple-gating system	Walker & Severson (1992); http://store.cambiumlearning.com
TeenScreen	Ages 11–18 screening for depression, suicide, and other mental health issues	National Center for Mental Health Checkups at Columbia University; www.teenscreen.org

---

ESSENTIALS

- Screening for identification of a mental health problem in broad categories is often not adequate for use in designing interventions at Tier 2.

- The closer a targeted intervention is related to the specific problems exhibited by students, the more effective it will be.

- More comprehensive behavior rating scales can be used to design appropriate interventions.

CHALLENGES TO THE USE OF UNIVERSAL SCREENING FOR MENTAL HEALTH IN SCHOOLS

Despite clear evidence that universal screening is critical to getting children and youth needed mental health supports and that schools can play a vital role in the process, schools can face a number of barriers to implementing screening programs of this kind. One often-voiced concern is that using school time for screening and such activities as social emotional learning (SEL) programs might detract from instructional time and result in lower academic outcomes. Research has found, however, that this is not the case and that, in fact, school-wide academic outcomes *improve* by about 11 percentile points on average when SEL programs are present (Durlak, Weissberg, Dymnicki, Taylor, & Schellinger, 2011). Computer-assisted administration and scoring methods make use of screening strategies increasingly feasible for school use.

Perhaps the greatest challenge to widespread adoption of universal screening lies in its ac-

ceptability to parents, teachers, administrators, and even some school mental health professionals. The main concerns are usually that screening might lead to increased medication of students, and the possibility that students and parents might be stigmatized and embarrassed.

"Quality screening and early intervention should occur in readily accessible, low-stigma settings, such as primary health care facilities and schools...."
(*The President's New Freedom Commission on Mental Health, p.* 60)

There are also a variety of legal and ethical issues to consider regarding the use of universal screening in schools. Three issues are particularly important: (a) parental prior notice and student assent, (b) the possibility of student stigmatization, and (c) ensuring that the school has the resources to follow-up with students identified through the screening (Jacob, Decker, & Hartshorne, 2011). In developing a screening program, the school should consider legal and ethical requirements, including those of the Protection of Pupil Rights Amendment (2001), FERPA, state laws, district policies, and professional ethics codes. Procedures should be implemented that allow parents or guardians to inspect the screening tools prior to their use and to exempt their child from screening, to inform students about the use of screening data and give them a chance to opt out of the screening, and to protect confidentiality of the results (Jacob et al., 2011). Screening procedures should be integrated into the ongoing activities of the general education program so as to reduce the potential for stigmatizing individual students.

KEY MESSAGES TO CONVEY ABOUT UNIVERSAL SCREENING

- Screening will not occur without the consent of parents and assent of students.

- Screening can identify students at risk for emotional and behavioral problems that can have lifelong implications if left untreated.

- Mental health problems that warrant diagnosis do not simply go away by themselves

- Interventions that improve student outcomes can be implemented by school mental health professionals.

- In the case of depression and its close link to suicide, screening can even save lives.

- Appropriate screening and talking about depression and suicide do not cause distress among students.

When conducting a screening program, schools must ensure that identified students receive services (Jacob et al., 2011). Although about 10%–15% of the student population is typically identified as at risk by a screening, note that the actual percentage of *newly* identified students would be lower because many of them will already be known to school mental health providers and not all the rest will need service. A precaution must be taken to train whoever is actually administering the screening instrument to look through each of the protocols immediately after administration for key items suggesting the possibility of suicide so that those students can be seen immediately by a school mental health professional (i.e., there should be no delay in referral of those students). Reviewing plans with the school district attorney prior to implementing a screening program is good practice.

These are reasonable concerns that need to be openly discussed with all members of the home–school community. Embedding screening as part of an integrated continuum of social, emotional, and behavioral health services; establishment of collaborative relationships; respectful discussion of the issues; and education about screening prior to implementing the screening program are needed to help mitigate these concerns. Developing and using consistent key messages in communications can reduce confusion about and resistance to implementing universal screening (see inset box). When done well, screening and talking about topics such as depression and suicide do not cause distress among students (Robinson et al., 2011). The evidence for the value of screening for depression and suicide is overwhelming (Mazza & Reynolds, 2008). Decreasing costs, improved efficiency and feasibility, and increasing awareness in the home–school community of the importance of prevention and early intervention are slowly gaining acceptance and helping to make screening more of a mainstream concept.

"Despite the potential challenges inherent in implementation, some version of universal screening for depression and other mental disorders should be established in each school district. "

Once a decision has been made about what to screen for, the choice of instruments can be fairly straightforward and will probably be based on issues of affordability, feasibility, and acceptance by the home–school community.

HOW OFTEN SHOULD SCREENING BE DONE?

Universal screening of all students has a variety of advantages including efficiency and broad coverage. In many schools, however, the cost of such an approach may be prohibitive. In these cases, a more manageable approach might be to focus screening efforts based on the developmental stage of the students or on times of significant transitions. In the case of depression, this would mean focusing screening mostly on middle and high school students (because of the higher incidence of depressed behavior in those groups), and at transition points such as entrance to middle school and high school. This is clearly a second-best approach, however, because it neglects elementary students and sacrifices the best chance for earliest intervention.

Universal academic screening within an RTI framework is typically conducted three times a year as part of the benchmarking process. The same could be done for depression and other mental health issues, but perhaps more feasible would be to screen twice per year, once during the fall benchmarking period and then again during the winter benchmarking period. Even with universal screening twice per year, it must be remembered that symptoms of depression (as well as other mental health issues) wax and wane over the course of a year and there is no guarantee that a twice-yearly screening will occur at the same time that individual students are experiencing and reporting these symptoms. Moreover, provision would need to be made for students who transfer in to a school and miss universal screenings: They would need to be individually screened at admission or would need to wait for the next benchmarking period. Despite these limitations, universal screening of this kind is likely to be the most effective in identifying students at risk for depression and other mental health problems. Indeed, more

---

ESSENTIALS

■ Risk factors can be identified among young children.

■ An early experience of depressive symptoms predicts later depression.

■ Reducing initial episodes of depressed behavior reduces the probability of later episodes.

■ Screening of students in early grades can be an important part of efforts to reduce depressed behavior of students throughout school and adult life.

important than how many times it is done or when it is done is that some form of screening takes place during the school year.

SCREENING IN THE PRIMARY GRADES

Most schools do not routinely assess first and second graders for risk factors associated with depression. However, recent research has shown that risk factors can be identified in young children (NRC & IOM, 2009), that children are able to reliably report symptoms of anxiety and depression, and that these reports are predictive of depression in adolescence (Ialongo, Edelsohn, & Kellam, 2001; Mazza et al., 2010). This line of research confirms that early experience of anxious or depressed behavior contributes to the emergence of later depressive symptoms, suggesting that reducing initial episodes of depression should be given the highest priority (Munoz, Beardslee, & Leykin, 2012). Given that risk factors for depression can be identified during the primary grades and that, indeed, children in first and second grade can reliably report some of these themselves, screening at this age may be an important part of any campaign to reduce depression throughout school and adult life.

ESSENTIALS

- Considerations for timing of mental health screenings are essentially the same as those for academic screenings.

- More important than how many times a year or what time of year screenings are done is that some form of screening for depression and other mental health issues take place during the school year.

RTI CONNECTIONS

- Universal screening for students at risk for academic problems is already a part of the RTI process.

- Begin to incorporate universal screening for mental health problems into the RTI process in your school.

ACTION PLAN

Despite the potential challenges inherent in implementation, some version of universal screening for depression and other mental disorders should be established in each school district. This is best done as part of a comprehensive, coordinated continuum of support for the social, emotional, and behavioral development of students.

- Establish a collaborative team comprising key family–school–community stakeholders to investigate, develop, and implement a mental health screening process for the school or district.

- Decide what you want to screen for: protective or risk factors, depression alone, depression plus suicide, or a broader array of mental health risks.

- Choose an appropriate screening procedure on the basis of affordability, feasibility, and acceptance.

- Consider legal and ethical issues and consult with the district's attorney to ensure that any procedures developed meet legal requirements.

- Provide professional development for school personnel on risk factors, signs, symptoms, outcomes, and methods of referral for students exhibiting depressed behavior. Discuss the benefits of mental health screening, how it is to be conducted, and how the results are to be used. Dispel any misunderstandings about mental health screening and promote buy-in among staff.

- Conduct parent education sessions on risk factors, signs, symptoms, outcomes, and methods of referral for students exhibiting depressed behavior. Discuss the benefits of mental health screening, how it is to be conducted, and how the results are to be used. Dispel any misunderstandings about mental health screening.

- Implement the screening process and use results to plan individual and school-wide interventions.

- Evaluate the outcomes of the screening process.

KEYS TO COLLABORATION

- Establish a family–school–community collaborative team prior to planning and initiating a mental health screening process.

- Bring all parents and school staff into the process through a series of professional development activities for staff and parent education activities for families.

RESOURCES

The chapter by J. A. Baker (2008) entitled "Assessing School Risk and Protective Factors" in the book by B. Doll and J. A. Cummings entitled *Population-Based Approaches to Promoting the Competency and Wellness of Children* is an excellent overview of the topic of screening. It provides an overview of key issues, models, and examples of screening processes for school use.

An authoritative discussion of risk and protective factors for depression and other mental health problems, as well as a wide-ranging overview of prevention and intervention for behavioral and mental health problems in children and adolescents, may be found in a publication by the National Research Council and Institute of Medicine (2009), *Preventing Mental, Emotional, and Behavioral Disorders Among Young People: Progress and Possibilities* (http://www.nap.edu/openbook.php?record_id=12480&page=R1).

REFERENCES

Baker, J. A. (2008). Assessing school risk and protective factors. In B. Doll & J. A. Cummings, *Transforming school mental health services: Population-based approaches to promoting the competency and wellness of children* (pp. 43–65). Thousand Oaks, CA: Corwin Press (a joint publication with the National Association of School Psychologists.

Beaver, B. R. (2008). A positive approach to children's internalizing problems. *Professional Psychology Research and Practice, 39*(2), 129–136. doi:10.1037/0735-7028.39.2.129

Burns, M. K., Deno, S. L., & Jimerson, S. R. (2007). Toward a unified response-to-intervention model. In S. R. Jmerson, M. K. Burns, & A. M. VanDerHeyden (Eds.). *Handbook of response to intervention: The science and practice of assessment and intervention* (pp. 428–440). New York, NY: Springer.

Durlak, J. A., Weissberg, R. P., Dymnicki, A. B., Taylor, R. D., & Schellinger, K. B. (2011). The impact of enhancing students' social and emotional learning: A meta-analysis of school-based universal interventions. *Child Development, 82*(1), 405–432.

Felver-Gant, J., & Merrell, K. W. (2009, February). *Teacher ratings of student's assets and resilience: Development of the Sears-T.* Paper presented at Meeting of the National Association of School Psychologists, Boston, MA. Retrieved from http://strongkids.uoregon.edu/SEARS/FelverGant2009.pdf

Ialongo, N.S., Edelsohn, G., & Kellam, S.G. (2001). A further look at the prognostic power of young children's reports of depressed mood and feelings. *Child Development, 72*, 736–747.

Jacob, S., Decker, D. M., & Hartshorne, T. S. (2011). *Ethics and law for school psychologists (6th ed.).* Hoboken, NJ: Wiley.

Levitt, V. H., & Merrell, K. W. (2009). Linking assessment to intervention for internalizing problems of children and adolescents. *School psychology forum: Research and practice, 3*(1), 13–26.

Mazza, J. J., Fleming, C. B., Abbott, R. D., Haggerty, K. P., & Catalano, R. F. (2010). Identifying trajectories of adolescents' depressive phenomena: An examination of early risk factors. *Journal of Youth and Adolescence, 39*(6), 579–593. doi:10.1007/s10964-009-9406-z

Mazza, J. J. & Reynolds, W. M. (2008). School-wide approaches to prevention of and intervention for depression and suicidal behaviors. In B. Doll & J. A. Cummings, *Transforming school mental health service: Population-based approaches to promoting the competency and wellness of children.* Thousand Oaks, CA: Corwin Press (a joint publication with the National Association of School Psychologists).

Merrell, K. W. (2008). *Social-emotional assets and resilience scales (SEARS).* Lutz, FL.: Psychological Assessment Resources, Inc.

Munoz, Beardslee, & Leykin, Y. (2012). Depression can be prevented. *American Psychologist, 67*, 285–295.

National Association of School Psychologists. (2009). *Appropriate behavioral, social, and emotional supports to meet the needs of all students* (Position Statement). Bethesda, MD: Author. Retrieved from http://www.nasponline.org/about_nasp/positionpapers/AppropriateBehavioralSupports.pdf

National Assembly on School-Based Health Care. (n.d.). *Screening and assessment.* Retrieved from http://www.nasbhc.org/site/c.ckLQKbOVLkK6E/b.7697107/apps/s/content.asp?ct=11072845

National Center for Mental Health Checkups at Columbia University. (2003). *Support for screening.* Retrieved from TeenScreen at http://www.teenscreen.org/about/support-endorsements

National Research Council and Institute of Medicine. (2009). *Preventing mental, emotional, and behavioral disorders among young people: Progress and possibilities.* Washington, DC: National Academies Press. Retrieved from http://www.nap.edu/openbook.php?record_id=12480&page=R1

The President's New Freedom Commission on Mental Health. (2003). *Achieving the promise: Transforming mental health care in america.* Retrieved from http://govinfo.library.unt.edu/mentalhealthcommission/reports/reports.htm

Robinson, J., Pan Yuen, H., Martin, C., Hughes, A., Baksheev, G. N., Dodd, S., ... Yung, A. R. (2011). Does screening high school students for psychological distress, deliberate self-harm, or suicidal ideation cause distress—And is it acceptable? *Crisis: The Journal of Crisis Intervention and Suicide Prevention, 32*(5), 254–263. doi:10.1027/0227-5910/a000087

Seligman, M. E. P., Steen, T. A., Park, N., & Peterson, C. (2005). Positive psychology progress: Empirical validation of interventions. *American psychologist, 60*(5), 410–421. doi:10.1037/0003-066X.60.5.410

Walker, B. A. (2010). Effective schoolwide screening to identify students at risk for social and behavioral problems. *Intervention in School and Clinic, 46*(2), 104–110. Retrieved from http://isc.sagepub.com/content/46/2/104.full.pdf+html

Walker, H. M., & Severson, H. (1992). *Systematic screening for behavior disorders (2nd ed.).* Longmont, CO: Sopris West.

Weist, M. D., Rubin, M., Moore, E., Adelsheim, S., & Wrobel, G. (2007). Mental health screening in schools. *Journal of School Health, 77*(2), 53–58.

CHAPTER 10

ASSESSMENT OF DEPRESSION IN CHILDREN AND ADOLESCENTS

Identifying students with depression is the first step toward providing them with appropriate services. At Tier 1 of the response-to-intervention (RTI) model, this is accomplished primarily through the use of universal screening of students for signs and symptoms of depressed behavior. The goal at this level is to identify students at risk for depression who might need targeted (Tier 2) interventions. At this level of intervention, more individualized screening and assessment strategies are often used. The goals of assessment at this tier are to help determine appropriate interventions, assess whether students are responding adequately to intervention, determine whether and when a student might transition back to Tier 1 or on to more intensive services at Tier 3, and determine whether to refer the student for a comprehensive evaluation to determine special education eligibility and classification. At Tier 3, assessment is much more individualized and comprehensive, often involving the use of formal assessment instruments and functional behavioral assessments. Eligibility for special education is often a consideration at this level of assessment. There are two main reasons to conduct an assessment of depression: (a) to determine a diagnosis or special education eligibility classification and (b) to assist in intervention planning.

ASSESSMENT FOR DIAGNOSIS AND CLASSIFICATION

In non-educational settings, the diagnosis of depression is usually made based on DSM-IV-TR criteria. The DSM-IV-TR is also sometimes used in educational settings. More typically, however, the diagnostic categories of IDEA are used in school practice because they are required by law for special education identification. While in many ways they mean the same thing, the term *diagnosis* is most often used in non-school settings and is based on DSM-IV-TR and the term *classification* is used in school settings and is based on IDEA special education categories.

ESSENTIALS

- Identifying students with depression is the first step toward providing them with services.

- In non-educational settings, the DSM-IV-TR is usually used for diagnosis; the IDEA classification system is typically used in schools.

Diagnosis and Classification Using the DSM-IV-TR

Both of the DSM-IV-TR and IDEA classification systems employ discrete diagnoses; that is, either a student has a diagnosis or not—subclinical levels of depressed behavior are not considered. The DSM-IV-TR lists several major diagnostic categories in which symptoms of depression are prominent: (a) depressive disorders (major depressive disorder, dysthymic disorder, depressive disorder not otherwise specified), (b) bipolar disorders (bipolar I, bipolar II, cyclothymic disorder, bipolar disorder not otherwise specified), (c) mood disorder due to a general medical condition, (d) substance-induced mood disorder, and (e) adjustment disorder with depressed mood (see Table 1 for a description of some of them). Other diagnoses can also have symptoms of depression as a related symptom (e.g., anxiety disorders, posttraumatic stress disorder, schizoaffective and schizophrenic disorders,

Table 1. DSM-IV-TR Disorders Having Depressed Behavior as a Prominent Symptom

DSM-IV-TR Diagnostic Category See DSM-IV-TR for subcategories	Primary DSM-IV-TR Symptoms See DSM-IV-TR for specific criteria
Major depressive disorder	Depressed mood; loss of interest or pleasure in activities; weight loss or gain; sleep disturbance; psychomotor retardation or agitation; fatigue; loss of energy; feelings of guilt or worthlessness; reduced ability to think, concentrate, or make decisions; recurrent thoughts of death.
Dysthymic disorder	Symptoms similar to major depressive disorder but chronic (occurring most days for at least one year) and less severe.
Bipolar I disorder	Manic episodes or manic episodes cycling with depressive episodes.
Bipolar II disorder	Recurring depression with hypomanic (i.e., milder than manic) episodes.
Cyclothymic disorder	Periods of depressive and hypomanic symptoms occurring numerous times over a period of at least one year.
Mood disorder due to a general medical condition	Disturbance of mood that is a direct physiological result of a medical condition.
Substance-induced mood disorder	Disturbance of mood resulting from exposure to a substance (drugs, medications, toxins).
Adjustment disorder with depressed mood	Symptoms of depression generally lasting a few months in reaction to stress.
Source: *American Psychiatric Association* (2000).	

and personality disorders). Children and adolescents with a diagnosed depressive disorder also are very likely to have co-occurring disorders. Specifically, they are most susceptible to anxiety, conduct disorder, eating disorders, and substance abuse, with anxiety and behavior disorders the most commonly co-occurring disorders (Avenevoli, Knight, Kessler, & Meridangas, 2008).

> *"Not all students with a DSM-IV-TR diagnosis will qualify for special education (they also must meet the requirement of needing special education)."*

Characteristics of Depression in Children and Adolescents

Diagnostic decisions within the DSM system are based on specific criteria for each disorder. Criteria used for the diagnosis of depression and the related disorders listed in Table 1 are—with minor variation—applied to both children and adults. Nevertheless, while the core symptoms of sadness and hopelessness are present at all ages, there is evidence that variation in symptoms of depression can occur at different stages of development in physiological, social–emotional–behavioral, and cognitive domains (Garber, Gallerani, & Frankel, 2009; Rudolf, 2009). Indeed, children and adolescents often exhibit other signs of depression in addition to those listed in Table 1. Complaints about physical symptoms (watch visits to the nurse's office for stomach aches

and other recurrent, minor maladies) and irritability are two of the most common of these (Merrell, 2008). Physiological, social–emotional–behavioral, and cognitive characteristics of childhood and adolescent depression are summarized below.

> *"It must be kept in mind that not everyone who exhibits these symptoms is depressed; referral to a school mental health professional is a good first step for teachers or parents who have concerns."*

Physiological Signs of Depression in Children and Adolescents

- Changes in sleep patterns, difficulty falling asleep, staying asleep; sleeping much more than is typical for the child's age.

- Unusually low energy, fatigue; sluggishness in moving, talking, reacting; reduced amount of activity or playing.

- Restlessness and agitation, increased fidgeting, squirming; reduced ability to sit still.

- Changes in eating patterns: increased or decreased appetite; weight gain or loss.

- Frequent physical complaints: complaints about illnesses, especially vague ones such as headaches, stomachaches, muscle aches, and tiredness.

Social–Emotional–Behavioral Signs of Depression in Children and Adolescents

- Disengagement from friends, family, teachers; seeking solitude; difficulty with interpersonal relationships.

- Excessive time alone with videogames and other solo activities.

- Reduced participation in previously enjoyed activities; dropping sports and clubs.

- Classroom misbehavior; lack of cooperation.

- Decreased performance in school.

- Tardiness and absence from school.

- Running away or talking about running away.

- Suicidal talk or attempts; reckless behavior; self-injurious behavior.

- Alcohol and/or drug abuse.

- Lack of grooming and self-care.

- Decreased ability to appropriately cope with social events, extracurricular activities, hobbies, and family events.

- Decreased ability to cope with responsibilities.

- Increased sensitivity to failure, rejection, and criticism.

- Increased irritability, anger, brooding, or hostility.

- Increased dependency and insecurity.

- Feelings of sadness, isolation, hopelessness, worthlessness, anxiety, or guilt.

- Crying or verbal outbursts without apparent cause.

Cognitive Signs of Depression in Children and Adolescents

- Poor attention and concentration.

- Poor memory.

- Difficulty completing tasks.

- Difficulty making decisions.

- Pessimistic world-view; perceiving things as worse than they are; negative attributions.

- Negative view of self, life, world, and future.

- Helplessness and hopelessness; belief that there is nothing that can be done about their depression and that this is the way it always will be.

- Low self-esteem; over-focus on one's deficiencies and failures.

- Thoughts of suicide or death; self-destructive thoughts.

ESSENTIALS

- Anxiety, behavior disorders, and substance abuse often accompany depressed behavior.

- Different symptoms of depression can occur at different ages.

Depressed children and adolescents do not necessarily display all of these signs and symptoms. Moreover, some of them are more common at one developmental stage than at another. For example, Cash (2010) noted the following variations in signs of depression in children ages 3 through 12 years.

- Ages 3–5: accident proneness, phobias, exaggerated fears, delay or regression in developmental milestones, and excessive apologies for minor mistakes (e.g., for spilling food).

- Ages 6–8: vague physical complaints, aggressive behavior, clinging to parents, avoidance of new people and challenges.

- Ages 9–12: insomnia, self-blame, morbid thoughts, extreme worry about schoolwork or about disappointing parents and teachers.

Adolescents experience more excessive sleep, weight loss, suicidal thoughts and behavior, lack of energy, and feelings of helplessness and hopelessness than do children (Rudolf, 2009). These symptoms are less visible to school personnel, so close attention is essential. It is important to observe changes in adolescents' usual behavior patterns and activities. For example, excessive sleep may manifest in tardiness or absences that are a change in the student's attendance history. Lack of energy may manifest in a change in completion of homework and other assignments, preparation for tests with a change in academic performance or a change in participation in usual school activities. Helplessness or hopelessness may manifest in a withdrawal from all usual academic and social activities or be evident in the content of assignments. The key is to be aware of changes in behavior that are manifestations of depressive symptoms.

Finally, it must be kept in mind that not everyone who exhibits these symptoms is depressed. Referral to a school mental health professional is a good first step for teachers or parents who have concerns. That professional can then determine whether further assessment or intervention may be needed.

Diagnosis and Classification Using IDEA

Diagnosis according to the IDEA classification system is guided by IDEA regulations and is focused on determining whether the student has one of the 13 disabilities listed in IDEA and whether the student needs special education (typically interpreted as a need for specialized instruction). Depression and other internalizing disorders would generally fall under the *emotional disturbance* classification in this system. The IDEA 2004 regulations define emotional disturbance as:

> (i) Emotional disturbance means a condition exhibiting one or more of the following characteristics over a long period of time and to a marked degree that adversely affects a child's educational performance: (A) An inability to learn that cannot be explained by intellectual, sensory, or health factors; (B) An inability to build or maintain satisfactory interpersonal relationships with peers and teachers; (C) Inappropriate types of behavior or feelings under normal circumstances; (D) A general pervasive mood of unhappiness or depression; (E) A tendency to develop physical symptoms or fears

associated with personal or school problems. (ii) Emotional disturbance includes schizophrenia. The term does not apply to children who are socially maladjusted, unless it is determined that they have an emotional disturbance under paragraph (c)(4)(i) of this section. (34 C.F.R. Sec. 300.8[c][4])

School IEP teams are authorized to determine whether a student has an emotional disturbance and whether that student requires special education. They are guided in this effort not only by the federal definition provided above, but also by state laws and regulations. Some students exhibiting depressed behavior may also be classified under another IDEA classification. For an excellent overview of the legal issues regarding IDEA and Section 504, see the chapters entitled, "Ethical–Legal Issues in the Education of Students With Disabilities Under IDEA" and "Section 504 and the Americans With Disabilities Act" in Jacob, Decker, and Hartshorn (2011). Also, most state departments of education have websites that provide more information about the process for special education classification within their states.

It is important to note that a DSM-IV-TR diagnosis is not necessary for IDEA classification under the emotional disturbance category. If the school decides that a medical diagnosis is required to determine eligibility, obtaining that diagnosis must be provided at no cost to the family. Moreover, not all students with a DSM-IV-TR diagnosis will qualify for special education (they also must meet the

requirement of needing special education). A DSM-IV-TR diagnosis of depression is very persuasive regarding whether a student has a qualifying disability, but the ultimate responsibility for determining whether a student does have such a disability and whether that student needs special education rests with the IEP team.

ESSENTIALS

- Depression is usually classified as *emotional disturbance* under IDEA.

- Some depressed students may be eligible for special education under a different IDEA classification.

- Not all students with depression are eligible for special education.

Diagnosis and Classification Under Section 504

Section 504 of the Rehabilitation Act of 1973 and its subsequent amendments requires school districts to provide a free, appropriate public education to students with disabilities, "regardless of the nature or severity of the disability" (U.S. Department of Education Office for Civil Rights, 2011). Section 504 covers students who have a physical or mental impairment (including any mental or psychological disorder, such as depression) that substantially limits a major life activity (e.g., concentrating, thinking, reading, learning). Schools are required to individually evaluate a student before classifying him or her as a person with a disability. A school-based multidisciplinary team determines what form the evaluation should take and ultimately decides on whether the student is identified. If the school decides that a medical diagnosis is needed in order to determine eligibility, the evaluation must be provided at no cost to the family. If a student is identified as eligible under Section 504, the multidisciplinary team develops a Section 504 plan for that student specifying the accommodations and modifications that will be made:

> Section 504 requires recipients to provide to students with disabilities appropriate educational services designed to meet the individual needs of such students to the same extent as the needs of students without disabilities are met. An appropriate education for a student with a disability under the Section 504 regulations could consist of education in regular classrooms, education in regular classes with supplementary services, and/or special education and related services. (U.S. Department of Education Office for Civil Rights, 2011)

The process is in most ways similar to that employed by schools for identification of students for special education under IDEA. The definition of disability and the eligibility requirements for Section 504 identification are significantly less stringent than those for special education and, indeed, are intended to be "construed in favor of broad coverage of individuals" (ADAA, 2008, Sec. 12102[4][A]). Many students with depression who do not qualify for school support under IDEA may qualify under Section 504.

"If the school decides that a medical diagnosis is needed in order to determine eligibility, the evaluation must be provided at no cost to the family."

Just as with eligibility determination in special education, having a medical diagnosis does not automatically make a student eligible for identification under Section 504; the school multidisciplinary team must consider that diagnosis along with a range of other information to determine whether the student is eligible.

The Americans With Disabilities Act Amendments Act of 2008

The Americans With Disabilities Act Amendments Act of 2008 amends certain aspects of Section 504. Of most significance for the discussion in this book is the amendment's broad expansion of the definition of students eligible for services under Section 504. Some important provisions of the act are listed below (Source: U.S. Department of Education Office for Civil Rights, 2012).

- If a student is not eligible for special education, but does have a physical or mental impairment that substantially limits (but not necessarily significantly restricts) a major life activity such as learning, thinking, or concentration, and the student requires only related services to meet his or her needs, the student is eligible for those services under Section 504.

- "Mitigating measures," such as medication taken by a student to treat his or her disability, may not be considered when determining whether the student has a substantially limiting impairment.

- An impairment that is episodic or in remission is still considered a disability if, when active, it substantially limits a major life activity. As an example, a student with bipolar disorder would be covered if, during the active manic or depressive episodes, he or she is substantially limited in a major life activity.

Components of a Diagnostic Assessment of Depression

A school-based assessment for the purpose of classification or diagnosis of depression typically involves the use of behavior rating scales, self-report instruments, and interviews (the most valid, reliable, and practical methods; Merrell, 2008). Other assessment methods are also sometimes used. Moreover, a comprehensive assessment of depression (or other internalizing disorder) should consider multiple settings where the behavior might occur (e.g., home, school), incorporate information from multiple informants (e.g., student, parent, teacher), and use multiple methods (e.g., rating scales, observation; Levitt & Merrell, 2009). Using "the rule of two" is recommended; that is, as a *minimum*, the assessment should comprise at least two settings, two informants, and two methods.

Behavior Rating Scales

Two examples of commonly used behavioral rating scales that may be completed by parents, teachers, and other observers are listed in Table 2 along with their age ranges and websites. Both instruments measure a number of clinical areas in addition to depression.

Self-Report Instruments

Because the symptoms of depression and other internalizing disorders are often private (internal to the student), student self-report measures are essential to their assessment with all but very young children (Merrell, 2008). Some self-report measures are part of broadband instruments that measure depression along with a number of other diagnostic categories (see Table 3). Others are narrowband, measuring only depression. Broadband instruments have the advantage of helping to screen for a variety of possible co-occurring conditions. Some commonly used narrowband self-report instruments that measure depression are listed in Table 4.

Table 2. Examples of Behavior Rating Scales

Name	Age Range	Access
Achenbach System of Empirically Based Assessment (ASEBA)	Ages 6–18	http://www.aseba.org
Behavior Assessment System for Children, 2nd Edition (BASC-2)	Ages 2–21	http://www.pearsonassessments.com/HAIWEB/Cultures/enus/Productdetail.htm?Pid=PAa30000

Table 3. Examples of Broadband Instruments

Name	Age Range	Access
Achenbach System of Empirically Based Assessment (ASEBA)	Ages 11–18	http://www.aseba.org
Behavior Assessment System for Children, 2nd Edition. (BASC-2)	Ages 8–18	http://www.pearsonassessments.com/HAIWEB/Cultures/en-us/Productdetail.htm?Pid=PAa30000
Minnesota Multiphasic Personality Inventory – Adolescent (MMPI-A)	Ages 14–18	http://psychcorp.pearsonassessments.com/HAIWEB/Cultures/en-us/Productdetail.htm?Pid=PAg522
Personality Inventory for Youth (PIY)	Ages 9–19	http://portal.wpspublish.com/portal/page?_pageid=53,102890&_dad=portal&_schema=PORTAL

Table 4. Examples of Narrowband Instruments

Name	Age Range	Access
Children's Depression Inventory, 2nd Edition (CDI-2)	Ages 7–17	http://www.pearsonassessments.com/HAIWEB/Cultures/en-us/Productdetail.htm?Pid=015-8044-762
Reynolds Adolescent Depression Scale, 2nd Edition (RADS-2)	Ages 11–20	http://www4.parinc.com/Products/Product.aspx?ProductID=RADS-2
Reynolds Child Depression Scale, 2nd Edition (RCDS-2)	Ages 7–13	http://www4.parinc.com/Products/Product.aspx?ProductID=RCDS-2

Interviews

Huberty (2012) noted that well-developed structured interviews designed specifically for the assessment of depression in children and adolescents do not yet exist. There are, however, a number of semi-structured interview formats that may be used specifically for the purpose of assessing depression.

- Merrell (2008) discusses semi-structured interviewing techniques as part of an assessment of depression and recommends that questions incorporate the areas of medical history, developmental history, social and emotional functioning, educational progress, and community involvement.

- Huberty (2012, pp. 220–223) provides formats for use with children, parents, and teachers that survey cognitive, behavioral, and physiological symptoms of depression.

ESSENTIALS

- Diagnoses and classifications are not very useful for intervention planning.

- Intervention planning requires the use of a problem-solving method that integrates assessment and intervention.

- Functional behavioral assessment is a methodology that can be used to derive effective intervention strategies for depressed behavior.

- Progress monitoring of interventions is a critical component of a problem-solving approach to treating depressed behavior.

ASSESSMENT FOR INTERVENTION PLANNING

As previously discussed, diagnoses are often required in order for students to access specialized programs (e.g., special education) and funding sources (e.g., health insurance). They sometimes also suggest broad categories of intervention (psychotherapy, hospitalization, special education) that could be used with students. Diagnoses and classification categories, however, are generally not useful in guiding more specific recommendations for intervention (e.g., a recommendation for self-monitoring and positive reinforcement for getting out of bed on time). For intervention planning at this level, the use of a problem-solving model that integrates assessment and intervention is more appropriate. Both forms of assessment have their purposes, but assessment designed only for the purpose of providing a diagnosis is rapidly becoming an obsolete practice, especially in schools. Contemporary best practice stresses the linkage between assessment and intervention; that is, a major purpose of assessment is to drive the development of effective interventions for students.

"Assessment designed only for the purpose of providing a diagnosis is rapidly becoming an obsolete practice, especially in schools."

Functional Behavioral Assessment

An assessment approach that has proven most effective in this regard is *functional behavioral assessment*. The sophisticated use of this approach involves assessing the antecedents and consequences of a target behavior and using that information to develop three categories of intervention:

- *preventive strategies* (such as classroom accommodations and curricular modifications) that reduce the likelihood that the behavior will occur,

- *consequence strategies* that reduce interfering behavior and increase positive behavior, and

- *alternative behavior strategies* that teach coping skills and more socially appropriate ways for students to attain social goals for which they otherwise exhibit the target behavior in order to attain.

Functional behavioral assessment has been used so far mostly to develop interventions for externalizing behavior, but this form of assessment is just as applicable to internalizing disorders such as depression. Moreover, functional behavioral assessment strategies are useful for designing interventions for at-risk students at Tier 2 as well as those at Tier 3 and special education. Functional behavioral assessment is an important step in an overall problem-solving model that essentially involves four steps: (a) identification of the problem, (b) collection of assessment data, (c) development of the intervention, and (d) evaluation of intervention outcome. In this model, the cycle of problem identification, as-

sessment, intervention, and evaluation may be repeated until the problem is solved.

Excellent books on school-based functional behavioral assessment include *Tier 3 of the RTI Model: Problem Solving Through a Case Study Approach* by Hunley and McNamara (2010) and *Conducting School-Based Functional Behavioral Assessments: A Practitioner's Guide (2nd ed.)* by Steege and Watson (2009). The Office of Special Education Programs Center for Positive Behavioral Interventions and Supports provides a video overview of the functional behavioral assessment process (see Lewis, n.d.).

"Contemporary best practice stresses the linkage between assessment and intervention; that is, a major purpose of assessment is to drive the development of effective interventions for students."

Progress Monitoring

Progress monitoring is a required component of any response-to-intervention or problem-solving approach to assessment and intervention. Collecting data on the extent to which an intervention is working, and making decisions about whether to continue or modify interventions based on progress-monitoring data, is critical to attaining the best possible outcomes for students. The books mentioned above (Hunley & McNamara, 2010; Steege &

Watson, 2009) discuss a number of techniques to monitor a student's response to an intervention and *Evaluating Educational Interventions: Single-Case Design for Measuring Response to Intervention* by Riley-Tillman and Burns (2009) provides a thorough discussion of this topic.

ESSENTIALS

■ African American, American Indian, and Native Alaskan students are disproportionately identified as emotionally disturbed.

■ Assessment of culturally and linguistically diverse students for mental health problems requires a sophisticated level of cultural competency that needs to be regularly updated.

ASSESSMENT OF CULTURALLY AND LINGUISTICALLY DIVERSE STUDENTS

The proportion of African American, American Indian, and Native Alaskan students identified under IDEA as emotionally disturbed is greater than that of any other racial or ethnic group, according to the U.S. Department of Education Office of Special Education Programs (2011). It is critical that professionals conducting assessments of depression among culturally and linguistically diverse students possess a high degree of cultural competency in order to reduce bias in the process. Indeed, because graduate training programs often do not provide adequate training in this area and because the knowledge base of culturally competent practice continues to progress at a great rate, most professionals currently working in schools will need to update their skills on a regular basis (Ortiz, Flanagan, & Dynda, 2008).

The disproportionate identification of culturally and linguistically diverse students as emotionally disturbed has resulted in questions about the validity of the assessment and diagnostic procedures used to identify them and, indeed, whether there might be a higher likelihood of misidentification with this group than with other groups in the school (Sullivan et al., 2009). School mental health professionals must use evidence-based procedures validated for the population they are serving, and at the same time take a very broad approach to assessment, especially as they assess the context of the student's environment at the early stages of the assessment process (Lau & Blatchley, 2009).

"It is critical that professionals conducting assessments of depression among culturally and linguistically diverse students possess a high degree of cultural competency in order to reduce bias in the process."

RTI CONNECTIONS

The same framework of assessments done within an RTI framework for academic behavior can be used for depression:

■ Tier 1: Screening.

■ Tier 2: In-depth screening and other assessment for intervention design.

■ Tier 3: Comprehensive assessment and functional behavioral assessment.

■ Progress monitoring for all interventions.

Good assessment practices and interventions at the lower tiers can avoid the problems associated with using full-scale evaluation procedures with culturally and linguistically diverse students.

A three-tiered model of assessment is recommended, beginning with screening and less formal assessments prior to initiating a comprehensive assessment for diagnosis and classification. The importance of this approach becomes very clear when considering culturally and linguistically diverse students. Good assessment practices at the lower tiers can focus attention on prevention, early intervention, and changes in classroom and school procedures, thereby obviating the need for referral to a full-scale evaluation and avoiding the problems associated with using these procedures with culturally and linguistically diverse students (Lau & Blatchley, 2009).

Considerations at Tier 1

Depression and other internalizing disorders are not well defined for teachers (even the IDEA definition of emotional disorder is hard to interpret) and are often difficult to observe because the symptoms are typically internal to the student. For this reason, universal screening for these problems at Tier 1 is recommended. A systematic approach to screening at Tier 1, often involving self-report or other behavioral rating scales, can result in a more accurate identification of at-risk students. However, caution must be exercised in the use of typical screening methods such as rating scales and interviews with culturally and linguistically diverse students. Many items on behavioral rating scales and questions on interview protocols are not easily understood by culturally and linguistically diverse students and parents. Even interpreters and cultural liaisons can have difficulty understanding and communicating the underlying psychological nuances of some of these questions. School mental health professionals using interpreters to help with assessments need to train and supervise interpreters on the tests and procedures used in assessment (Lau & Blatchley, 2009; Lopez, 2008). Moreover, they need to be able to employ a broader, more in-depth screening process when working with these students and families (Lau & Blatchley, 2009).

ESSENTIALS

■ Behavioral observations can help determine whether a student's behavior is significantly different from that of others from similar backgrounds.

■ Interventions should be evidence-based and effective for the cultural and linguistic group with which the student is associated.

■ Behavioral assessment of depression may be less biased than other methods.

Examination of system-wide results of these screenings can help a school or district determine whether particular groups of students are disproportionally identified and what steps might be taken to resolve that issue (e.g., provide professional development about depression and, in particular, cultural or linguistic considerations).

> *"Examination of system-wide results of these screenings can help a school or district determine whether particular groups of students are disproportionally identified and what steps might be taken to resolve that issue."*

Before deciding to advance students from culturally and linguistically diverse backgrounds to Tier 2 assessment, the school team should determine whether Tier 1 universal interventions (e.g., classroom rules, social and emotional learning programs, school climate initiatives) were appropriate for the students and were implemented with integrity (i.e., implemented the way the designers intended). Data regarding how the student responded to these interventions should also be reviewed.

Considerations at Tier 2

Culturally and linguistically diverse students identified as at risk through a universal screening at Tier 1 may require a more in-depth fol-low-up screening at Tier 2, including consideration of the student's stage of acculturation. New immigrants, in particular, are subject to numerous stressors, including disruptions of social connections and supports that can be the cause of depression, anxiety, and other psychological problems (Lau & Blatchley, 2009).

Direct observation of the student by a school mental health professional may be a necessary part of an in-depth screening to determine how the student's behavior compares to that of other students from similar cultural or linguistic backgrounds. Observations of antecedents and consequences of behavior indicative of depression can shed light on ecological factors associated with the student's behavior. Similarly, a parent interview could help determine whether depressive symptoms are evident only at school (suggesting a contextual cause) or more pervasively at home and in the community.

Before deciding to advance a student to Tier 3 assessment, the school mental health team should determine whether the Tier 2 interventions employed were evidence-based and known to be effective for the cultural and linguistic population with which the student is associated. The team should also determine whether the interventions were implemented with integrity and examine data showing how the student responded to those interventions.

Considerations at Tier 3

Assessment procedures at Tier 3 are more comprehensive than at the other tiers and often are used to help determine a student's eligibility for special education. All of the assessment information gathered at Tiers 1 and 2 may be incorporated and expanded upon at Tier 3. Low-inference, behavioral approaches to assessment (e.g., functional behavioral assessment) are generally less biased than other approaches and are, therefore, preferred for culturally and linguistically diverse students.

ACTION PLAN

- Integrate assessment and intervention for depression into the school's RTI framework.

- Shift the focus of assessment to include an emphasis on intervention planning and progress monitoring in addition to the traditional emphasis on classification and diagnosis.

- Most schools have good capacity to conduct comprehensive assessments of depression at Tier 3 of an RTI framework. Through professional development, broaden the base of people in the school capable of conducting screening and progress monitoring at Tiers 1 and 2 (assessing for prevention and intervention with at-risk students). Make use of computerized assessment and data management systems (e.g., AIMSweb Behavior).

- Increase the use of direct, low-inference assessments (e.g., functional behavioral assessment) that directly link to generating strategies for intervention.

- Assess the entire continuum of depression (not just the clinical levels) starting with universal screening of all students for depression and other mental health problems.

- Provide professional development for school staff on the signs and symptoms of depression.

KEYS TO COLLABORATION

- A high level of multicultural competence is required to effectively collaborate with people from culturally and linguistically diverse backgrounds.

- Effective collaboration will result in more valid assessments, more appropriate interventions, and increased cooperation among all stakeholders in the process.

RESOURCES

Assessment of depression and other internalizing disorders is a complex process. Two comprehensive textbooks addressing assessment in detail are:

- Huberty, T. J. (2012). *Anxiety and depression in children and adolescents: Assessment, intervention, and prevention.* New York, NY: Springer.

- Merrell, K. W. (2007). *Behavioral, social, and emotional assessment of children and adolescents.* New York, NY: Routledge.

The U.S. Department of Education Office for Civil Rights webpage entitled *Disability Discrimination* (http://www2.ed.gov/policy/rights/guid/ocr/disability.html) provides answers to frequently asked questions about Section 504 (and the Americans with Disabilities Act Amendments Act of 2008) relative to students with disabilities.

The U.S. Department of Education Office for Civil Rights also maintains a webpage entitled *Questions and Answers on the ADA Amendments Act of 2008 for Students With Disabilities Attending Public Elementary and Secondary Schools* (http://www2.ed.gov/about/offices/list/ocr/docs/dcl-504faq-201109.html) that provides additional guidance for interpreting Section 504.

Resources providing information for working with culturally and linguistically diverse (CLD) students and families may be found in Table 5.

Table 5. Resources for Working With Culturally and Linguistically Diverse Students and Families

Topic	Resource	Source
Overviews of some of the key issues in working with CLD students and families	*The Psychology of Multiculturalism in the Schools: A Primer for Practice, Training, and Research* (Jones, 2009)	Booksellers
	Best practices in working with culturally diverse children and families. Ortiz, Flanagan, & Dynda, (2008). Chapter in Thomas & Grimes, *Best practices in school psychology V*	
	Best practices in increasing cross-cultural competence (Miranda, 2008). Chapter in Thomas & Grimes, *Best practices in school psychology V*	
	Handbook of Multicultural School Psychology: An Interdisciplinary Perspective (Esquivel, Lopez & Nahari, 2007)	
	Communicating effectively with culturally and linguistically diverse families (Guerrero & Leung 2008)	http://www.nasponline.org/publications/cq/mocq368commmatters.aspx

Topic	Resource	Source
Assessment of CLD students	A comprehensive, multidimensional approach to assessment of culturally and linguistically diverse students (Lau and Blatchley, 2009). Chapter in Jones, *The Psychology of Multiculturalism in the Schools: A Primer for Practice, Training, and Research*	Booksellers
	Personality and behavioral assessment: Considerations for culturally and linguistically diverse individuals (Kohn, Scorcia, & Esquivel, 2007). Chapter in Esquivel, et al., *Handbook of Multicultural School Psychology: An Interdisciplinary Perspective*	
Working with interpreters during assessment	Best practices in working with school interpreters (Lopez (2008). Chapter in Thomas & Grimes, *Best practices in school psychology V*	
Communicating and working with Black students and families	*Effective Communication With Black Families and Students* (Chandler, A'Vant, & Graves, 2008)	http://www.nasponline.org/publications/cq/mocq373blackfamilies_handout.aspx
Communicating and working with families of Indigenous Americans	*Home–School–Community Communication With Indigenous American Families* (Dauphinais, Charley, Robinson-Zañartu, Melroe, & Bass, 2009)	http://www.nasponline.org/publications/cq/mocq375indigenous_american_family.aspx
Communicating and working with Asian parents and families	*Communicating With Asian Parents and Families* (Leung, Wu, Questin, & Le, 2008)	http://www.nasponline.org/publications/cq/mocq368asianfamilies.aspx
Communicating and working with Latino families	*Communicating With Latino Parents and Families* (Peña, Silva, Claro, Gamarra, & Parra, 2008)	http://www.nasponline.org/publications/cq/mocq374latino_families.aspx

REFERENCES

American Psychiatric Association. (2000). *Diagnostic and statistical manual of mental disorders*, Fourth Edition, Text Revision. Washington, DC: Author.

Americans with Disabilities Amendments Act. (2008). Retrieved from http://www.ada.gov/pubs/adastatute08mark.htm

Avenevoli, S., Knight, E., Kessler, R. C., & Merikangas, K. R. (2008). Epidemiology of depression in children and adolescents. In J. R. Z. Abela & B. L. Hankin, *Handbook of depression in children and adolescents* (pp. 6–32). New York, NY: Guilford.

Cash, R. E. (2010). Depression in young children. In A. Canter, L. Z. Paige, & S. Shaw (Eds.), *Helping children at home and school III: Handouts for families and educators* (pp. S5H10-1–S5H10-4). Bethesda, MD: National Association of School Psychologists.

Chandler, D., A'Vant, E. R., & Graves, S. L. (2008). Effective communication with Black families and students. *NASP Communiqué, 37*(3). Retrieved from http://www.nasponline.org/publications/cq/mocq373blackfamilies_handout.aspx

Dauphinais, P., Charley, E., Robinson-Zañartu, C., Melroe, O. & Baas, S. (2009). Home–school–community communication with Indigenous American families. *NASP Communiqué, 37*(5). Retrieved from http://www.nasponline.org/publications/cq/mocq375indigenous_american_family.aspx

Esquivel, G. B., Lopez, E. C., & Nahari, S. (2007). *Handbook of multicultural school psychology: An interdisciplinary perspective*. Mahway, NJ: Erlbaum.

Garber, J., Gallerani, C. M., & Frankel, S. A. (2009). Depression in children. In I. H. Gotlib & C. L. Hammen, *Handbook of depression, 2nd edition* (pp. 405–443). New York, NY: Guilford.

Guerrero, C., & Leung, B. (2008). Communicating effectively with culturally and linguistically diverse families. *NASP Communiqué, 36*(8). Retrieved from http://www.nasponline.org/publications/cq/mocq368commmatters.aspx

Huberty, T. J. (2008). Best practices in school-based interventions for anxiety and depression. In A. Thomas & J. Grimes, *Best practices in school psychology V* (pp. 1473–1486). Bethesda, MD: National Association of School Psychologists.

Huberty, T. J. (2012). *Anxiety and depression in children and adolescents: Assessment, intervention, and prevention*. New York, NY: Springer.

Hunley, S., & McNamara, K. (2010). *Tier 3 of the RTI model: Problem solving through a case study approach*. Thousand Oaks, CA: Corwin (A joint publication with the National Association of School Psychologists).

Jacob, S., Decker, D. M., & Hartshorne, T. S. (2011). *Ethics and law for school psychologists (6th ed.)*. Hoboken, NJ: Wiley.

Jones, J. (Ed.). (2009). *The psychology of multiculturalism in the schools: A primer for practice, training, and research*. Bethesda, MD: National Association of School Psychologists.

Kohn, S. W., Scorcia, D., & Esquivel, G. B. (2007). Personality and behavioral assessment: Considerations for culturally and linguistically diverse individuals. In G. B. Esquivel, E. C. Lopez, & S. Nahari (Eds.), *Handbook of multicultural school psychology: An interdisciplinary perspective* (289–308). Mahwah, NJ: Erlbaum.

Lau, M. Y., & Blatchley, L. A. (2009). A comprehensive, multidimensional approach to assessment of culturally and linguistically diverse students. In J. Jones (Ed.), *The psychology of multiculturalism in the schools: A Primer for practice, training, and research*. Bethesda, MD: National Association of School Psychologists.

Leung, B., Wu, T., Questin, M., Staresnick, J., & Le, P. (2008). Communicating with Asian parents and families. *NASP Communiqué, 36*(8). Retrieved from http://www.nasponline.org/publications/cq/mocq368asianfamilies.aspx

Lewis, T. (n.d.). *Functional behavioral assessment* [video]. Office of Special Education Programs Center for Positive Behavioral Interventions and Supports. Retrieved from http://desemo.adobeconnect.com/p65667851/?launcher=false&fcsContent=true&pbMode=normal

Lopez, E. C. (2008). Best practices in working with school interpreters. In A. Thomas & J. Grimes, *Best practices in school psychology V* (pp. 1751–1769). Bethesda, MD: National Association of School Psychologists.

Merrell, K. W. (2007). *Behavioral, social, and emotional assessment of children and adolescents.* New York, NY: Routledge.

Merrell, K. W. (2008). *Helping students overcome depression and anxiety (2nd ed.).* New York, NY: Guilford.

Miranda, A. H. (2008). Best practices in increasing cross-cultural competence. In A. Thomas & J. Grimes, *Best practices in school psychology V* (pp. 1739–1749). Bethesda, MD: National Association of School Psychologists.

Ortiz, S. O., Flanagan, D. P., & Dynda, A. M. (2008). Best practices in working with culturally diverse children and families. In A. Thomas & J. Grimes, *Best practices in school psychology V* (pp. 1721–1738). Bethesda, MD: National Association of School Psychologists.

Peña, A. M., Silva, A., Claro, C., Gamarra, A., & Parra, E. (2008). Communicating with Latino parents and families. *NASP Communiqué, 37*(4). Retrieved from http://www.nasponline.org/publications/cq/mocq374latino_families.aspx

Riley-Tillman, T. C., & Burns, M. K. (2009). *Evaluating educational interventions: Single-case design for measuring response to intervention.* New York, NY: Guilford.

Rudolf, K. D. (2009). *Adolescent depression.* In I. H. Gotlib & C. L. Hammen, *Handbook of depression, 2nd edition* (pp. 444–466). New York, NY: Guilford.

Steege, M. W., & Watson, T. S. (2009). *Conducting school-based functional behavioral assessments: A practitioner's guide (2nd ed.).* New York, NY: Guilford.

Sullivan, A. L., A'Vant, E., Baker, J., Chandler, D., Graves, S., McKinney, E., & Sayles, T. (2009). Confronting inequity in special education, part I: Understanding the problem of disproportionality. *NASP Communiqué, 38*(1). Retrieved from http://www.nasponline.org/publications/cq/mocq381disproportionality.aspx

U.S. Department of Education Office for Civil Rights. (2011). *Protecting students with disabilities: Frequently asked questions about Section 504 and the education of children with disabilities.* Retrieved from http://www2.ed.gov/about/offices/list/ocr/504faq.html

U.S. Department of Education Office for Civil Rights. (2011). *Questions and answers on the ADA amendments act of 2008 for students with disabilities attending public elementary and secondary schools.* Retrieved from http://www2.ed.gov/about/offices/list/ocr/docs/dcl-504faq-201109.html) that provides additional guidance for interpreting Section 504

U.S. Department of Education, Office of Special Education and Rehabilitative Services, Office of Special Education Programs. (2011). *30th annual report to Congress on the implementation of the Individuals with Disabilities Education Act, 2008.* Washington, DC: Author. Retrieved from http://www2.ed.gov/about/reports/annual/osep/2008/parts-b-c/30th-idea-arc.pdf

CHAPTER 11

IT TAKES A VILLAGE: COLLABORATIVE AND INTEGRATED SERVICE DELIVERY

Intervention for students with depression invariably requires the efforts of a number of people within the family, school, and community. It is well-established that collaborative relationships among these critical stakeholders result in the most favorable outcomes for students and that collaborative teams offer the most promise for designing efficient and effective interventions for children and adolescents with depression.

Students with depression often have complex needs involving multiple professionals in both assessment and intervention. The potential for deriving effective outcomes from these services is great. But there is also the potential for miscommunication, inefficiency resulting from overlapping services and unforeseen gaps between these services, and even for service providers inadvertently working against one another's goals. Delivery of services for students exhibiting symptoms of depression should be one component of a comprehensive and integrated school-wide approach to promoting the mental health of all students in the school. It should not be established as a separate, stand-alone program that is designed for only a few targeted students, delivered by a few specialized personnel, in a short-term or sporadic manner. All school staff members need to be involved at various levels in a collaborative effort to provide these services.

Moreover, community providers (whether housed within the school or externally) need to be woven into that system in a coordinated, integral way. In a comprehensive program, all stakeholders (parents, teachers, administrators, school mental health professionals, and community resources and providers) work together to provide a seamless continuum of service. The need for truly collaborative professional teaming is critical for students who are depressed or at risk for depression.

"Delivery of services for students exhibiting symptoms of depression should be one component of a comprehensive and integrated school-wide approach to promoting the mental health of all students in the school. "

Teams of various kinds are ubiquitous features of public school operation. Called by various names (e.g., school improvement teams, educational support teams, multidisciplinary teams, learning supports resource team, data teams), they accomplish much of the work done in schools, from individual student interventions to district-wide systems change. All of these teams may be associated with words such as cooperation, partnership, team work, association, organization, and assistance, but are they truly collaborative?

WHAT IS COLLABORATION?

Collaboration is one of those processes that everyone seems to value but is seldom fully implemented. It is not the same as cooperation (Eason, Atkins, & Dyson, 2000; Walsh, Brabeck, & Howard, 1999), whereby professionals work together on a team in the interests of the student but do so from their own professional perspectives as more or less independent entities on that team. Collaboration moves beyond cooperation in that the team becomes more of an entity unto itself and less a group of individual people around a table. When professionals collaborate, they operate from a stance of respect for the skills of the other professionals involved and are willing to modify their own conceptualizations of a case in favor of the opinion of the team as a whole. They are willing to move outside of their realm of specialization and be a part of broader, more integrated conceptualizations of the problem and of potential solutions. Professional competition is minimized. Whereas the result of professional cooperation is the sum of the efforts of each independent team member, the results of collaboration are frequently greater than the sum of those parts. There is a synergy within collaborative teams that usually produces better decisions and more integrated approaches to problems than those resulting from mere cooperation. People can *feel* the difference between cooperative and collabo-

rative professional interaction. If cooperation is like a dating relationship, collaboration is like a marriage: The partners maintain their individual professional identities and make unique contributions to the relationship. At the same time, there is something greater that includes but supersedes the contributions of the partners and is based on a complete mutuality of interests, respect, and goals.

> *"If cooperation is like a dating relationship, collaboration is like a marriage: The partners maintain their individual professional identities and make unique contributions to the relationship."*

A Continuum of Collaboration

The amount of collaboration exhibited by teams of various sorts exists along a continuum. Four models of collaboration (Glaser, Quimet, & Shaw, 2010) represent various points along that continuum and correspond to increasing ability to generate comprehensive and integrated interventions (see Table 1). In the *independent functions model*, based on a medical consultation model, communication is limited to referral and feedback between independent professionals; there is little chance for mutual development or ongoing discussion of interventions (Drotar as cited in Glaser et al., 2010). In the *multidisciplinary team*

CHARACTERISTICS OF COLLABORATIVE TEAMS

- Trust and mutual respect

- Effective communication

- Shared vision and goals

- Flexibility and blurring of professional roles; members take on functions based on the needs of the students

- Focus on solutions and resources

model, each professional contributes input in his or her area of specialization, resulting in multiple intervention recommendations for the student, but there is little consideration of how these interventions might work together as a whole program (e.g., overlaps and gaps in services may result). In the *interdisciplinary team model*, an integrated and coordinated set of interventions is developed by consensus of all the participants involved, and there is fre-quent follow-up by the team (Drotar as cited in Glaser et al., 2010). In the *transdisciplinary team model*, an integrated and coordinated set of interventions is developed, and there is a blurring of professional roles as team members take on functions based on individual com-petencies, available resources, and the needs of the individual student. These four models represent an increasing level of collaboration resulting in progressively comprehensive and coordinated care. The cost—in terms of time needed for planning and meeting—also in-creases with the level of collaboration. Inter-vention planning for students with depression requires a high degree of collaboration, with the level of necessary collaboration increasing with the complexity of the student's situation. It would be useful for readers of this book to assess their own teams in terms of which mod-el they are using and where they are located along the continuum of collaboration.

Table 1. Models of Increasing Levels of Collaboration

Model	Description
Independent Functions Model	Referral and feedback among professionals with little ongoing discussion of interventions
Multidisciplinary Team Model	Each professional contributes interventions but with little dis-cussion of how they might work together as a whole
Interdisciplinary Team Model	Integrated, coordinated set of interventions developed by con-sensus and followed up by the team
Transdisciplinary Team Model	Integrated, coordinated set of interventions developed with functions of team members determined by the needs of the student
Source: Glaser, Quimet, & Shaw (2010)	

ESSENTIALS

- Collaboration results in a more systemic view of problems and solutions, more comprehensive intervention plans, and a mutual stake in the plan's success.

- Effective collaboration results in increased likelihood of solving student problems.

Collaborative relationships are characterized by trust and mutual respect among the participants, effective communication, a shared vision, and agreed-upon goals. Effective collaborative teams maintain a focus on solutions and resources more than problems, recognizing that problems are maintained by a variety of factors and solutions may come from a variety of sources.

Benefits of Collaboration

Evidence-based interventions are not always available for all the needs presented by students with depression, meaning that the pooled clinical experience of multiple practitioners is needed in order to develop a comprehensive intervention plan. Authentic collaboration among professionals offers the best chance of developing an effective intervention. Moreover, when intervention plans are developed collaboratively, all participants (e.g., school and community mental health providers, teachers, parents) take common ownership of the plan and have a personal stake in its success. Collaborative teams also provide a context for open discussion of gaps, overlaps, strengths, and resources in programs available for students with depression and can be a powerful platform for systems

change. The end result of effective collaboration for students is increased academic achievement and fewer social, emotional, and behavioral problems.

OVERCOMING CHALLENGES TO COLLABORATION

If collaboration is such a fundamental component of intervention with depressed students, then why is it sometimes so difficult to establish authentic collaboration between school-based and community-based providers, and even among providers within the same school? There are many reasons for this, including a historical one: The independent functions model is still in existence to some degree in schools and in the broader community. Changing how programs are organized and how people from various disciplines work together is often difficult.

The broad scope of responsibility held by school nurses may contribute to the persistence of independent functions in the face of the need to collaborate around student mental health. The role of school nurses encompasses both health and mental health needs, and addressing the major health problems experienced by students (American Academy of Pediatrics Council on School Health, 2008). There are eight components to the role of the school nurse, including school health services (e.g., screening, immunizations, injuries and emergencies, interventions for acute and chronic illness, addressing health concerns from dental disease to sexually transmitted infections to adolescent pregnancy). In addition, school nurses are expected to provide leadership or collaborate with respect to health education, health promotion for faculty and staff, school nutrition services, physical education programs, healthy school environment, family and community involvement, and counseling, psychological, and social services (National Association of School Nurses, 2008).

This breadth in the scope of practice for the school nurse is in contrast with the more specific scope of responsibility for school counselors, psychologists, and social workers. Yet the National Association of School Nurses has taken the position that "mental health is as critical to academic success as physical well-being" and that "as members of interdisciplinary teams, school nurses play a vital role in supporting early assessment, planning, intervention, and follow-up of children in need of mental health services" (National Association of School Nurses, 2008). It is easy for the more immediate demands of students' physical health needs to take precedence over collaborative efforts to address mental health needs. The challenge is to move beyond the focus on physical health, and to collaborate as part of the team of school mental health professionals. Depending on where along the continuum of collaboration a given group is located, it is reasonable to expect that it could take 3 to 5 years of effort to move toward a much more collaborative stance.

Finding a group of people who recognize the need for a more collaborative approach to prevention and intervention and who have the motivation and leadership qualities necessary

to sustain a change effort over a significant length of time is the first challenge to overcome. Differences in professional vocabularies, ways of conceptualizing problems and solutions, and expectations based on perceptions of professional status (e.g., of physicians, educators, school nurses) are examples of the kinds of challenges that need to be negotiated and overcome. Fortunately, the very process of resolving these issues can become an opportunity for developing and practicing the skills needed for authentic collaboration.

"School administrators are critical change agents and key members of any collaborative team effort to help students with depression."

School administrators are critical change agents and key members of any collaborative team effort to help students with depression. Administrators can marshal financial and staff resources, help with the organization of team process and service delivery, help arrange classroom accommodations for students, and advocate for system change. They can help establish a tone of understanding, acceptance, and competence in working with these students.

Overcoming Systemic Challenges to Collaboration

Adelman and Taylor (n.d.) at the University of California, Los Angeles, Center for Mental Health in Schools have explored the systemic impediments to collaboration and identified three main causes. These include: overspecialization of providers and the resulting narrow focus of each one, fragmentation and marginalization of support services delivered to students, and competition among specialists for scarce resources. Each of these factors reinforces the other. All three must be addressed in order to improve services to students within the school system.

Overspecialization

Most professionals are trained in specialized programs and identify with their chosen specialties. Professionals from those disciplines work very hard to differentiate themselves from each other—recognizing their overlapping competencies but stressing their differences in order to promote their uniqueness and their special mission within the system. They often carve out narrowly defined spheres of practice based upon specialty. For example, a system might evolve where school counselors might only do college planning, school nurses are assigned to caring only for students with acute health issues, school psychologists only conduct testing, and school social workers only provide counseling. Specialists remain in their respective silos with separate and rigidly defined funding streams, departments, administrators, and roles. This is seen not only in large districts, but also in small schools where each "department" can consist of one or a very small number of individuals.

> *"The trend in school improvement is toward less emphasis on intervention ownership and more attention to accomplishing desired outcomes through flexible and expanded roles and functions for staff. This trend recognizes underlying commonalities among a variety of school concerns and intervention strategies...."*
> - Adelman & Taylor, 2006b, pp. 245–246

While each has its own unique skills, there is a tremendous amount of overlap among the competencies or skills of the various professionals employed by schools who can provide mental health services. All school counselors, nurses, psychologists, and social workers have competence in the delivery of school-based prevention and universal interventions as well as screening and early identification of students at risk for depression. Most are competent to deliver universal or targeted school interventions. Some are competent to deliver more intensive interventions for students who are highly at risk for depression or who are already depressed, either through intensive school interventions with community support or in intensive community interventions with school support (National Association of School Nurses, 2008; National Association of School

Psychologists, 2006). This underlying commonality of training and experience needs to be recognized and respected in building collaborative teams in support of children and adolescents with depression. The greatest amount of flexibility in terms of developing and delivering interventions will be gained when roles and functions of team members are determined by individual competencies matched to the needs of individual students and the school as a whole rather than by preconceived ownership of interventions based on specialty (UCLA Center for Mental Health in Schools, n.d.).

"While each has its own unique skills, there is a tremendous amount of overlap among the competencies or skills of the various mental health specialists employed by schools."

Fragmentation

A school program for a student with depression might include group counseling, individual counseling, a check-and-connect program to support school engagement, and special education support. In addition, the student might also have medication prescribed by a physician or nurse practitioner (administered and monitored by the school nurse) and counseling with a community-based provider. The parents need to interface with all of these services and may require services themselves.

With more than a half-dozen programs administered by a variety of professionals in different settings—all without adequate collaboration or even cooperation—the fragmentation is obvious and the risk is high for significant overlap, gaps, or conflicts in service. A highly collaborative team would have the capacity to assess these inefficiencies and develop a more comprehensive, integrated, and effective program for this student without increasing cost.

Marginalization

From a big-picture point of view, not only are school learning support services fragmented, but—even when considered as a whole—they are also marginalized as secondary to the instructional and administrative components of the school program (Adelman & Taylor 2006b, 2010). Despite all the evidence to the contrary, they are usually seen as supplementary, and not integral to the central academic mission of the school. As a result, these services often do not receive the same level of coordination, funding, and supervision that, for example, a program in reading would receive. Efforts at reform need to focus on bringing school learning supports into parity with instruction and administration. As a starting point at the school or district level, it is important that all stakeholders within the school community are made aware of the connection between students' mental health and academic achievement. There is no doubt that as the social, emotional, and behavioral functioning of students improves, their engagement with school and academic achievement will also improve. This is true not just for students suffering from depression, but for all students.

"Efforts at reform need to focus on bringing school learning supports into parity with instruction and administration."

Competition Among Specialists

School personnel are probably well acquainted with some of the (often unstated) competition that exists between school-based and community-based mental health service providers. Similar levels of competition can also exist within the very same school or school district among professionals from various specialties. During periods of budgetary constraint, this competition can become pretty stark and serves to maintain overspecialization and fragmentation of programs even when professionals know that service to students suffers. Yet, there is plenty of work to do and more students in need of intervention than there are providers to serve them.

Overcoming Challenges to Family–School Collaboration

The challenges to collaboration between parents and school personnel are in many ways the same as those that exist between professionals. Particular challenges for families might also include lack of time, transportation, and childcare; family health issues; unsafe neighborhoods; cultural and linguistic differences; conflicting work schedules; and poverty. Specific challenges for school and community professional staff often include lack of training in enhancing family–school collaboration, lack of training in cultural and linguistic diversity, and beliefs about families' lack of interest in their children's schooling. For these reasons and many others, trust can often be a basic challenge for both parties. Families are sometimes reluctant to tell school or community professionals that their child has depression, is on medication, or is seeing a therapist. Professionals worry that full collaboration with families not only makes frank discussion and brainstorming of ideas impossible, but perhaps leaves them open to violations of due process or legal proceedings.

These challenges can all be resolved, and there is a sizeable literature describing strategies to do so. These strategies generally fall under the key ideas listed below (Esler, Godber, & Christenson, 2008):

- Make school–family collaboration central to the practices and policies of the school.

- Have a specific plan for enhancing family–school collaboration starting with an assessment of the kinds of communication and involvement wanted by families in the school.

- Be proactive and persistent with efforts to communicate with families.

- Adopt a positive style of communication with families that expresses the beliefs that their child can learn, that families can be helpful, that the school will welcome their involvement, and that solutions are possible.

- Personalize contacts based upon the school's knowledge of the family's situation.

- Provide specific information to families about how they can help their child.

- Evaluate progress toward enhancement of family–school collaboration on a yearly basis.

- Act in ways that reflect a core belief in the process of family–school collaboration.

Overcoming Challenges to Collaboration with the Healthcare Community

Some students who are depressed receive medication prescribed by their physician (mostly pediatricians) or nurse practitioner. Some students receive service through community agencies that operate on a medical model, and some, particularly those with severe symptoms or suicidal behavior, require hospitalization. Each of these situations requires collaboration between school mental health professionals and healthcare providers.

The challenges to collaboration outlined above often apply to these situations. In addition, collaboration between schools and medical personnel often has its own set of unique challenges. These can include differences in professional vocabulary; ethical standards; systems of diagnosis (schools typically use the IDEA diagnostic system; medical personnel typically employ the *Diagnostic and Statistical Manual of Mental Disorders [DSM]* or the *International Classification of Diseases [ICD]* system); and approaches to treatment and service de-

livery (Glaser et al., 2010), Moreover, lack of payment for time spent on prevention, school meetings, and other time-consuming activities makes it difficult for physicians to take time from their practices for such collaborative activities.

Confidentiality requirements are a particular challenge to collaboration. Under FERPA, parents have access to the education records of their children, including any health information contained in those education records. However, the HIPPA (the Health Insurance Portability and Accountability Act of 1996) Privacy Rule protects health information but excludes information governed by FERPA. Accordingly, parents have access to protected health information for their minor children but they do not have access to information that pertains to services for which minors may legally grant consent or when they have already agreed to confidentiality protections. Furthermore, the HIPPA Privacy Rule governs health records maintained by school-based health clinics that are not funded by the school district. Thus, information in the records of such school-based health centers are subject to HIPPA and cannot be shared with school personnel. Given that the HIPPA Privacy Rule affects the sharing of information between school mental health professionals and health care providers in community clinics and school-based health clinics, a key operating principle must be to have a signed consent for release of information between students/parents and their health care providers. FERPA will apply to the records of school nurses and other mental health professionals that are a part of students' education records.

"A key operating principle must be to have a signed consent for release of information between students/parents and their health care providers. "

Strategies for enhancing collaboration specifically between school and medical personnel include the following (Glaser et al., 2010):

- Assign someone on the team to be the contact or liaison with the physician or medical agency. The school nurse or nurse practitioner is the obvious choice for this role in most cases, although school psychologists serve this function in some schools.

- Keep communications with physicians concise, factual, and jargon-free.

- Build relationships with community medical providers (e.g., invite them to collaborate on school-based health promotion activities, invite them to planning meetings for students who are their patients).

- Help parents improve their ability to keep lines of communication open between the school and healthcare provider.

School mental health professionals serve vital functions such as coordinating medical services within the school, monitoring behavioral effects of medication, and coordinating transitions between hospital and school placements (Glaser et al., 2010). School nurses hold partic-

ular responsibility for developing and implementing 504 plans, the health portion of the Special Education Individual Education Plan (IEP), and the Individualized Healthcare Plan (IHP) (National Association of School Nurses, 2008), and for "providing a link between educational and medical systems" (DeSocio & Hootman, 2004), with this linkage also including families (National Association of School Nurses, 2011). Solid collaboration between school and healthcare providers can ensure that students receive the best possible care in both settings.

KEY CONCEPTS FOR COLLABORATION WITH COMMUNITY PROVIDERS

- A full continuum of care for students with depression cannot exist without community (including healthcare) resources.

- Even when community services are based in schools, school mental health professionals must maintain responsibility for their students and guide the integration of those services into the school.

- All school-based mental health services must link to the educational mission of the schools.

Overcoming Challenges to Collaboration With Community Resources

As collaborative teams develop, they can work toward expanding the list of people who might be recruited for various levels of collaboration. Just as school members of a collaborative team can extend beyond the obvious school mental health providers and include people such as health teachers and school safety officers, community members are not confined to mental health agencies and healthcare providers and may include people such as clergy and community youth leaders. Nearly everyone has the potential to play a role in supporting students with depression in one way or another.

Conversely, merely linking or coordinating community services—or even locating them on school campuses—may or may not represent true collaboration. Adelman and Taylor (1999) point out that such arrangements can enhance student accessibility to community services but that disadvantages can include competition (school staff may feel devalued relative to community services staff) and the possibility that infusion of community services into schools may result in a corresponding reduction in funding for school services. Merely placing a community program within the school walls does not guarantee collaboration. Building collaboration is an ongoing process regardless of the organizational structure developed. Critical concepts for school personnel to keep in mind when working with external or school-based community resources are listed in the box on this page.

School based health centers or clinics (SBHCs) offer unique potential for collaboration with school nurses and other school mental health providers. SBHCs provide primary health care and serve as a medical home in the school setting or on school grounds. They offer a comprehensive set of health services provided by nurse practitioners, registered nurses, physician assistants, social workers, physicians, and other health professionals. Typically, SBHCs require parents to sign written consents for their children to receive the full scope of services provided by the clinic. Most SBHCs have a mental health provider and through collaboration with school mental health professionals, the mental health and productivity of students can be optimized. With active school mental health professionals, it is likely that the mental health provider in the SBHC will be a psychiatric mental health nurse practitioner (PMHNP) or psychiatrist, and assume a role in terms of psychiatric assessment and diagnosis, and pharmacotherapy. School mental health providers can then readily provide other school-based interventions. Again, because the HIPPA Privacy Rule applies to SBHC records, a release of information will be necessary in order to ensure collaborative care for the student. Additional information about school-based health clinics can be found at the website for the National Assembly on School-Based Health Care (http://www.nasbhc.org) . The National Association of School Nurses and National Assembly of School-Based Health Care have issued a joint statement on the partnership between the school nurse and school based health center and a shared vision of collaboration that would readily extend to all school health/mental health professionals (National Association of School Nurses, 2011).

"Merely placing a community program within the school walls does not guarantee collaboration. "

Overcoming Challenges to Collaboration Within a Response-to-Intervention Process

Some schools are implementing a response-to-intervention (RTI) process for behavior (Sprick, Booher, & Garrison, 2009; Malecki & Demaray, 2007) and there is interest in developing RTI models that integrate supports for academics and behavior in one process (Graden, Stollar, & Poth, 2007; Bohanon, Goodman, & McIntosh, n.d.). Adopting this approach brings with it some inherent advantages in enhancing collaboration around development of interventions for students with depression. One of these is that RTI teams are already a major part of the overall school organization and generally have the full backing of the school administrative and instructional infrastructure. Including interventions for students with depression within this infrastructure reduces the problem of marginalization of such services as previously described. Moreover, RTI teams have embedded within them some of the fundamental characteristics of collaborative teams: a common vision and goals, a focus on solutions and resources, a multidisciplinary approach to developing interventions, and a foundation for effective communication that is built into the problem-solving process.

CREATING COORDINATED, COLLABORATIVE, INTEGRATED SUPPORTS FOR STUDENTS WITH DEPRESSION

Creating a coordinated, collaborative, and integrated approach to serving students with depression can seem like a tall order for school professionals who often do not have the authority (or time and resources) to change the structure or policies of the service delivery process in their districts, let alone those of community agencies and providers. For these professionals, a practical approach to improvement may be conceptualized as a process of change through a series of concentric circles with the individual practitioner at the center and each larger circle representing increasingly larger and more complex systems. Adelman and Taylor (2006b) refer to this approach as "building from localities outward" (p. 156).

RTI CONNECTIONS

- Including assessment and intervention for depressed students within the RTI framework brings these services into the mainstream of school organization, reducing marginalization.

- RTI teams already have many of the characteristics of collaboration.

From this perspective, the process of improving services to students with depression appears more manageable. Individual professionals can begin with the resolution to review and improve their own practices in terms of collaboration and partnership with colleagues. Start with an assessment of the current efforts at collaboration. Actively support all efforts to create family–school collaboration. Actively support all systemic efforts to reduce fragmentation and marginalization of support services. At the next level, groups comprising two or more professionals of various specialties within the school critically evaluate how they serve students and make changes that increase the level of collaboration and integration. Other school personnel (notably administrators and teachers) are then brought into the process to develop a school-wide approach to helping these students. Work toward integrating the care of students with depressed behavior into pre-existing collaborative teams (e.g., through behavioral RTI teams or integrated behavioral–academic RTI teams). Develop a written agreement among collaborating partners about the structures and processes they will follow to accomplish the team's shared vision and goals. Develop plans for building collaboration with key stakeholders such as school administrators, school mental health professionals, and healthcare personnel.

"Broad school-district reform may be needed, but sometimes reform has to come from the bottom up."

Ultimately, these efforts can be expanded into other schools, the district as a whole, and the community. Broad school-district reform may be needed, but sometimes reform has to come from the bottom up. The ultimate goal is authentic family–school–community collaboration, but it is important to recognize that building such a system could take several years of focused effort. Students with depression frequently have complex needs involving multiple professionals for both assessment and service provision. The need for truly collaborative professional teaming is critical for helping these students, their families, and their teachers.

ACTION PLAN

- Start from the default position that students with depressed behavior will be best served by (a) a comprehensive and integrated school-wide approach to assessment, prevention, and intervention; and (b) truly collaborative and inclusive family–school–community teams that are fully integrated with the instructional and managerial infrastructure of the school.

- Enlist a group of people interested in improving family–school–community collaboration. Administrators are critical members of such a group.

- Assess the degree of collaboration within local teams for areas of needed improvement, and actively implement a plan to address these areas directly. Promote frank discussion of problems and solutions related to overspecialization of professional roles, fragmentation of mental health services, and marginalization of these services within the school.

- Advocate for bringing learning supports such as mental health services into parity with instructional and managerial structures within the school. Consider integrating services for students with depression and other mental health problems into the school's RTI framework.

- Work to improve family–school collaboration by implementing the recommendations of Esler and colleagues (2008) described earlier in this chapter.

- Provide professional development for school personnel regarding family–school collaboration, especially regarding culturally and linguistically diverse families.

- Develop a process for collaboration with the healthcare community along the lines of the suggestions of Glaser and colleagues (2010) described in this chapter. School mental health professionals should maintain primary responsibility for their students regardless of where they might be receiving services (e.g., healthcare offices, school-based health centers, hospitals).

- As the family–school–community team is strengthened, reach out to community resources such as clergy, librarians, youth leaders, and others to broaden the base for potential intervention with depressed students.

- Provide professional development making all staff aware of the connection between students' mental health and academic achievement.

RESOURCES

Three websites have resources useful for facilitating analysis of when FERPA and HIPPA rules apply:

- National School Boards Association (http://www.nsba.org/SchoolLaw)

- National Law Review. Particularly relevant to the discussion in this chapter is the document entitled "Understanding the Privacy Rights of HIPAA and FERPA in Schools" (http://www.natlawreview.com/article/understanding-privacy-rights-hipaa-ferpa-schools).

- National Assembly on School-Based Health Care (http:www.nasbhc.org). Of particular relevance is the article entitled "The HIPAA Privacy Rule and FERPA: How Do they Work in SBHCs?"

An outstanding source of information and materials for a wide range of issues in school mental health is the University of California, Los Angeles, School Mental Health Project: The Center for Mental Health in Schools (smhp.psych.ucla.edu). Below are some examples of resources found there that are of particular relevance to the discussion in this chapter.

- Adelman, H. S., & Taylor, L. (2008). *Rebuilding for learning: Addressing barriers to learning and teaching and re-engaging students.* New York, NY: Scholastic. This is a handbook for enhancing the full continuum of school–community supports for students. Retrieved from http://smhp.psych.ucla.edu/rebuild/RebuidlingV11RD28.pdf

- UCLA Center for Mental Health in Schools. (n.d.). *Framing new directions for school counselors, psychologists, and social workers.* Los Angeles, CA: Author. This report describes how the roles of school mental health professionals might be reframed to better address challenges to learning faced by students. Retrieved from http://smhp.psych.ucla.edu/pdfdocs/Report/framingnewdir.pdf

- UCLA Center for Mental Health in Schools. (2010). *Synthesis and analysis of recommendations to Congress for ESEA reauthorization from the perspective of addressing barriers to learning & teaching.* Los Angeles, CA: Author. Ostensibly about the reauthorization of the Elementary and Secondary Schools Act, this document is also brief summary of the work of Howard Adelman and Linda Taylor. Retrieved from http://smhp.psych.ucla.edu/pdfdocs/esearecs.pdf

Two books by Adleman and Taylor (2006, a, b), *The Implementation Guide to Student Learning Supports in the Classroom and Schoolwide: New Directions for Addressing Barriers to Learning* and *The School Leader's Guide to Student Learning Supports: New Directions for Addressing Barriers to Learning,* are comprehensive guides to restructuring schools in order to reduce fragmentation and marginalization of student support services and remove barriers to learning for all students. These books also provide extensive information (including forms, checklists, and other tools) about ways for schools to build collaborative teams.

The Harvard Family Research Project: Family Involvement website (http://www.hfrp.org/family-involvement) is a professional resource for articles and research on family–school collaboration issues.

The National Association of School Nurses has two excellent resources for school nurses that provide important information on collaboration:

- *School Nursing: Scope and Standards of Practice,* 2nd Edition (2011), jointly published by the National Association of School Nurses and the American Nurses Association, provides the standards of practice and their associated competencies. The standards provide authoritative statements on the responsibilities of school nurses and how outcomes can be measured. Collaboration is a standard of practice.

- *School Nursing: A Comprehensive Text,* 2nd Edition (2012) was edited by Janice Selekman, DNSc, RN, NCSN and published by the National Association of School Nurses. This is an excellent resource on all aspects of school nursing. Two chapters have relevance to this chapter: Chapter 3, Standards of Practice and Chapter 7, Collaboration with the Community. This text is also a resource for IEPs, 504 plans, and emergency plans.

The National Association of School Psychologists offers a series of handouts on their website for families (http://www.nasponline.org/families/index.aspx) and educators (http://www.nasponline.org/educators/index.aspx). Some of these are available in Spanish or audio formats as well as in English. Titles in this series that are particularly relevant to family–school collaboration include:

- Family–School Partnerships: Information and Approaches for Educators

- Home–School Conferences: A Guide for Parents

- Immigrant Parents and the School

- Homeless Students in the Schools: Information for Educators

- Home–School–Community: Communicating With Indigenous American Families

- Communicating With Latino Parents and Families

- Effective Communication With Black Families and Students

- Communication Matters: Communicating Effectively With Culturally and Linguistically Diverse Families

- Communicating With Asian Parents and Families

- Culturally Competent Schools: Guidelines for Secondary School Principals (reprint from *Principal Leadership*, March 2006)

The National Parental Information and Resource Center (PIRC) is funded by the U.S. Department of Education and provides information and technical assistance to PIRCs across the country. PIRCs were created to encourage parental involvement in school policies, programs, and activities that would lead to improvement in student academic achievement and strengthen partnerships among parents, teachers, principals, administrators, and other school personnel

in order to better meet the educational needs of students. A webinar series titled *Achieving Excellence and Innovation in Family, School, and Community Engagement* is among these resources. This resource is the result of partnerships between the U.S. Department of Education and United Way Worldwide, National Parent Teacher Association, SEDL, and Harvard Family Research Project. This series of nine webinars provides an opportunity for school personnel and parents to learn about best practices and innovations that make a difference in student learning. The webinar titles include:

- Webinar 1: Transforming Schools Through Family, School, and Community Engagement

- Webinar 2: A New Day: Family, School, and Community Engagement in Education Reform

- Webinar 3: Data Driven: Making Student and School Data Accessible and Meaningful to Families

- Webinar 4: The Teacher–Parent Relationship: Using Professional Development to Improve Family and Community Engagement

- Webinar 5: Building Strategic Partnerships to Foster Community Engagement in Education

- Webinar 6: Ensuring School Readiness Through Successful Transitions

- Webinar 7: Successful Transitions to High School: Promoting High School Success and Facilitating College Readiness

- Webinar 8: Evaluating Family Engagement Strategies: Addressing Measurement Challenges

- Webinar 9: Bringing it All Together: Family and Community Engagement Policies in Action

More information and access to the webinars may be found at http://www.nationalpirc.org.

The Nebraska Center for Research on Children, Youth, Families, and Schools: Future of School Psychology Task Force on Family–School Partnerships offers a wide variety of resources on their website (http://fsp.unl.edu/future_index.html), including handouts, PowerPoint presentations, and training modules for staff development in the area of family–school collaboration. Training modules cover such areas as:

- Overview of Family–School Partnerships

- Family–School Interventions: Preschool

- Parent Consultation

- Parent Education, Training, Interventions

- Family–School Collaboration

The national PTA publishes *National Standards for Family–School Partnerships* along with other resources on its website (http://www.pta.org/national_standards.asp).

Segool, N. K., Mathiason, J. B., Majewicz-Hefley, A., & Carlson, J. S. (2009). Enhancing student mental health: Collaboration between medical professionals and school psychologists. *NASP Communiqué, 37*(7), 1, 23–26.

Shaw, S. R., Clayton, M. C., Dodd, J. L., & Rigby, B. T. (2004). Collaborating with physicians: A guide for school leaders. *Principal Leadership, 5*(1). Retrieved from http://www.nasponline.org/resources/principals/nassp_collab.aspx

Shaw, S. R., & Woo, A. H. (2008). Best practices in collaborating with medical personnel. In A. Thomas & J. Grimes (Eds.), *Best practices in school psychology V* (pp. 1707–1717). Bethesda, MD: National Association of School Psychologists.

For a very readable overview of the status of home–school–community collaboration and suggestions for improvement, read *School-Community Relations: Policy and Practice* by Taylor & Adelman (2003; http://smhp.psych.ucla.edu/publications/39%20school%20community%20relations%20policy%20and%20practice.pdf).

The National Wraparound Initiative website (http://www.nwi.pdx.edu/index.shtml) contains a collection of information, tools, and strategies for collaboration through the wraparound model.

The book by Sprick, Booher, and Garrison (2009), *Behavioral Response to Intervention: Creating a Continuum of Problem-Solving and Support*, is a very good introduction to this topic and amounts to a how-to text on implementing a response-to-intervention model for social, emotional, and behavioral concerns.

REFERENCES

Adelman, H. S., & Taylor, L. (1999). Mental health in schools and system restructuring. *Clinical Psychology Review, 19*(2), 137–163. Retrieved from http://smhp.psych.ucla.edu/publications/17%20mental%20health%20in%20schools%20and%20system%20re-structuring.pdf

Adelman, H. S., & Taylor, L. (2006a). *The implementation guide to student learning supports in the classroom and schoolwide: New directions for addressing barriers to learning.* Thousand Oaks, CA: Corwin Press.

Adelman, H. S., & Taylor, L. (2006b). *The school leader's guide to student learning supports: New directions for addressing barriers to learning.* Thousand Oaks, CA: Corwin Press.

Adelman, H. S., & Taylor, L. (n.d.). *Impediments to enhancing availability of mental health in schools: Fragmentation, overspecialization, counterproductive competition, and marginalization.* Los Angeles, CA: UCLA Center for Mental Health in Schools. Retrieved from http://smhp.psych.ucla.edu/pdfdocs/impediments.pdf

American Academy of Pediatrics (AAP), Council on School Health. (2008). The American Academy of Pediatrics policy statement: The role of the school nurse in providing school health services. *Journal of School Nursing, 24,* 269–274. doi:10.1177/1059840508323781

DeSocio, J., & Hootman, J. (2004). Children's mental health and school success. *Journal of School Nursing, 20,* 189–196. doi:10.1177/10598405040200040201

Esler, A. N., Godber, Y., & Christenson, S. L. (2008). Best practices in supporting school–family partnerships. In A. Thomas & J. Grimes (Eds.), *Best practices in school psychology V* (pp. 917–936). Bethesda, MD: National Association of School Psychologists.

Glaser, S., Ouimet, T., & Shaw, S. R. (2010). Collaboration between educators and medical professionals: Models, barriers, and implications. In P. C. McCabe & S. R. Shaw (Eds.), *Pediatric disorders: Current topics and interventions for educators* (pp. 8–21). Thousand Oaks, CA: Corwin (a joint publication with the National Association of School Psychologists).

Graden, J. L., Stollar, S. A., & Poth, R. L. (2007). The Ohio Systems Model: Overview and lessons learned. In S. R. Jimerson, M. K. Burns, A. M. VanDerHeyden (Eds.), *Handbook of response to intervention: The science and practice of assessment and intervention* (pp. 288–299). New York, NY: Springer.

Malecki, C. K., & Demaray, M. K. (2007). Social behavior assessment and response to intervention. In S. R. Jimerson, M. K. Burns, A. M. VanDerHeyden (Eds.), *Handbook of response to intervention: The science and practice of assessment and intervention* (pp. 161–171). New York, NY: Springer.

National Association of School Nurses (NASN). (2011). *Position statement: Role of the school nurse.* Retrieved from http://www.nasn.org/positions

National Association of School Nurses (NASN). (2011). *Joint statement: School nurse/school-based health center partnership.* Retrieved from http://www.nasn.org/positions

National Association of School Nurses (NASN). (2008). *Position statement: Coordinated school health programs.* Retrieved from http://www.nasn.org/positions

National Association of School Nurses (NASN). (2008). *Position statement: Mental health of students.* Retrieved from http://www.nasn.org/positions

National Association of School Psychologists. (2006). Communication planning and message development: Promoting school-based mental health services. *Communiqué, 35*(1). Bethesda, MD: Author. Available from publisher.

Segool, N. K., Mathiason, J. B., Majewicz-Hefley, A., & Carlson, J. S. (2009). Enhancing student mental health: Collaboration between medical professionals and school psychologists. *NASP Communiqué, 37*(7), 1, 23–26.

Shaw, S. R., Clayton, M. C., Dodd, J. L., & Rigby, B. T. (2004). Collaborating with physicians: A guide for school leaders. *Principal Leadership, 5*(1). Retrieved from http://www.nasponline.org/resources/principals/nassp_collab.aspx

Shaw, S. R., & Woo, A. H. (2008). Best practices in collaborating with medical personnel. In A. Thomas & J. Grimes (Eds.), *Best practices in school psychology V* (pp. 1707–1717). Bethesda, MD: National Association of School Psychologists.

Sprick, R., Booher, M., & Garrison, M. (2009). *Behavioral response to intervention: Creating a continuum of problem-solving and support.* Eugene, OR: Pacific Northwest Publishing.

Taylor, L., & Adelman, H. S. (2003). School-community relations: Policy and practice. In M. S. Fishbaugh, T. R. Berkeley, & G. Schroth (Eds.), *Ensuring safe school environments: Exploring issues–seeking solutions* (pp. 107–132). Mahway, NJ: Erlbaum. Retrieved from http://smhp.psych.ucla.edu/publications/39%20school%20community%20relations%20policy%20and%20practice.pdf

UCLA Center for Mental Health in Schools. (2010). *Synthesis and analysis of recommendations to Congress for ESEA reauthorization from the perspective of addressing barriers to learning & teaching.* Los Angeles, CA: Author. Retrieved from http://smhp.psych.ucla.edu/pdfdocs/esearecs.pdf

UCLA Center for Mental Health in Schools. (n.d.). *Framing new directions for school counselors, psychologists, and social workers.* Los Angeles, CA: Author. Retrieved from http://smhp.psych.ucla.edu/pdfdocs/Report/framingnewdir.pdf

169

CHAPTER 12

DEPRESSION WITHIN A RESPONSE-TO-INTERVENTION FRAMEWORK

The creation of a comprehensive, coordinated range of services has been the holy grail of mental health service delivery—long sought but seldom realized. Multi-tiered problem-solving approaches, especially when paired with student progress monitoring, can be very effective ways of providing these services. Typically, these models deliver a continuum of services across three tiers of intensity:

- Tier 1: *Universal* prevention activities for everyone in a population, including those who are not currently experiencing problems.

- Tier 2: *Targeted* interventions for those at risk for developing social, emotional, or behavioral problems.

- Tier 3: *Intensive* interventions for those who are at very high risk or already experiencing a significant mental health problem.

As the primary provider of service for students with depression and other mental health problems, schools need to organize their services to students according to this model.

In fact, an increasing majority of schools already are incorporating aspects of a three-tiered problem-solving model into their programs through a response-to-intervention (RTI) framework. Considering its origins in the field of public health, it is ironic that most schools are using the model to organize, deliver, and evaluate the effectiveness of *academic* interventions for their students—and not so much mental health interventions. Moreover, most schools using the RTI infrastructure for addressing behavioral issues use positive behavior support (PBS) strategies of various kinds, which, except for interventions designed to improve general school climate, primarily focus on improving externalizing behaviors, not internalizing behaviors such as depression and anxiety. Nonetheless, RTI has the potential to at last provide a means for integrating school mental health services, including those for students with depression, into the mainstream of school organization. At the same time, it may provide the framework for a coordinated continuum of service for students with mental health needs. The three-tiered system typically seen in RTI approaches is readily applied to both academic and behavioral interventions.

WHAT IS RTI?

"A practice of providing high-quality instruction and interventions matched to student need, monitoring progress frequently to make decisions about changes in instruction or goals and applying child response data to important educational decisions."

(National Association of State Special Education Directors, 2006, p. 3).

ADDRESSING DEPRESSION THROUGH RESPONSE TO INTERVENTION

Whether a school district uses an RTI framework or not, the school mental health team should work toward organizing its services and interventions according to a multi-tiered problem solving model such as RTI. The aspects of RTI that have made it such a successful problem-solving model for academic behavior make it a very powerful method for intervening with depression. These aspects, which should be incorporated into applications with all social, emotional, and behavioral problems, include the following:

- Multi-tiered problem-solving model of service delivery

- Emphasis on prevention and early intervention

- Use of evidence-based interventions

- Assessment and data-based decision-making used for screening, diagnosis, intervention planning, progress monitoring, and program evaluation

While schools are only beginning to incorporate mental health services into this model, the RTI approach has tremendous potential for making the delivery of school mental health services much more efficient and effective.

"The aspects of RTI that have made it such a successful problem-solving model for academic behavior make it a very powerful method for intervening with depression."

Universal, Tier 1 Intervention

Within the social, emotional, and behavioral realm, universal interventions (Tier 1 of an RTI framework) might include such interventions as in-service professional development and training for staff, a social–emotional learning (SEL) program, consistent and effective classroom management and school-wide disciplinary procedures, various programs designed to improve student connectedness to school, home–school partnership, and universal screening. Giving students authoritative information about their difficulties, teaching cognitive–behavioral strategies, and coping skills instruction may all be integrated into a universal SEL program. School-wide efforts to increase protective factors and decrease risk factors are also important interventions at this tier. All school mental health service providers are able to provide Tier 1 services. Indeed, most teachers and school administrators—with appropriate in-service training—are also able to provide many of these services.

172

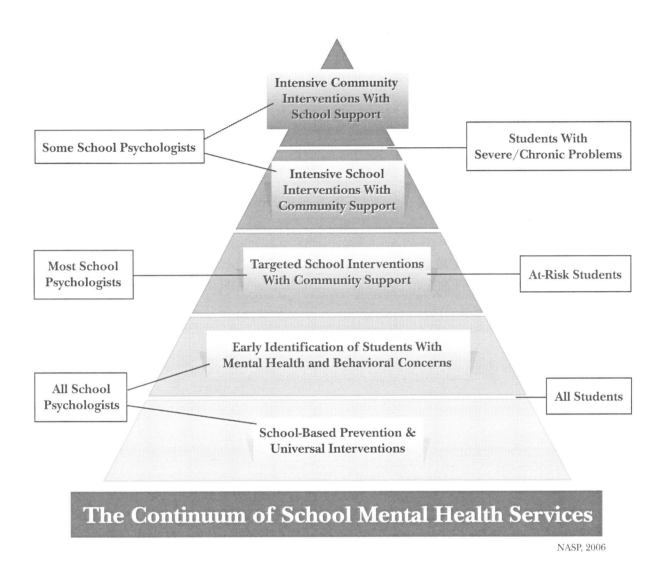

Figure 1. The Continuum of Mental Health Services

Adapted with permission from "Communication Planning and Message
Development: Promoting School-Based Mental Health Services" in *Communiqué*, Vol. 35, No. 1.
National Association of School Psychologists.

Targeted, Tier 2 Intervention

Targeted (Tier 2) services are those designed for the approximately 5% to 15% of students whose emotional and behavioral needs are not met by Tier 1 interventions. These services might include more intensive versions of interventions found at Tier 1. Such interventions might involve more frequent or intensive SEL programs, small-group counseling, more specialized in-service training for small groups of teachers, social or cognitive–behavioral skills training for small groups of students, education for parents of targeted students, and in-depth screening of at-risk students. Promotion of protective factors and reduction of risk factors for at-risk groups of students are also important interventions at this tier. Nearly all school mental health professionals are able to provide such services.

ESSENTIALS

- An RTI framework in the schools may be used for both academic and social–emotional–behavioral service issues, including depression.

- RTI provides a framework for integrating mental health with the overall educational mission of the school.

- Using an RTI framework would allow early assessment, prevention, and intervention for students with depression.

Intensive, Tier 3 Intervention

Intensive interventions are provided to the approximately 5% of students who do not respond to social, emotional, and behavioral interventions in the first two tiers. These services are more intense, more frequent, and more specialized. They may include more intensive versions of Tier 2 services, or more individualized interventions such as individual counseling, behavior management, case management (including wraparound service models using community-based services), and special education. Functional behavioral assessment and function-based interventions are frequently used at this tier. Promoting protective factors, mitigating risk factors, and building student skills continue to be important components of comprehensive planning at this tier. Some, though not necessarily all, school mental health professionals are equipped to provide these services.

Some students with depression will require referral to community agencies and providers such as community- and school-based health services, possibly including hospitalization and other intensive treatment options. Students with severe depression or depression accompanied by drug abuse, suicidal behavior, gang-related behavior, history of child abuse, and complex family involvement are all possible examples of those who may need this level of service. In all cases, however, school mental health providers must maintain a high level of involvement and collaboration in order to provide a comprehensive, coordinated intervention program integrating services from the school and community.

The Role of Diagnosis

Service provision within an RTI approach is not based on a student's DSM-IV-TR diagnosis or IDEA classification; rather, the intensity of interventions provided is determined by initially assessing the intensity of intervention the student requires, monitoring the student's response to that intervention, and increasing or decreasing the intensity of intervention based on the student's response. Even students at Tier 3 may not have a formal diagnosis, although many certainly could. For an academic example, students with reading difficulties may receive interventions at various tiers based on their needs and on their response to intervention (not on whether or not they have a diagnosed learning disability in reading). Similarly, students with depression may receive interventions at various tiers based not on whether they have a formal diagnosis, but on their needs and on their response to intervention. Section 2 of this book provides examples of the kinds of interventions applicable at each RTI tier.

INTEGRATING ACADEMIC AND BEHAVIORAL RESPONSE TO INTERVENTION

While it is possible for a school mental health team to develop multi-tiered problem-solving approaches in schools that do not have RTI frameworks in place, it is much easier in schools that already have this structure. The same teams, procedures, and data management systems used in the academic realm may be used for social, emotional, and behavioral concerns. In these cases, services for students with depression may be integrated into existing RTI programs and procedures.

"The same teams, procedures, and data management systems used in the academic realm may be used for social, emotional, and behavioral concerns."

Advantages of Integrating Academic and Behavioral Response to Intervention

Including social, emotional, and behavioral interventions within a school's RTI infrastructure goes a long way toward reducing the fragmentation, marginalization, and overspecialization of mental health services described by Adelman and Taylor (2006). Some of the advantages of an integrated RTI framework that incorporates both academic and social–emotional–behavioral functioning include the following (McIntosh, Goodman, & Bohanon, 2010):

■ Academic and behavioral skill development are positively related; that is, improving academic skills improves social, emotional, and behavioral skills and improving social, emotional, and behavioral skills improves academic skills. Incorporating social, emotional, and behavioral skills into the school's RTI framework substantially supports students' positive outcomes in academic achievement. As an example, adding a universal SEL component to the school curriculum results on average in an 11 percentile-point gain in school-wide academic achievement (Durlak, Weissberg, Dymnicki, Taylor, & Schellinger, 2011).

■ Students who are struggling with both academic and social–emotional–behavioral difficulties are at significantly higher risk of negative outcomes than students who have difficulty in only one of these domains. An RTI team that only considered one of these areas in isolation would very likely not identify students who functioned just below cutoffs in each area, yet it is these students who might be most at risk for negative outcomes. An integrated approach would be capable of identifying these students.

■ Because academic and behavioral RTI approaches share the same basic principles and structures, adding a social–emotional–behavioral component to existing RTI frameworks involves very little additional orientation of staff and does not require building another separate set of

procedures. There are efficiencies to be gained by using one system for both skill areas.

Adoption of an RTI model of service delivery for students with depression ensures (a) a prevention and early-intervention orientation toward depression, (b) a continuum of services integrated with mainstream school organizational patterns, (c) progress monitoring and a mechanism for students to move from one level of service to another, and (d) the involvement and collaboration of all stakeholders (not just specialists) in a multidisciplinary approach to intervention on behalf of students with depression. It also supports a focus on the context of depression and the use of evidence-based interventions.

KEYS TO COLLABORATION

■ RTI teams that equally consider academic and social–emotional–behavioral development will require a great deal of collaboration among school staff in order to be effective.

■ Administrators and school mental health professionals have substantial expertise in consultation and collaboration and should work together to improve collaboration on an integrated team.

■ Even within an RTI context, school mental health professionals will need to collaborate with medical and other community resources for some students with depression.

ACTION PLAN

- Develop a multi-tiered problem-solving approach to delivering a comprehensive and coordinated range of interventions for students with depression.

- If the school has an existing RTI structure, procedures for serving students with depression and other social, emotional, and behavioral problems should mirror the procedures used in the school's RTI approach to academic skill development. Consider developing an integrated RTI system for both mental health and academic concerns. Such an approach is more efficient than having two separate systems and all students might be better served.

- Train a broad base of school personnel to provide evidence-based interventions for depression at each tier of the RTI framework. Because interventions that support students with depression are also effective with students who have other mental health problems, doing so helps build capacity throughout the system.

- Collaboration and integration with community resources will help ensure that students have access to the full continuum of services they need.

RESOURCES

Response to Intervention: Policy Considerations and Implementation (2006), published by the National Association of State Directors of Special Education, is a standard introduction to the basic concepts of RTI.

An easy-to-read general introduction to RTI and it implementation is *Implementing Response to Intervention: A Principal's Guide*, by Susan Hall.

There are also a number of websites that provide general information about RTI as well as specific strategies for implementation. Two examples are:

- The National Center on Response to Intervention (http://www.rti-4success.org).

- The RTI Action Network (http://www.rtinetwork.org). A series of articles particularly relevant to this chapter is one entitled *Integrating Academic and Behavior Supports Within an RTI Framework* by Bohanon, Goodman, and McIntosh (http://www.rtinetwork.org/learn/behavior-supports/integrating-behavior-and-academic-supports-general-overview).

Most state governments also provide online RTI information that is specifically relevant to each state.

The Council for Exceptional Children (CEC; 2011) has published a position statement (*RTI for Emotional/Behavior Disorders Shows Promise*) supporting the integration of academic and behavioral RTI and discussing some of the issues surrounding implementation (http://www.cec.sped.org/AM/Template.cfm?Section=Home&TEMPLATE=/CM/ContentDisplay.cfm&CONTENTID=11297).

A National Association of School Psychologists (2009) position statement (*Appropriate Behavioral, Social, and Emotional Supports to Meet the Needs of All Students*) supports "the use of multi-tiered problem-solving strategies to address the behavioral, social, emotional, and academic needs of all students" (http://www.nasponline.org/about_nasp/position-papers/AppropriateBehavioralSupports.pdf).

Two books that provide comprehensive approaches to developing and implementing behavioral RTI programs in schools are *Behavioral Response to Intervention: Creating a Continuum of Problem-Solving and Support* by Sprick, Booher, and Garrison (2009) and *Behavioral Interventions in Schools: A Response-to-Intervention Guidebook* by Hulac, Terrell, Vining, and Bernstein (2011). Neither book focuses primarily on depression or internalizing disorders, but both describe how to develop a behavioral RTI program, and both provide an outline of processes that could easily be adapted to address a range of social, emotional, and behavioral problems, including internalizing disorders.

■ The book by Sprick et al. (2009) lays out plans, forms, and resources for the development of behavioral RTI processes in schools. It is an excellent introduction to the topic written in reader-friendly terms for those wishing to start or improve a behavioral RTI approach in their district or school.

■ The Hulac et al. (2011) book provides a guide to implementing a problem-solving model within a behavioral RTI program in elementary and middle schools. The focus, however, is on positive behavioral supports and externalizing behavior.

There are a number of chapters in various textbooks that address behavioral RTI. One particularly relevant example is a chapter by Seeley, Rohde, and Jones (2010) entitled "School-Based Prevention and Intervention for Depression and Suicidal Behavior." This chapter provides general background on depression as well as a summary of some of the interventions appropriate for each tier of prevention. It may be found in *Interventions for Achievement and Behavior Problems in a Three-Tier Model Including RTI* by Shinn and Walker (2010).

REFERENCES

Adelman, H. S., & Taylor, L. (2006a). *The implementation guide to student learning supports in the classroom and schoolwide: New directions for addressing barriers to learning.* Thousand Oaks, CA: Corwin Press.

Bohanon, H., Goodman, S., & McIntosh, K. (n.d.). *Integrating Academic and Behavior Supports Within an RTI Framework, Part 1: General Overview.* Retrieved from (http://www.rtinetwork.org/learn/behavior-supports/integrating-behavior-and-academic-supports-general-overview)

Bohanon, H., McIntosh, K., & Goodman, S. (n.d.). *Integrating Academic and Behavior Supports Within an RTI Framework, Part 4: Tertiary Supports.* Retrieved from (http://www.rtinetwork.org/learn/behavior-supports/integrating-academic-and-behavior-supports-tertiary-supports)

Council for Exceptional Children. (2011). RTI for emotional/behavior disorders shows promise. Retrieved from http://www.cec.sped.org/AM/Template.cfm?Section=Home&TEMPLATE=/CM/ContentDisplay.cfm&CONTENTID=11297

Durlak, J. A., Weissberg, R. P., Dymnicki, A. B., Taylor, R. D., & Schellinger, K. B. (2011). The impact of enhancing students' social and emotional learning: A meta-analysis of school-based universal interventions. *Child Development, 82*(1), 405–432.

Goodman, S., McIntosh, K., & Bohanon, H. (n.d.). *Integrating Academic and Behavior Supports Within an RTI Framework, Part 2: Universal Supports.* Retrieved from (http://www.rtinetwork.org/learn/behavior-supports/integrating-academic-and-behavior-supports-universal-supports)

Hall, S. L. (2008). *Implementing response to intervention: A principal's guide.* Thousand Oaks, CA: Corwin Press.

Hulac, D., Terrell, J., Vining, O., & Bernstein, J. (2011). *Behavioral interventions in schools: A response-to-intervention guidebook.* New York, NY: Taylor and Francis.

McIntosh, K., Bohanon, H., & Goodman, S. (n.d.). *Integrating Academic and Behavior Supports Within an RTI Framework, Part 3: Secondary Supports.* Retrieved from (http://www.rtinetwork.org/learn/behavior-supports/integrating-academic-and-behavior-supports-secondary-supports)

McIntosh, K., Goodman, S., & Bohanon, H. (2010). Toward true integration of academic and behavior response to intervention systems–part one: Tier 1 support. *NASP Communiqué, 39*(2). Retrieved from http://www.nasponline.org/publications/cq/mocq392RTISystemsSupport.aspx

National Association of School Psychologists. (2009). *Appropriate behavioral, social, and emotional supports to meet the needs of all students* (Position Statement). Bethesda, MD: Author. Retrieved from http://www.nasponline.org/about_nasp/positionpapers/AppropriateBehavioralSupports.pdf

National Association of State Directors of Special Education. (2006). *Response to intervention: Policy considerations and implementation.* Alexandria, VA: Author.

Seeley, J. R., Rohde, P., & Jones, L. B. (2010). School-based prevention and intervention for depression and suicidal behavior. In M. R. Shinn & H. M. Walker (Eds.), *Interventions for achievement and behavior problems in a three-tier model including RTI* (pp. 363–396). Bethesda, MD: National Association of School Psychologists.

Shinn, M. R., & Walker, H. M. (Eds.). (2010). *Interventions for achievement and behavior problems in a three-tier model including RTI.* Bethesda, MD: National Association of School Psychologists.

Sprick, R., Booher, M., & Garrison, M. (2009). *Behavioral response to intervention: Creating a continuum of problem-solving and support.* Eugene, OR: Pacific Northwest Publishing.

Vannest, K. J., Reynolds, C. R., & Kamphaus, R. W. (2008). *BASC-2 intervention guide for behavioral and emotional issues.* Minneapolis, MN: Pearson.

CHAPTER 13

SUICIDE PREVENTION AND INTERVENTION

"The noblest goal of an organization or individual is to save lives."

– Gene Cash (2009), former president of the National Association of School Psychologists

The results of the 2011 Youth Risk Behavior Surveillance System survey conducted by the Centers for Disease Control and Prevention (CDC, 2012a) tell a sobering story about suicidal behavior among youth in the United States. Asked to report their behavior during the year preceding the survey, students in grades 9 through 12 revealed the following:

- 15.8% seriously considered attempting suicide.

- 12.8% made a plan about how they would attempt suicide.

- 7.8% made one or more suicide attempts.

- 2.4% made a suicide attempt that resulted in the need for medical attention.

In other words, in an average high school of 1,000 students, these percentages suggest that during 2011, approximately 158 students had seriously considered suicide and 24 of them made an attempt requiring medical attention as a result (CDC, 2012a). Nationally, approximately 157,000 young people per year go to emergency rooms for self-inflicted injuries (CDC, 2012b). As with depression, however, much of this suffering often goes undetected by mental health professionals.

ESSENTIALS

- The CDC reports that, in 2011, 15.8% of high school students considered attempting suicide and 2.4% made an attempt resulting in medical attention.

- Approximately 4,400 young people commit suicide each year.

- 40% of students who attempt suicide make their first attempt before high school.

The problem actually starts in elementary school: 40% of students who attempt suicide first do so in elementary or middle school (Mazza, Catalano, Abbott, & Haggerty, 2011), although suicide before age 12 is rare. Suicide is the third leading cause of death among school-age children and adolescents; approximately 4,600 young people commit suicide each year (CDC, 2012b). In the United States, the rate of completed suicides among children 10 to 14 years of age is about one (0.9) per 100,000; among adolescents ages 15 to 19, it is seven (6.9) per 100,000 (NIMH, 2010). Clearly, the risk of suicide increases with the age of the student. In 2009, more adolescents and young adults, ages 15 to 24 years, died from suicide than from cancer, heart disease, congenital birth defects, influenza, pneumonia, pregnancy and childbirth, cerebrovascular disease, and lower respiratory diseases *combined* (Kochanek, Xu, Murphy, & Miniño, & Kung, 2011).

ESSENTIALS

■ Students will often disclose suicidal behavior through screening programs.

RECOGNIZING STUDENTS AT RISK FOR SUICIDE

The process of recognizing students who might be at risk for suicide parallels the process used to identify students at risk for depression. That is, both processes of recognition rely upon: (a) educating all school staff about risk factors, warning signs, and how to access help; (b) universal screening of all students; (c) school mental health professionals trained in suicide risk assessment; and (d) collaborative interconnections with community mental health providers.

Screening Programs for Suicide Prevention

Universal screening of all students is an important component of suicide prevention programs (SAMHSA, 2012). While students usually do not disclose suicidal behavior to adults, they will often answer questions about it when directly asked; screening pro-

cedures take advantage of this fact. Two commonly used evidence-based universal suicide-screening programs are TeenScreen for grades 6–12 (www.teenscreen.org) and SOS (Signs of Suicide; http://www.mentalhealthscreening. org/programs/youth-prevention-programs/ sos) for grades 8–12.

An alternative to this kind of screening is to identify students as possibly at risk based on the presence of known risk factors for suicide. These include: history of psychopathology (including conduct problems and substance abuse); history of suicidal or self-injurious behavior; depression, hopelessness, and mental pain; lack of family support; lack of connectedness or feelings of expendability; and being lesbian, gay, bisexual, or transgendered (Miller, 2011; Van Orden, Witte, Selby, Bender, & Joiner, 2008).

ESSENTIALS

■ All school staff should be trained to recognize the risk factors and warning signs for suicide.

■ Depression is a risk factor. However, not all depressed students commit suicide and not all suicidal students are depressed.

Depression as a Risk Factor for Suicide

The probability of suicide among adolescents with mood disorders is substantially higher than among adolescents without that diagnosis. However, not all students with depression exhibit suicidal behavior and not all students who exhibit suicidal behavior are depressed; there is no such thing as the prototypical suicidal student. In fact, there is a significant co-occurrence of a variety of psychological problems with suicidal behavior, most notably depression, conduct disorder, and substance abuse, with students exhibiting more than one of these problems being at greatest risk (Berman, Jobes, & Silverman, 2006).

Warning Signs

Many suicidal students exhibit observable warning signs of suicide risk. While the presence of risk factors suggests that school staff should monitor a student for possible suicidal behavior, the presence of warning signs suggest that such behavior is already present (Brock, Sandoval, & Hart, 2006). School staff and mental health professionals should be mindful of students who evidence any of the following warning signs (Lieberman, Poland, & Cassel, 2008):

- Feelings of depression, helplessness, and hopelessness.

- Sudden changes in behavior.

- Previous suicide attempt.

- Direct or indirect threats to kill oneself.

- Having a plan and method for killing oneself and access to the means to do so; the more detailed the planning, the greater the risk.

- Making final arrangements such as giving away possessions or writing goodbye notes.

In its handout entitled "Know the Warning Signs," the American Association of Suicidality (AAS, n.d.) offers a mnemonic to remember

warning signs: IS PATH WARM? The letters stand for:

- I – Ideation
- S – Substance Abuse
- P – Purposelessness
- A – Anxiety
- T – Trapped
- H – Hopelessness
- W – Withdrawal
- A – Anger
- R – Recklessness
- M – Mood Changes

ESSENTIALS

- Possibly suicidal students should be immediately referred for a risk assessment by a school mental health professional.

- Confidentiality cannot be promised during this process.

- Students should not be left alone during this process and parents should be informed of the assessment regardless of its results.

All school staff should be trained in the risk factors and warning signs of suicide. Read the chapter in this book entitled "Recognizing Depressed Students: Screening for Prevention" for additional information about approaches to screening and how to implement a screening program in your school. For more detailed information, read *Preventing Suicide: A Toolkit for High Schools* (SAMHSA, 2012), which provides detailed guidelines for developing a school-based suicide screening program.

Suicide Risk Assessment

Each school should have at least one school mental health professional with competence in suicide risk assessment. Students who have been identified as possibly suicidal, either through a screening process, referral, or crisis situation, need to be administered a suicide risk assessment by a school mental health professional in order to determine the level of suicide risk and the interventions that are necessary to address that risk. Parents should be notified whenever a risk assessment is performed, regardless of its outcome. Documentation of all actions taken should be part of the school's procedures.

Risk assessments should include multiple sources of data (e.g., interviews with teachers, use of psychometric instruments), but all should involve an interview with the student (Miller, 2011) that is conducted in a calm, nonjudgmental,

developmentally appropriate way (Tishler, Reiss, & Rhodes, 2007) and an interview with the parent (Lieberman et al., 2008). Lieberman and colleagues (2008) recommend questions to ask during interviews (also available on the Los Angeles County Youth Suicide Prevention Project website). They recommend that suicide risk assessments include consideration of the following:

- Observed warning signs

- Sudden changes in behavior

- Suicidal thoughts or threats

- Previous suicide attempts

- Planning for the suicide

- Lethality and accessibility of the planned method of suicide

- Student's support system

- History of mental illness

- History of recent loss, trauma, or victimization

Table 1. Sample Suicide Assessment Instruments

Name	Age Range	Access
Beck Scale for Suicide Ideation	Ages 17+	http://www.pearsonassessments.com/HAIWEB/Cultures/en-us/Productdetail.htm?Pid=015-8018-443&Mode=summary
Suicide Ideation Questionnaire	Grades 10–12	http://www4.parinc.com/Products/Product.aspx?ProductID=SIQ
Suicide Ideation Questionnaire–JR	Grades 7–9	http://www4.parinc.com/Products/Product.aspx?ProductID=SIQ
Suicide Probability Scale	Ages 14+	http://portal.wpspublish.com/portal/page?_page-id=53,69317&_dad=portal&_schema=PORTAL

During interviews and other suicide risk assessment procedures, confidentiality cannot be promised to the student and should not be maintained. Students should not be left alone during this process.

There are a great number of psychometric assessment instruments available for use with children and adolescents (see Goldston, 2000, for a review). Examples of some that have an adequate evidence base and take about 10 minutes to administer are provided in Table 1.

As mentioned previously, suicide assessment instruments alone are not adequate for suicide risk assessment; they should always be used as one part of a multi-method assessment.

Linking Level of Risk to Intervention

Rudd (2006) defines suicidal risk along a continuum, from minimal to extreme, and provides general guidelines for actions at each level. Table 2 summarizes his description of each level of risk and recommendations for actions to be taken at each level.

ESSENTIALS

- School-based suicide prevention is based on a comprehensive and collaborative continuum of assessment and intervention services.

- Best practice is to integrate suicide prevention activities within a comprehensive program designed to promote student mental health.

Table 2. Levels of Risk and Responses (Rudd, 2006)

Risk Level	Indicators	Actions to Be Taken
Minimal	No identifiable suicidal ideation.	No change in program.
Mild	Suicidal ideation of limited frequency, intensity, duration, specificity.	Monitor suicidal ideation for changes in risk level.
Moderate	Frequent suicidal ideation of limited intensity and duration, some specificity of plan, and no associated intent.	Assess need for hospitalization. Increase psychotherapy, family involvement. Assess 24-hour availability of crisis services. Frequent reevaluation of risk and treatment plan. Consideration of medication.
Severe	Frequent, intense, enduring suicidal ideation; specific plan; no subjective intent but some objective markers of intent (e.g., choice of lethal method).	Immediate evaluation for hospitalization.
Extreme	Frequent, intense, enduring suicidal ideation; specific plan, clear intent.	Hospitalization for stabilization.

Table 3. Levels of Risk and Responses (Lieberman et. al, 2008)

Level of Risk	Indicators	Actions to Be Taken
Low	Current or recent suicidal ideation; depression; signs such as direct or indirect threats, personality change, change in friends or behavior; evidence in written or art work; visits to "dark" Internet sites.	Warn parents; Supervise student and develop safety plan; Connect with school and community resources; Suicide-proof environments.
Medium	Current suicidal ideation and history of previous suicidal behaviors; recent history of mental health hospitalization, loss, victimization, psychotropic medication; substance abuse; repetitive self-injury; risky behavior.	Supervise student; release student only to law enforcement, psychiatric mobile response, or parent who commits to seeking immediate assessment; Prepare reentry plan and circle of care with family, school-based providers, and community providers.
High	Current suicidal ideation, plan, method, and access; refusal to commit to safety plan; goodbye messages and/or giving away possessions.	

ESSENTIALS

■ Regardless of whether the school implements a more comprehensive program of suicide prevention, they must have in place protocols for helping students at risk for suicide, responding to suicide, and preventing additional suicides.

RTI CONNECTIONS

■ In too many cases, attention to suicide first occurs at the most intensive level of a three-tiered problem-solving model. Effective suicide prevention starts with universal screening and prevention programming and progresses to targeted and increasingly intensive interventions, an approach entirely consistent with a response-to-intervention (RTI) model.

Rudd's (2006) levels of risk and responses constitute a guideline for classification of suicidal risk in people of all ages. Lieberman and colleagues (2008) define suicidal risk along a continuum of low–medium–high for school-age youth and provide general guidelines specifically for school-based clinical action at each level. Table 3 summarizes their description of each risk level and their recommendations for actions to be taken at that level of risk (also available on the Los Angeles County Youth Suicide Prevention Project website at http://preventsuicide.lacoe.edu/admin_staff/administrators/guidelines_suicide.php).

Additional indicators and actions, along with much more detailed descriptions of risk assessment, are summarized in both Rudd (2006) and Lieberman et al. (2008).

SCHOOL-BASED STRATEGIES FOR PREVENTING SUICIDE

Just as strategies for assessment of depression and suicide parallel each other, strategies for suicide prevention are, in many ways, similar to strategies for the prevention of depression. That is, suicide prevention activities are best thought of as part of a comprehensive, integrated, and collaborative continuum of services designed to enhance student mental health and prevent or treat mental health problems. Interventions along such a continuum may be universal (delivered to all students), targeted (for at-risk students), or intensive (for suicidal students) in nature.

Components of School-Based Suicide Prevention Programs

Berman and colleagues outline seven components of comprehensive school-based suicide prevention programs (Berman et al., 2006):

1. All students and faculty are taught the risk factors and signs associated with suicide and how to refer students to a mental health professional.
2. Resources within the school and community are identified for possible referral. Students are made aware of these resources, especially those available within the school.
3. Various strategies are employed to make help-seeking more the norm among students.
4. School staff are specifically trained in youth suicide, including risk factors, signs, and referral methods.

5. Parents are also trained in youth suicide, including risk factors, signs, and referral methods.
6. Universal school programs designed to teach skills that promote positive mental health are incorporated into the curriculum starting in elementary school.
7. Interventions following a suicide attempt or death by suicide are in place within the school.

The U.S. Department of Health and Human Services Substance Abuse and Mental Health Services Administration (SAMHSA, 2012) also recommends the development of comprehensive suicide prevention programs in schools. Ideally, such programs would include protocols for specifically addressing suicide that are integrated within a comprehensive, coordinated approach to promoting student mental health. This is because such programs, by addressing the risk and protective factors for suicide before overt suicidal behavior occurs, are ultimately more helpful than focusing on remedial actions once students become suicidal (Berman et al., 2006). Nevertheless, two components that every school should immediately have in place regardless of whether they implement any other suicide prevention activities are protocols for (a) helping students who are at risk or who attempt suicide and (b) responding to suicide and preventing additional suicides. Once these protocols are in place, the next steps are to (a) train all staff in recognizing risk factors and signs of suicide, (b) train selected staff in assessment and referral of at-risk students, (c) educate parents and students about behavioral risk promotion and suicide prevention, and (d) screen students for suicide risk (SAMHSA, 2012). *Preventing Suicide: A Toolkit for High Schools* (SAMHSA, 2012) is a comprehensive guide to the tools and strategies needed for a school to accomplish this and is available online free of charge.

Suicide Prevention Programs

Once foundational protocols are in place for protecting students at risk for suicide, schools can turn their attention to building a more comprehensive program of suicide prevention that incorporates universal, targeted, and intensive levels of intervention.

Universal Interventions

Universal programs are those that are delivered to all students in a school or district. Berman et al. (2006) stress the importance of universal prevention programming (here called primary prevention) in schools:

> ■ Taking the long view, the most effective and probably the most cost-effective strategy is that of primary prevention, incorporating any number of programs designed to teach health-enhancing behavior through teaching behavioral skills. These programs must begin in the primary grades, be reinforced through follow-up training, and focus on adaptive skills and competencies. (p. 320)

Preventing Suicide: A Toolkit for High Schools (SAMHSA, 2012) provides a listing of such programs for high school students, including brief descriptions of each. Some of the evidence-based programs described in that publication and websites for each one are listed below:

- American Indian Life Skills Development/Zuni Life Skills Development

- Lifelines (http://www.ihs.gov/nonmedicalprograms/nspn)

- Signs of Suicide (SOS; http://www.mentalhealthscreening.org/programs/youth-prevention-programs/sos)

- Ask 4 Help! Suicide Prevention for Youth (http://www.sprc.org/sites/sprc.org/files/bpr/

- Helping Every Living Person (HELP) Depression and Suicide Prevention Curriculum (http://www.yspp.org/curriculum/HELP_curriculum.htm)

- LEADS for Youth: Linking Education and Awareness of Depression and Suicide (http://www.save.org/index.cfm?fuseaction=home.viewPage&page_id=45DFBB66-7E90-9BD4-CEB81505D25E7ED1)

- Response: A Comprehensive High School-Based Suicide Awareness Program (http://www.columbia-care.org/Page.asp?NavID=99)

Another program listed, Sources of Strength (http://sourcesofstrength.org), is designed to train peer leaders to lead a suicide prevention campaign in their school.

ESSENTIALS

■ Intensive school-based interventions focus on keeping the student safe, performing a risk assessment, warning parents, coordinating and documenting services provided, and preparing services that will be needed after the crisis has been resolved.

■ School mental health professionals support families and provide referral to and collaboration with community service providers such as hospitals, physicians, and therapists.

Targeted Interventions

Targeted interventions are those designed for students who are at risk for suicidal behavior. Students who are depressed fall into this category. Two targeted programs for high school students at risk for suicide are listed in *Preventing Suicide: A Toolkit for High Schools* (SAMHSA, 2012):

■ Coping and Support Training (CAST; http://www.reconnectingyouth.com/programs/cast)

■ Reconnecting Youth (http://www.reconnectingyouth.com/ry/what_main.html)

ESSENTIALS

■ School mental health professionals provide support to staff members affected by a student's suicidal behavior.

■ Following a completed suicide, they coordinate the postvention activities of the school. A major goal of such activities is to prevent additional suicides.

Other targeted interventions that might be useful in a comprehensive school-based suicide prevention program are focused on the factors that put the identified students at risk. For example, interventions designed to decrease depression and hopelessness, increase connectedness, address substance abuse, and decrease conduct problems all have an evidence base supporting their use (Miller, 2011). Targeted interventions for depressed behavior are described in the chapter of this book entitled "Evidence-Based Interventions for Students at Risk for Depression."

Intensive Interventions

Intensive interventions are designed for students at high risk for suicide or for those in the midst of a suicidal crisis. School-based interventions at this level are often focused on: keeping students safe (including removing access to weapons or other means of harm); performing a risk assessment; notifying parents, police, or community supports; coordinating activities undertaken on behalf of the student; and preparing services that will be required once the crisis is resolved (Miller, 2011). Counseling services are also usually provided, either within the school or through community providers. It is at this intensive level of intervention that it is most critical to have protocols and checklists in place as recommended by SAMHSA (2012) and others so that appropriate services and procedures are provided and documented. School mental health professionals typically have a central role in collaborating with all members of the home–school–community system.

Generally speaking, the most intensive interventions for students at risk for suicide (psychopharmacology, hospitalization, long-term psychotherapy) are not provided within the schools (Seeley, Rohde, & Jones, 2010). School mental health professionals often need to provide referrals for such services. They must then continue to collaborate with the family, hospital, therapist, and others in providing school-based supports and coordinating interventions post-crisis when the student returns to school. They also, of course, have a central role in providing support and interventions for students and school staff also affected by the suicidal behavior.

Following a completed suicide, school mental health professionals need to provide a variety of postvention activities to help survivors cope with the suicide, prevent further suicides, identify at-risk students, and facilitate the grieving process for the school community. Of particular concern is preventing the occurrence of imitative suicides following the completed suicide (Lieberman, et al., 2008). A good resource for postvention planning is *After a Suicide: A Toolkit for Schools*, published by the American Foundation for Suicide Prevention and Suicide Resource Center (2011).

NONSUICIDAL SELF-INJURY

Nonsuicidal self-injury (NSSI) is defined as deliberate bodily harm without suicidal intent, and includes cutting, burning, rubbing, mutilating, or other methods of trauma to one's own body tissue (Wilkinson, 2011). Self-injury or self-mutilation also includes inserting objects under the skin or in body orifices, scratching or picking at the skin and hair pulling (McDonald, 2006). It usu-

ally begins in adolescence, but may occur at any age. While it is not a suicidal behavior, it is associated with depression and suicide (Miller & Brock, 2010). In fact, the most prevalent risk factor associated with NSSI is depression (Wilkinson, 2011). In a recent study of adolescents with chronic treatment-resistant depression, histories of NSSI were found for 38% of those studied (a rate more common than suicide attempts), and a history of NSSI at the beginning of treatment, even with no history of suicide attempts, predicted suicide attempts over the next 6 months (Asarnow et al., 2011).

The factors that cause and maintain NSSI are not entirely known, but an important function of the behavior appears to be the reduction of psychological pain (Miller & Brock, 2010). It is considered a coping mechanism and a means of regulating affect, albeit dysfunctional (Wilkinson, 2011). Beyond an isolated incident, NNSI is a pattern of behavior with a certain number of adolescents found to become addicted to the emotional relief or high associated with self-injury (Wilkinson, 2011). While rates of NSSI have varied across studies (Asarnow et al., 2011), it is likely that NSSI occurs at a higher rate than suicide attempts.

ESSENTIALS

- Nonsuicidal self-injury represents a risk factor for suicide but is not, in itself, a suicidal behavior.

- The most prevalent risk factor associated with NSSI is depression.

It is clear that NSSI is a concern in itself and is a risk factor for suicide. As such, early identification of NSSI behavior can provide school mental health professionals the opportunity for intervention and referral before more se-

---

KEYS TO COLLABORATION

- The need for collaboration around the issues of depression and suicide are essentially the same. At the most intense levels of intervention, where community psychotherapists, physicians, and hospitals may be involved, the need for collaboration also intensifies.

- School nurses are the natural connection to community medical personnel and services. School nurses and school psychologists can also collaborate with community services in coordinating school and community interventions, monitoring effects of medical and other interventions and reporting those to community providers, and helping family members to be active participants in their child's treatment.

---

rious suicidal behavior occurs (Reynolds & Mazza, 1999). Indeed, if a student is referred for NSSI, the school mental health professional should obtain a complete mental health history and conduct a suicide risk assessment (Lieberman & Poland, 2006). Although students can be very creative at hiding the evidence of NSSI, dressing in long-sleeved shirts or concealing outfits and avoiding sports or other activities where skin exposure may occur can be an indicator in the context of other risk factors for depression. Peers tend to be the ones to alert school mental health professionals, teachers, or coaches (Wilkinson, 2011).

ACTION PLAN

- Make sure everyone in the school knows the number for the National Suicide Prevention Lifeline (1-800-273-TALK).

- Use the materials in SAMHSA's (2012) *Preventing Suicide: A Toolkit for High Schools* to guide suicide prevention procedures in your school and district.

- Review the school's suicide prevention procedures. Update them as necessary with checklists and protocols for responding to suicidal behavior. Forms, tools, checklists, and protocols are available in SAMHSA (2012).

- Ensure that school mental health professionals have competence in suicide prevention and are familiar with the protocols and tools in the school's suicide prevention procedures. Integrate these procedures with those of the school crisis team. Identify a school staff member with competence in suicide assessment, intervention, and referral to take the lead during suicidal crises.

- Collaborate with community providers to establish methods of providing services to students in crisis in a timely manner.

- Train all staff to recognize risk factors and warning signs of suicide and to appropriately refer students to school mental health professionals.

- Educate parents about suicide and how to avail themselves of resources available to them when they have concerns.

- Collaborate with the school crisis team, behavioral RTI team, or other problem-solving team within the school to incorporate a universal prevention program in the curriculum.

- Implement specific procedures for universal mental health screening, including screening for suicide risk.

- Build school capacity to implement targeted interventions for students at risk for suicide and other mental health problems.

- Use collaborative teams to continually evaluate and improve the effectiveness of the school's comprehensive, integrated approach to suicide prevention. Ensure that parents and community providers are included in this process.

RESOURCES

The National Suicide Prevention Lifeline 1-800-273-TALK (1-800-273-8255) will connect a caller to a crisis counselor in the area 24 hours a day.

Berman, A. L., Jobes, D. A., & Silverman, M. M. (2006). *Adolescent suicide: Assessment and intervention* (2nd ed.). Washington, DC: American Psychological Association. This authoritative textbook is an outstanding overview of suicide research, clinical practice, and prevention.

Miller, D. N. (2010). *Child and adolescent suicidal behavior: School-based prevention, assessment, and intervention*. New York, NY: Guilford Press. One of the few books specifically focused on school-based practice, this book covers assessment, prevention, and treatment in a highly readable and practical fashion.

Rudd, M. D. (2006). *The assessment and management of suicidality*. Sarasota, FL: Professional

Resource Press. This is a short but authoritative book on suicide risk assessment and how to manage suicidal clients.

Brock, S. E., Sandoval, J., & Hart, S. (2006). Suicidal ideation and behaviors. In G. G. Bear & K. M. Minke (Eds.). *Children's needs III: Development, prevention, and intervention* (pp. 225–238). Bethesda, MD: National Association of School Psychologists. This chapter provides an overview of key information needed for the recognition, prevention, and treatment of suicidal behavior from the perspective of school-based practice. Included are helpful tables of information about risk factors and warning signs, general suicide interventions for school staff, risk assessment procedures, and recommendations for memorial services.

The *Suicide Prevention* website maintained by the Substance Abuse and Mental Health Services Administration (SAMHSA) contains a variety of resources and publications on suicide prevention. An outstanding publication, entitled *Preventing Suicide: A Toolkit for High Schools* (SAMHSA, 2012), contains 230 pages of information on how to develop a comprehensive approach to suicide prevention in schools. The book is essentially a collection of tools, guidelines, protocols, handouts, forms, and other resources for school staff to use in helping students at risk for suicide and responding to a suicide and its aftermath. Also provided in this book are lists of programs for students, staff education, parent outreach and education, and screening. The toolkit is available for free online (http://store.samhsa.gov/product/SMA12-4669) and is a must-have resource for school mental health professionals.

Suicide Prevention Resource Center. This website, funded by the U.S. Department of Health and Human Service's Substance Abuse and Mental Health Services Administration (SAMHSA), provides training materials, publications, and resources on suicide. Of particular interest are two publications:

- *The Role of School Health and Mental Health Providers in Preventing Suicide* (http://www.sprc.org/sites/sprc. org/files/library/SchoolHealth-MentalHealth.pdf).

- *After a Suicide: A Toolkit for Schools* (http://www.sprc.org/sites/sprc. org/files/library/AfteraSuici-deToolkitforSchools.pdf)

Also of interest are a variety of free training courses, including:

- Counseling on Access to Lethal Means

- Choosing and Implementing a Suicide Prevention Gatekeeper Training Program

- Locating, Understanding, and Presenting Youth Suicide Data

- Planning and Evaluation for Youth Suicide Prevention

- The Research Evidence for Suicide as a Preventable Public Health Issue

The American Association of Suicidology (http://www.suicidology.org/home) has checklists, fact sheets, warning signs, and links to resources. A variety of certification programs are also offered, including a School Suicide Prevention Accreditation Program, an online train-

ing program for school professionals wishing to become more expert in designing and providing suicide prevention programs.

The Los Angeles County Youth Suicide Prevention Project website (http://preventsuicide. lacoe.edu/index.php) is an extensive source of authoritative information for students, parents, and school personnel. It provides handouts and intervention guidelines on all aspects of suicide and nonsuicidal self-harm, videos, training modules, and other resources.

The National Association of School Psychologists makes a number of handouts freely available for downloading from its website (www. nasponline.org). Of particular interest are:

- *Preventing Youth Suicide: Tips for Parents and Educators* by Andrea Cohn (2006, NASP *Communiqué, 35*(4); http://www.nasponline.org/publications/cq/cq354suicide.aspx)

- *Death: Dealing With Crisis at School– Practical Suggestions for Educators* (http://www.nasponline.org/resources/crisis_safety/neat_poland.aspx)

- *Death and Grief: Supporting Children and Youth* (http://www.nasponline. org/resources/crisis_safety/death-grief.pdf)

- *Memorial Activities at School: A List of Do's and Don't's* (http://www. nasponline.org/resources/crisis_ safety/memorialdo_donot.pdf)

- *Memorials/Activities/Rituals Following Traumatic Events: Suggestions for Schools* (http://www.nasponline. org/resources/crisis_safety/memorials_general.aspx)

The American Foundation for Suicide Prevention and Suicide Prevention Resource Center provides information and materials at its website. Of particular interest is the publication, *After a Suicide: A Toolkit for Schools* (2011), which provides information and resources for suicide postvention activities. It is available free of charge at http://www.sprc.org/sites/sprc.org/files/library/AfteraSuicideToolkitforSchools.pdf

The Jason Foundation website (http://www.jasonfoundation.com) provides educational materials about suicide about suicide and support to parents, young people, and school personnel.

The Yellow Ribbon Suicide Prevention Program (http://www.yellowribbon.org) website provides resources and training. There are Yellow Ribbon chapters in many states that provide speakers and resources to local organizations, including schools.

Miller, D. N., & Brock, S. E. (2011). *Identifying, assessing, and treating self-injury at school.* New York, NY: Springer. This volume is a comprehensive resource that, unlike most books on this subject, focuses on the perspective of school-based practice.

Lieberman, R., & Poland, S. (2006). Self-mutilation. In G. G. Bear & K. M. Minke (Eds.). *Children's needs III: Development, prevention, and intervention* (pp. 965–976). Bethesda, MD: National Association of School Psychologists. This chapter provides a good overview of nonsuicidal self-injury, its prevention, and treatment in school-based practice.

http://www.selfharm.net – This site, maintained by Deb Martinson, provides information on all aspects of NSSI and features interactive components including Web boards, questionnaires and surveys, and resources.

REFERENCES

American Association of Suicidality. (n.d.). *Know the warning signs*. Retrieved from http://www.suicidology.org/web/guest/stats-and-tools/suicide-warning-signs

American Foundation for Suicide Prevention and Suicide Prevention Resource Center. (2011). *After a suicide: A toolkit for schools*. Newton, MA: Education Development Center, Inc. Retrieved from http://www.sprc.org/sites/sprc.org/files/library/AfteraSuicideToolkitforSchools.pdf

Asarnow, J. R., Porta, G., Spirito, A., Emslie, G., Clarke, G., Wagner, K. D., … Brent, D. A. (2011). Suicide attempts and nonsuicidal self-injury in the treatment of resistant depression in adolescents: Findings from the TORDIA study. *Journal of the American Academy of Child and Adolescent Psychiatry, 50,* 772–781.

Berman, A. L., Jobes, D. A., & Silverman, M. M. (2006). *Adolescent suicide: Assessment and intervention* (2nd ed.). Washington, DC: American Psychological Association.

Cash, R. E. (2009). *NASP President's call to action to prevent suicide*. Retrieved from http://www.nasponline.org/advocacy/suicidecalltoaction.aspx

Centers for Disease Control and Prevention. (CDC; 2012a). *2011 High school youth risk behavior survey data.* Retrieved from http://apps.nccd.cdc.gov/youthonline

Centers for Disease Control and Prevention (CDC; 2012b). *Suicide prevention: Youth suicide.* Retrieved September 23, 2012, from http://www.cdc.gov/violenceprevention/pub/youth_suicide.html

Goldston, D. (2000). *Assessment of suicidal behaviors and risk among children and adolescents.* Technical report submitted to NIMH under Contract No. 263-MD-909995. Retrieved from http://www.suicidology.org/c/document_library/get_file?folderId=235&name=DLFE-141.pdf

Kochanek, K. D., Xu, J., Murphy, S. L., Miniño, A. M., & Kung, H. (2011). Deaths: Preliminary data for 2009. *National Vital Statistics Reports, 59*(4), 30. Retrieved from http://www.cdc.gov/nchs/data/nvsr/nvsr59/nvsr59_04.pdf

Lieberman, R., & Poland, S. (2006). Self-mutilation. In G. G. Bear & K. M. Minke (Eds.). *Children's needs III: Development, prevention, and intervention* (pp. 965–976). Bethesda, MD: National Association of School Psychologists.

Mazza, J. J., Catalano, R. F., Abbott, R. D., & Haggerty, K. P. (2011). An examination of the validity of retrospective measures of suicide attempts in youth. *Journal of adolescent health, 49,* 532–537.

McDonald, C. (2006). Self-mutilation in adolescents. *The Journal of School Nursing, 22,* 193–200. doi:10.1177/10598405050220040201

Miller, D. N. (2010). *Child and adolescent suicidal behavior: School-based prevention, assessment, and intervention.* New York, NY: Guilford Press.

Miller, D. N., & Brock, S. E. (2011). *Identifying, assessing, and treating self-injury at school.* New York, NY: Springer.

National Institute of Mental Health. (2010). *Suicide in the U.S.: Statistics and prevention.* Retrieved from http://www.nimh.nih.gov/health/publications/suicide-in-the-us-statistics-and-prevention/index.shtml#children

Lieberman, R., Poland, S., & Cassel, R. (2008). Best practices in suicide prevention. In A. Thomas & J. Grimes, *Best practices in school psychology V* (pp. 1457–1472). Bethesda, MD: National Association of School Psychologists.

Seeley, J. R., Rohde, P., & Jones, L. B. (2010). School-based prevention and intervention for depression and suicidal behavior. In M. R. Shinn & H. M. Walker (Eds.), *Interventions for achievement and behavior problems in a three-tier model including RTI* (pp. 363–396).

Substance Abuse and Mental Health Services Administration [SAMHSA]. (2012). *Preventing suicide: A toolkit for high schools.* HHS Publication No. SMA-12-4669. Rockville, MD: Center for Mental Health Services, SAMHSA. Retrieved from http://store.samhsa.gov/product/SMA12-4669

Van Orden, K. A., Witte, T. K., Selby, E. A., Bender, T. W., & Joiner, Jr., T. E. (2008). In J. R. Z. Abela & B. L. Hankin, *Handbook of depression in children and adolescents* (pp. 441–465). New York, NY: Guilford Press.

Wilkinson, B. (2011). Current trends in remediating adolescent self-injury: An integrative review. *The Journal of School Nursing, 27,* 120–128. doi:10.1177/1059840510388570

CHAPTER 14

BULLYING: PEER VICTIMIZATION AND DEPRESSION

ESSENTIALS

- Students vulnerable to bullying are also vulnerable to depression.

- School mental health professionals should assess for bullying whenever a student is experiencing depression.

The relationship between bullying and depression in students who are the subjects of peer victimization was clearly established over a decade ago when the first meta-analysis of the research on bullying and the consequences for psychosocial adjustment was published (Hawker & Boulton, 2000). The more complex matters of risk, causation, clinical presentation, and intervention have largely been addressed since then. Given the persistent link between bullying and depression, this chapter will address the topic generally and describe certain groups known to be particularly vulnerable to peer victimization.

Student groups that are vulnerable to bullying are also vulnerable to depression and students may, in fact, present to school nurses and other school mental health professionals seeking help for depression rather than the bullying. The implication, therefore, is to assess for bullying whenever a student is experiencing depression, especially if the student is a member of a vulnerable group.

In this chapter, the various forms of bullying will be defined and the consequences elaborated. Groups of students vulnerable to bullying will be described, including: those with tics and Tourette syndrome; those with coordination disorders; those who are obese or overweight; those who are lesbian, gay, bisexual, transsexual, or questioning; and those who have a history of child maltreatment. Finally, a brief summary of bullying interventions and resources will be provided.

BULLYING AND PEER VICTIMIZATION: DEFINITIONS AND OVERVIEW

Aggressive peer relationships characterize the many different terms for bullying and peer victimization. The position paper of the Society of Adolescent Medicine (Eisenberg & Aalsma, 2005) identified three central characteristics of the behavior reflected by the various terms: (a) aggressive or having an intention to harm, (b) repetitive over time, and (c) occurs in a relationship with an imbalance of power. The American Academy of Pediatrics (AAP) gave a definition of bullying in its 2009 policy statement that reflects these characteristics: "…a form of aggression in which one or more children repeatedly and intentionally intimidate, harass, or physically harm a victim who is perceived as unable to defend herself or himself" (AAP, 2009).

CHARACTERISTICS OF BULLYING

■ Having intention to harm

■ Repetitive over time

■ Occurs in a relationship with an imbalance of power

Most authors distinguish between direct and indirect bullying. Direct bullying is more obvious and includes physical and verbal aggression such as pushing, kicking, hitting, and name calling or other forms of verbal harassment. Indirect bullying is typically referred to as relational bullying or relational aggression, and includes ignoring, social exclusion, and spreading rumors in a way that damages a social relationship. These forms of victimization are considered traditional bullying. The most likely school sites for victimization are the playground, followed by classrooms, gym classes, lunchrooms, halls and stairs, and buses (Glew, Fan, Katon, Rivara, & Kernic, 2005).

Cyber bullying refers to victimization through social media and the use of computers and cell phones and is receiving growing attention from schools, mental health professionals, and researchers (Wang, Iannotti, Luk, & Nansel, 2010; AAP, 2011). Cyber bullying is the deliberate use of media to communicate false, embarrassing, or hostile information about another person (AAP, 2011). The opportunity for cyber bullying is widespread. The American Academy of Pediatrics estimates that 75% of adolescents have cell phones: a third of them use the cell phones for social media, over half (54%) use them for texting, and a fourth (24%) use them for instant messaging.

Core issues of popularity and status, sexual development, and risk-taking underlie students' vulnerability to cyber bully as they explore and experiment with social media. A recent study of bullying among adolescents found that one fourth (25%) of the 300 study participants engaged in cyber bullying (Sontag, Clemans, Graber, & Lyndon, 2011). Of those, nearly half (40%) engaged exclusively in cyber bullying whereas a third (31%) engaged in both traditional and cyber bullying. Although 40% of the students in the study experienced cyber victimization, they were more likely themselves to engage in reactive cyber bullying than victims of traditional bullying. Previous prevalence rates ranged from 16% to 35% (Hinduja & Patchin, 2008; Katzer, Getchenhauer, & Belschak, 2009) so that these more recent rates may reflect an increase in cyber aggression.

Among more than 3,500 elementary school students who were surveyed, nearly one out of four students (22%) reported being bullied and/or bullying others (Glew et al., 2005). As many as three quarters of young adolescents are thought to experience some type of bullying and perhaps a third experience more serious involvement (Nansel, Overpeck, Pilla, Ruan, Simons-Morton, & Scheidt, 2001; Eisenberg & Aalsma, 2005). Clearly, a significant proportion of students are involved in bullying across the school years (Hunt, Peters, & Rapee, 2012), with greater frequency among middle school students than high school students. Although there is some evidence that boys are more likely to be involved in bullying than girls (Nansel et al., 2001), both genders experience peer victimization. For male students, physical bullying and verbal bullying are common whereas

198

for female students, verbal bullying and relational aggression are more common.

When African American, Asian American, and Hispanic students have been included in studies on bullying, these studies have yielded conflicting results. Some research shows that African Americans are less likely than Caucasians and Hispanics to be victimized, Hispanics are slightly more likely to be bullied, and Asian Americans are the most frequently bullied whereas other studies found that the rates of victimization were comparable across ethnic groups (Fitzpatrick, Dulin, & Piko, 2010; Mouttapa, Valente, Gallaher, Rohrbach, & Unger, 2004; Nansel et al., 2001; Nishina, Juvonen, & Witkow, 2005; Shin, D'Antonio, Son, Kim, & Park, 2011; Wang et al., 2010). Derogatory statements about one's religion or ethnicity/race have been found to occur relatively infrequently in the context of bullying (Nansel et al., 2001) and research findings suggest that the reasons for being bullied could be broader than the context of discrimination (Shin et al., 2011). Much work remains to be done, however, before we understand the experience of minority students who are bullied in the context of stereotypes and discrimination. A research focus within ethnic and racial groups is required to examine intra-racial and intra-cultural dynamics (Fitzpatrick et al., 2010; Shin et al., 2011).

"Bullies suffer poor academic achievement and psychosocial outcomes."

Perpetrators of bullying tend to be characterized by externalizing behavior in the early years of preschool and elementary school, and that behavior often develops into conduct disorder and eventual criminal behavior. It is therefore not surprising that bullies suffer poor academic achievement and psychosocial outcomes (Eisenberg & Aslsma, 2005). Victims, on the other hand, are in some way *different*, perceived as weaker, and thought to have fewer friends. Similar antecedents and consequences are associated with peer victimization across cultures (Nishina et al., 2005).

CONSEQUENCES OF BULLYING

Peer victimization has similar psychological and behavioral correlates across cultures (Nishina, Jovonen, & Witkow, 2005). The victims of bullying are characterized by consequences in both the social and psychological domains. In the social domain, victims of bullying suffer from social anxiety as well as low global self-esteem and poor social self-concept (Hawker & Boulton, 2000). Those who are bullied also report poorer relationships with classmates and more difficulty making friends (Nansel et al., 2001). Initially, the consequences of bullying were thought to be largely social and to be, in essence, a social problem. However, the greatest and more serious consequences of being a victim of bullying have been in the psychological domain.

The largest effects from bullying have been depression and loneliness, results that are consistent across studies (Hawker & Boulton, 2000). Low self esteem and suicidal ideation have been implicated as consequences as well (Eisenberg & Aalsma, 2005). The more frequent the bullying, the more depressed, anxious, and lonely students feel, especially if they view themselves as targets for bullying (Nishina et al., 2005). Although depression is a serious consequence for victims of any type of bullying (Sontag et al., 2011), those that are exposed to all types (physical, verbal, social exclusion, rumors, and cyber bullying) experience even greater depression (Wang et al., 2010). Victims who are more frequently bullied experience comparable depression across types of bullying and more depression than those who are occasionally bullied (Wang, Nansel, & Iannotti, 2011).

> *"The largest effects from bullying have been depression and loneliness."*

Unfortunately, these internalizing symptoms are linked to more physical symptoms (Nishina et al., 2005) and injuries (Wang et al., 2010), and poorer physical health in later adolescence (Rigby, 1999). It may be that students that are bullied are at risk for becoming physically ill; the complex relationships between stress and the suppression of immune system functioning may make targets of chronic bullying more likely to get colds and other illnesses (Nishina et al., 2005). Alternatively, symptoms may elicit positive social attention. Notably, high levels of physical symptoms were not found to predict bullying, suggesting that the display of physical symptoms may prevent bullying; it may not be acceptable to bully those who are ill as opposed to those who are weak (Nishina et al., 2005). Whatever the underlying mechanism, these symptoms are likely connected to the greater number of excused and unexcused absences that characterize victims of bullying (Nishina et al., 2005). Lower academic achievement, then, may well result from the combination of depression, physical symptoms and illness, and more absences from school.

> *"Lower academic achievement may well result from the combination of depression, physical symptoms and illness, and more absences from school."*

Those who are bullied use more medication for sleeping problems and more medication for "nervousness"; female victims are especially more likely to use medication, especially if victimized by all types of bullying (Wang et al., 2010). Both depression and substance use has been associated with being bullied during adolescence but depression has actually been found to mediate the relationship between victimization and substance abuse in females (Luk, Wang, & Simons-Morton, 2010). This finding emphasizes the need to address the depression that results from being bullied in order to prevent not only substance abuse but perhaps the use of medications to treat the symptoms of sleeplessness and nervousness as well.

CONSEQUENCES OF BULLYING

- Depression

- Loneliness

- Suicidal ideation

- Substance abuse and use of medication to treat sleeplessness and anxiety

- Anxiety

- Low self-esteem

- Poor self-concept

- Difficulty making friends

- Physical symptoms and injuries

- Poor school functioning and achievement

The consequences of bullying tend to be the same across ethnic and racial groups; that is, victims of bullies experience depression, loneliness, low self esteem, social anxiety, physical symptoms, and poorer school functioning or achievement (e.g., Nansel et al., 2001; Nishina et al., 2005; Wang et al., 2010). Furthermore, the process by which victimization precedes psychosocial maladjustment and physical symptoms, which in turn predicts poor school functioning, is the same for African American, Hispanic, Asian American, and Caucasian students (Nishina et al., 2005). It appears that Hispanic- and Asian-American students who are bullied experience depression and other internalizing symptoms more intensely or at a higher level than African American and Caucasian students who are bullied (Shin et al., 2011; Wang et al., 2010), although recent research within an African American student sample found victims of bullying had levels of depression that exceeded national benchmarks (Fitzpatrick et al., 2010).

A clear link between bullying and suicide attempts has been established, and the experience of bullying in childhood is strongly correlated with suicidal ideation and attempts in adolescence (Cooper, Clements, & Holt, 2012). Furthermore, the effects of bullying appear to persist into adulthood. Of concern is that these findings have not yet influenced many policy makers and educators, translating into missed opportunities for targeted assessment and educational programs in the school setting (Cooper et al., 2012). Again, when seeing a student for physical symptoms or depression, it is crucial for school mental health professionals to ascertain whether the student is being bullied and what to types of bullying the student is being subjected.

VULNERABLE GROUPS

Those students who are perceived as different, as weaker, as having fewer friends, or otherwise "just don't fit in," are vulnerable to being bullied. Students with visible conditions that set them apart in some way from their peers are particularly vulnerable to victimization. Several conditions or circumstances have emerged as ones that are targeted by bullies, and the phenomenon of bullying among these has only recently been investigated. These include chronic tic disorders and Tourette syndrome, developmental coordination disorder, and obesity, and those who are lesbian, gay, bisexual, transsexual, or questioning. Students with a history of maltreatment may not have a visible condition but appear to engage in a style of interpersonal interaction or relationships that make them vulnerable to bullying.

Tourette Syndrome and Other Tic Disorders

Tourette syndrome and other chronic tic disorders represent the category of inherited neuropsychiatric conditions. Tourette syndrome affects one to ten children out of a thousand, and other tic disorders perhaps double that number. Children with neurodevelopment disorders are at greater risk for being bullied by their peers (Conti-Ramsden & Botting, 2004). Tourette syndrome and other chronic tic disorders are evidenced by tics, the repetitive, semi-voluntary irregular movements and/or vocalizations that are characteristic of these chronic disorders. The tics are typically preceded by unpleasant sensations or urges (premonitory urges) that are relieved by performing a tic. Other tic disorders involve only motor or vocal tics, rather than both, but are otherwise difficult to differentiate from Tourette syndrome. The severity of the tics is defined by the frequency, intensity, complexity, and number of tic types. The disruption or distraction caused by the urges and actual tic expressions often elicits unwanted attention. Chronic tic disorders often co-occur with attention deficit hyperactivity disorder, obsessive-compulsive disorder, mood and anxiety disorders, and explosive outbursts.

In the first study of bullying of children with Tourette syndrome and tic disorders, peer victimization was found to be common and most victims attributed their victimization to their tics (Zinner, Conelea, Glew, Woods, Budman, 2012). Those who were bullied had greater tic severity and complexity, and independent of tic severity the bully victims had greater

premonitory urges. As with other victims of bullying, victims with Tourette syndrome and tics were more likely to exhibit depression and anxiety, as well as more explosive anger outbursts. Potential interventions aimed at reducing bullying of the child address three areas (Zinner et al., 2012):

- Education of students and peers, which can promote acceptance of those with Tourette syndrome and other tic disorders so that it becomes more normative not to differentiate peers in this way.

- Working with or referring those afflicted with the disorders, to learn tic suppression and reduce the complexity and severity of the tics in order to diminish the students' vulnerability to bullying.

- Recognition and treatment of the comorbid conditions that will likely improve psychosocial well-being.

Developmental Coordination Disorder

Developmental coordination disorder (DCD) affects about 6% of children and is diagnosed when children do not develop normal motor coordination. It is usually first noticed when toddlers do not reach typical developmental milestones such as throwing or catching a ball, walking, or dressing themselves. There are six general groups of symptoms: unsteadiness and slight shaking, low muscle tone at rest, muscle tone that is consistently above normal, inability to move smoothly, inability to produce written symbols, and visual–perceptual problems (related to development of eye muscles). A formal diagnosis of DCD specifies that children have poor motor coordination that causes functional limitations in conducting the activities of daily living or academic achievement, and that these limitations are not caused by a general medical condition or severe learning difficulties. Children with this disorder appear clumsy, and suffer from frequent injuries or accidents.

Functional limitations of children with DCD in the school setting include difficulties in play activities because of an inability to perform the physical movements involved in sports and games. Children often avoid play, physical education, and other activities that make them uncomfortable or their deficits noticeable. Students with DCD often struggle with fine motor movements that impact their academic performance, such as letter formation, drawing objects, coloring pictures, and participating in art and crafts. A recent large cohort study (Lingam et al., 2012) found that, compared with typically developing children, those with probable DCD have a twofold increased risk of depression at 7 years of age and a fourfold increased risk for mental health problems at 9 to 10 years of age. Being bullied, lower global self-esteem, and poor social communication skills significantly increased the risk of negative outcomes.

Children with DCD are vulnerable to depression and bullying. Therefore, they may need to be screened for depression and, when screened, to be assessed for whether they are being bullied as well. Interventions that focus on addressing bullying, enhancing self-esteem, and improving social interaction skills are likely to alleviate some of the risk of de-

pression and subsequent mental health problems for these students (Lingam et al., 2012). Developing children's strengths and emphasizing their preferences in choosing activities can help them maximize their functioning in school. Treatments with occupational therapists that focus on skills for the playground or in the gym and physical training that allows the child to safely practice motor skills and control can be helpful as well.

Obesity and Overweight Status

The rising incidence of obesity and overweight status among children and adolescents is considered a growing epidemic (BeLue, Francis, & Colaco, 2009). Obese children are not only at risk for physical problems, such as diabetes and hypertension, but are at risk for psychosocial problems as well. Obese and overweight children are more likely to suffer from depression and low self-esteem (Giletta, Scholte, Engels, & Larsen, 2010; Goodman & Whitaker, 2002), social marginalization (Strauss & Pollack, 2003), and bullying (Giletta et al., 2010; Janssen, Craig, Boyce, & Pickett, 2004). More specifically, among adolescents 12 to 17 years of age, those who were overweight were more likely to suffer from depression and have a lower sense of self-worth, have problems coping with stress, have a behavior problem, and bully others (BeLue et al., 2009).

Overweight adolescents are more likely than their peers to report higher levels of distress and perceive that they are victimized (Giletta et al., 2010). In a national study, when race or ethnicity was considered, there were no associations between mental health problems and overweight status among African-American adolescents; the relationships held only for Caucasian and Hispanic adolescents (BeLue et al., 2009). It may be that cultural groups differ in the negative connotations attributed to weight status, suggesting that cultural, familial, or intrapersonal perspectives on weight status contribute to the experience. The direction of the relationship between obesity and overweight status, depression, and victimization cannot be assumed. These factors warrant assessment but must be explored with respect to intrapersonal factors in the context of race or ethnicity.

"For those students who are obese or overweight, school nurses and other mental health professionals must be alert to the attendant depression and vulnerability to bullying."

The prevention and treatment of obesity requires multiple strategies given the many health concerns, in addition to bullying, linked to obesity and overweight status. School nurses in particular hold a responsibility to promote the prevention of and address the needs of overweight and obese students (NASN, 2011). Collaboration with school personnel, students and families, and health care providers will optimize efforts to promote a healthy lifestyle. Nonetheless, for those students who are obese or overweight, school nurses and other mental health professionals must be alert to the attendant depression and vulnerability to bullying.

Lesbian, Gay, Bisexual, and Transgender Students

Gender nonconforming (LGBT; lesbian, gay, bisexual, and transgender) students face many obstacles and challenges in school (Toomey, Ryan, Diaz, Card, & Russell, 2010). A sizeable body of literature has found that LGBT youth report more depression, suicidality, and substance use or abuse than their gender-conforming heterosexual peers (Birkett, Espelage, & Koenig, 2009; Heck, Flentje, & Cochran, 2011; Marshal et al., 2011). Across studies, sexual minority (LGBT) adolescents are almost three times more likely to report a history of suicidal ideation than heterosexual adolescents, and bisexual students in particular are five times more likely to report suicidality (Marshal et al., 2011). These negative outcomes emerge in the transition from elementary school to middle school and persist through high school as adolescents begin to confront gender identity issues. In fact, students who question their sexuality are more likely to suffer than LGBT students. Those who are sexually questioning compared to those who assert a sexual orientation report higher rates of depression, suicidality, and substance use, and truancy (Birkett et al., 2009).

"Data from nearly 300 schools found that LGBT students in unsupportive surroundings had a 20% higher risk of attempting suicide than those in supportive surroundings."

It seems that, in large part, the reaction of others to one's sexual orientation is a key factor in higher risk for negative outcomes. When young people disclose their nonconforming status, parental rejection exacerbates the risk for depression and suicide attempts, whereas parental support mediates those negative outcomes (Heck et al., 2011). Family reactions to their children's sexual orientation can be more negative for African American and Hispanic students, who may experience homophobia from their respective racial or ethnic communities (Hightow-Weidman et al., 2011). An analysis of student data from nearly 300 schools found that LGBT students in unsupportive surroundings had a 20% higher risk of attempting suicide than those in supportive surroundings (Voelker, 2011).

The vulnerability to depression and suicidality among sexual minority students is exacerbated by victimization in middle and high school that is worse for LGBT students than for their heterosexual peers. Sexual minority and questioning students experience high levels of sexuality-related bullying, and the bullying predicts depression, suicidal ideation, and suicide attempts (Hightow et al., 2011; Marshall et al., 2011). The school environment is a moderator of these negative outcomes, particularly for homophobic teasing and physical harassment (Birkett et al., 2009). Although all victimization should be eliminated from the school environment, LGBT students targeted by bullies need to be protected in specific ways (Toomey et al., 2010). In fact, sexual minority students who attend high school with a gay-straight alliance experience less victimization because of their sexual

orientation, and have better outcomes related to depression and substance use (Heck et al., 2011).

"Sexual minority students who attend high school with a gay-straight alliance experience less victimization because of their sexual orientation, and have better outcomes related to depression and substance use."

School mental health professionals are positioned to intervene on several levels with students who identify as LGBT and are questioning their sexuality. First, students who present with depression must be carefully screened for past and current suicidal ideation and attempts, and a detailed plan for safety should be established even in the absence of current ideation. Second, LGBT students will likely benefit from interventions designed to help their families and social networks become more accepting of their sexual orientation and to help the students themselves achieve a positive view of self that encompasses both their sexual and racial identities (Hightow-Weidman et al., 2011). Third, students must be asked to what extent they are experiencing homophobic teasing and other forms of bullying and immediate strategies to protect the student must be identified.

Separate from intervention with individual students, school mental health professionals must engage as a team to advocate and promote a positive school climate in several ways. Anti-bullying campaigns such as It Gets Better (http://www.itgetsbetter.org) are important first steps (Hightow-Weidman et al., 2011), but they must be backed by other school-wide efforts. The recent literature endorses several approaches (Birkett et al., 2009; Toomey et al., 2010; Heck et al., 2011; Marshall et al., 2011; Voelker, 2011):

- Establish and publicize policies designed to help prevent bullying, harassment, and peer victimization.

- Train teachers and administrators to recognize teasing, harassment, and bullying based on sexual orientation, and to intervene when it occurs.

- Integrate information about sexual orientation and gender identity into educational curricula.

- Support the establishment of a gay–straight alliance or similar student organization, and identify teachers who would be willing to sponsor the group as an advisor.

Together, these approaches can begin to create a positive school climate for all students.

Maltreatment Experiences

Research evidence points to childhood maltreatment experiences as placing adolescents (and likely students of all ages) at risk for bullying victimization and perpetration in school (Hong, Espelage, Grogan-Kaylor, & Allen-Meares, 2012). Children who are victimized at home—whether physically, sexually, verbally, or through neglect—are also likely to experience a range of developmental, behavioral,

interpersonal, and school-related problems. Maltreated youth have consistently been found to have internalizing behaviors, including depression. These problems exacerbate their vulnerability and put these students at risk for bullying at school (Hong et al., 2012).

Parent–child relationships are thought to be the mechanism by which child maltreatment is linked to bullying victimization and perpetration by students in the school setting. Parent–child relationships have been found to influence peer relationships outside the home, and maltreatment by parents has been associated with peer rejection in elementary school as well as later in early adolescence (Shields, Ryan, & Cicchetti, 2001; Shields & Cicchetti, 2001). It may be that a pattern of submissiveness, learned in the abusive home, creates the vulnerability of these students. This submissiveness may be attended by a sense of powerlessness, a lack of assertiveness, and a lack of confidence. Emotional dysregulation is another outcome of maltreatment by parents that puts students at risk for bullying victimization and peer rejection on the one hand, and aggression and antisocial behavior— bullying perpetration—on the other. Together the pattern of submissiveness and emotional dysregulation can be broadly evidenced by a social skills deficit, leading to peer conflict and, again, victimization.

When students present to school mental health professionals with depression and a history of maltreatment, the presence of victimization by peers or perpetration of bullying must be ascertained as well. Again, the problem must be approached from several directions (Hong et al., 2012). If the child is involved with child welfare, school-related goals and objectives need to be developed, along with counseling to implement remediation and preventive strategies. These strategies necessarily include social and emotional learning approaches designed to help the student become self-aware, manage emotions, build social and friendship skills, and make positive decisions. The teacher–student relationship may also need attention given that supportive experiences with adults are pivotal in optimizing outcomes for maltreated children. In addition, teachers can promote positive peer interactions, intervene in peer conflicts, and prevent bullying incidents. Some students may need more intensive intervention to fully address the consequences of parental maltreatment.

ASSESSMENT OF BULLYING IN THE CONTEXT OF DEPRESSION

When students present to school mental health providers with depression, screening for bullying is crucial. Students experiencing bullying in conjunction with depression or suicidality during high school have been found to remain more impaired 4 years later compared to those who had reported depression or suicidality in the absence of bullying (Klomek et al., 2011). An assessment of bullying is recommended in any depression or suicide screening or assessment.

"An assessment of bullying is recommended in any depression or suicide screening or assessment."

Interviews have been used to assess students' victimization experiences, relationships with the perpetrators, circumstances and characteristics of the events, and emotional and behavioral responses (Crothers & Levinson, 2004). However, students may be reluctant to reveal information for fear of retaliation. In some cases, it may be sufficient to gain enough information to move to a systems-level intervention around the bullying while intervening with the student in terms of coping with the consequences. Middle and high school students may be more willing to engage in an interview assessment of victimization experiences, whereas elementary school students maybe more reluctant. Keeping the questions simple will help; the following examples could similarly be used in a paper and pencil or computer assisted self-report survey (Glew et al., 2005):

1. Do students at school make fun of you, bother you, or hurt you?

2. How often have you made fun of someone, or bothered or hurt another student at school?

These questions and follow-up probes need to also inquire about the nature and frequency of the victimization as well as the nature and frequency of any perpetration of bullying behavior.

3. Where have you been when made fun of or bothered or hurt?

This question needs to assess the time and location of the bullying. Self-report assessments should list location response options of the playground, playing field, gym classes, locker room, classroom, restroom, lunch room, hall-ways or stairs, school bus, bushes outside the school, and the route to and from school.

4. Have you told anyone that you have been made fun of or bothered or hurt? If yes, whom have you told?

This question is designed, in part, to identify adults to whom the student felt safe to disclose the victimization and how that disclosure was handled. It is also critical to find out whether the bullying has been witnessed by teachers, parents, or administrators and what their responses were. A lack of response or inadequate response is a form of collusion with the bullying as is any action by which vulnerable students are set apart or inadvertently identified for their differentness. Depending on state laws, it may also be grounds for complaint against the school.

If students are not forthcoming in an interview or self-report assessment about being bullied, observation on the playground, lunchroom, restroom, gym class, and any other probable setting for bullying may yield the necessary information. It is important to be as unobtrusive as possible and to vary the times and contexts of observations (Crothers & Levinson, 2004). Aspects of peer relationships such as social status, social isolation, and social withdrawal can be evaluated, and peer behavior that includes elements of domination, aggression, or exclusion can be discerned. Including teachers, playground monitors, and school mental health professionals can expand the scope of observations.

Two questionnaires were recently developed to assess school children's experiences of being bullied. The California Bully Victimization Scale (CBVS; Felix, Sharkey, Green, Furlong, & Tanigawa, 2011) is a self-report scale that measures the three-part definition of bullying without using the term *bully*. An elementary version asks about six forms of victimization that students have experienced at school and the secondary version for middle and high school students asks about seven forms of victimization. These include: teased or called names by another student; rumors spread or gossip behind the back; left out of a group or ignored; hit, pushed, or physically hurt; threatened; and possessions stolen or damaged. The secondary school version includes an additional item asking if sexual comments or gestures have been directed at them. Total victimization scores can be calculated, and students can be classified as non-victims, peer victims (victimization but no power imbalance), and bullied victims (power imbalance, intentional victimization, more frequent victimization). The CBVS was assessed for stability and validity with students in 5th through 12th grade in four schools (Felix et al., 2011). It is able to differentiate bullying from other forms of peer victimization, has good stability, and the responses are associated with indicators of well-being. This questionnaire can serve as an early screening for bullying and lead to a more in-depth interview or an interview can be supplemented by the questionnaire. When administered to a classroom, grade level, or school, it can serve as a screen to determine the extent of a bullying problem.

The Personal Experience Checklist (PECK; Hunt et al., 2012) is another recently developed self-report of students' experiences of being bullied. This 32-item measure has four subscales consistent with the domains of relational–verbal bullying, cyber bullying, physical bullying, and bullying based on culture. The items consist of specific bullying and victimization behaviors that begin with the stem, "Other kids…" and students are asked to rate the frequency other kids inflict each behavior on them. Analyses of three samples of students, ranging in age from 8 to 15 years of age, across nine schools revealed that the PECK is internally consistent and has adequate stability. Validity was established in relation to other scales of global, verbal, relational, and physical bullying. This measure is more comprehensive than the CBVS and may be warranted for more comprehensive assessment of bullying, whereas the CBVS is an excellent screening tool.

RTI CONNECTIONS

- Bullying prevention is best delivered as part of a comprehensive, coordinated program of social, emotional, and behavioral supports delivered throug multi-tiered framework such as RTI.

INTERVENTION WITH BULLYING

Interventions for bullying prevention are most effectively delivered as part of a comprehensive, coordinated program of social, emotional, and behavioral supports delivered through a multi-tiered framework such as response to intervention (RTI). Targeted (RTI Tier 2) or intensive (Tier 3) interventions with the victims

of bullying, especially with students who belong to one of the groups most vulnerable to bullying, or with the perpetrators of bullying, is important but insufficient. There are four groups involved in bullying: the victims, the bullies, the bully / victims, and the bystanders who encourage the bullying or fail to intervene in any way. Thus, school-based intervention must be directed not only to the victims, bystanders, or perpetrators of bullying (Tier 2), but also as universal (Tier 1) interventions for the whole school. A comprehensive continuum of interventions can include such programs as curriculum-based and school-wide interventions, targeted interventions with social skills training for victims, teacher and mentoring interventions, and more intensive interventions such as counseling for victims who are experiencing depression.

Universal interventions (Tier 1) have been found to reduce victimization and bullying more than interventions that only include classroom-level curriculum or social skills intervention (Vreeman & Carroll, 2007). Whole-school interventions involve administrators, teachers, student groups, and individual students, as well as the team of school mental health providers. The thrust of such programs is to alter the entire school environment as a systemic solution to the problem of bullying. The success of universal interventions suggests that bullying is a complex process of social interactions involving factors external to individual students' psychosocial problems (Vreeman & Carroll, 2007). As with universal approaches to depression, a whole-school approach to address bullying is relatively low cost and not stigmatizing.

> *"Commitment to reduce bullying requires resources and training for teachers, paraprofessionals, and other school personnel."*

Universal approaches to bullying prevention at the administrative level must address district and school policies that are enforceable and designed to create a safe school environment. Commitment to reduce bullying requires resources and training for teachers, paraprofessionals, and other school personnel. Only then can bullying be effectively addressed at the classroom level through classroom management and improved climate for teacher–student and peer–peer interactions. There are many facets to universal interventions that require concerted effort on the part of all personnel through the leadership of school mental health personnel.

> *"It is the responsibility of the school mental health professionals to mobilize as a team in order to engage school personnel in anti-bullying efforts."*

The context and climate of the classroom also needs to be addressed, especially in elementary school. Teachers and other school personnel need to monitor externalizing and bullying behavior; investigators have found that higher levels of adult monitoring seems to prevent students with externalizing or acting out behavior from bullying (Totura et al., 2008). This monitoring needs to be extended beyond the classroom to the school grounds, cafeteria, and other school locations in which bullying is likely to occur (Glew et al., 2005). However, school personnel must also be sensitive to situations in which those who are socially skilled and do not show visible externalizing behavior, especially girls, resort to covert strategies for bullying. In fact, some girls resent enhanced monitoring and develop covert systems for bullying (Totura et al., 2008). Structuring the classroom environment to decrease the opportunity for bullying to occur is crucial for the individual intervention strategies to be effective (Totura et al., 2008).

It is the responsibility of the team of school mental health professionals to work with educators to structure their classrooms, improve their skills for monitoring overt and covert bullying behavior, and intervene when they detect it. Unfortunately, intervention with the individual student, even with the structuring of classrooms and enhanced monitoring by adults, is pointless if the systemic issues and social environment are not addressed (Anthony, Wessler, & Sevian, 2010; Hong et al., 2012; Vreeman & Carroll, 2007). There are two approaches to addressing the systemic issues and school environment: whole-classroom intervention and whole-school intervention.

> *"Intervention with the individual student, even with the structuring of classrooms and enhanced monitoring by adults, is pointless if the systemic issues and social environment are not addressed."*

Whole-classroom interventions are broadly designed to promote anti-bullying attitudes within the classroom and to develop social skills. The programs tend to draw on the principles of cognitive–behavior therapy—increasing conflict resolution skills and self-efficacy—and serve to alter norms around bullying through changing attitudes (Vreeman & Carroll, 2007; Williford et al., 2012). Until recently, the classroom curricular approaches have been found to be more successful with younger students in elementary schools than with older students. In part, it was thought that this approach altered the attitudes and behavior of subgroups but failed to address bullying as a social group phenomenon that depended on different levels of power (Vreeman & Carroll, 2007).

However, a recently evaluated program was predicated on this principle that bullying is a group process in which the bully seeks to attain higher peer-group power and status through aggression, and that this process is reinforced by the ongoing apathy and encouragement of bystanders (Williford et al., 2012). The KiVa program, developed in Finland, was evaluated in 78 schools, with nearly 7,500 students participating, and found to successfully reduce bullying and victimization, as well as social anxiety (Williford et al., 2012). The program includes 20 hours of curriculum designed to increase anti-bullying attitudes in classrooms, as well as to increase defending behaviors and self-efficacy in bystanders. The lessons involve class discussions, group exercises, films about bullying, role-playing exercises, and an interactive computer game. An intervention component that addresses identified cases of bullying is also included, and requires the leadership of school mental health professionals to work with classroom teachers to resolve the issues with victims and bullies. The success of KiVa is attributed to its emphasis on explicitly addressing the power differential that exists between the bully and victim, and the social context that reinforces and maintains the behavior over time—a core component of bullying (Williford et al., 2012). More information about KiVa can be found at http://www.kivaprogram.net.

Other universal interventions that have a positive impact on bullying behavior in schools are listed below.

- Bully Busters (Available from Research Press at http://www.researchpress.com/books/455/bully-busters). Materials are available for grades K–5, 6–8, high school, and parents and may be used at Tiers 1, 2, and 3.

- Steps to Respect: Bullying Prevention for Elementary School (Available at http://www.cfchildren.org/steps-to-respect.aspx).

211

Intervention (at Tier 2 or 3) by school mental health professionals with victims of bullying who are also depressed needs to specifically include intervention for depression as well as to improve social skills. Specifically, strategies should be directed at changing cognitive and behavioral patterns, and strengthening interpersonal skills. Student strengths need to be identified and opportunities found for students to enhance and build on their abilities. Doing so will serve to improve self-concept and self-esteem, and facilitate how the students define themselves in relation to others. These efforts, in conjunction with tools for social problem solving (Totura, MacKinnon-Lewis, Gesten, Gadd, Divine, Dunham, & Kamboukos, 2008), can help develop an identity that is strength-based rather than victim-based, and thereby contribute to more positive peer interactions. Together, these strategies may alter the trajectory of the depressed and victimized students' experience in school.

KEYS TO COLLABORATION

- A collaborative school mental health team should include bullying prevention in its overall prevention planning efforts.

ACTION PLAN

- Ensure that all students in the school feel safe. Pay particular attention to students with conditions or circumstances that are often targeted by bullies.

- Assess gaps and strengths within school programs designed to improve school safety and reduce bullying. Use a collaborative team

approach to integrate bullying prevention into all aspects of school climate improvement plans. Rather than treat it as a stand-alone problem, bullying prevention is best approached through a comprehensive, coordinated program of social, emotional, and behavioral supports delivered through a multi-tiered framework such as response to intervention (RTI).

Assess students who are bullied for depression. Assess whether students with depression are also targets of bullying.

- Assess high-risk times and locations for bullying within the school and target those areas for increased intervention.

- Provide professional development for school personnel about bullying and its relationship to depression.

- Establish policies within the school requiring staff members to take concrete actions when witnessing bullying.

RESOURCES

The National Association of School Psychologists provides an easy-to-read policy brief about bullying authored by E. Rossen and K. C. Cowan titled *A Framework for School-Wide Bullying Prevention and Safety* (2012) that could be used for advocacy or as a basic guide to organizing a program (http://www.nasponline.org/resources/bullying/Bullying_Brief_12.pdf). The website also contains a variety of handouts and other materials for parents and educators on the topic of bullying prevention and intervention (http://www.nasponline.org/educators/index.aspx).

StopBullying.Gov is a U.S. Department of Health and Human Services website that contains resources (including information, videos, training, and policy advice) for parents, educators, and students. In 2012, a free training toolkit for educators was made available that includes PowerPoint slides and handouts that school mental health professionals could use as the basis of presentations in their schools.

The Stop Bullying Now website (http://www.stopbullyingnnow.com/index.htm) is a resource for strategies, interventions, and trainings to reduce bullying in schools based on the work of researchers in bully prevention. Information about bullying, evidence-based interventions, and other resources are provided.

The TeachSafeSchools.Org website (http://www.teachsafeschools.org/bullying-prevention.html) offers a variety of resources and information about bullying. In addition to information about bullying, the critical role of the principal is highlighted, assessment procedures for bullying are described, school-wide policies and practices are discussed, an overview of specific interventions is provided, and additional resources for information and handouts are provided. It is also possible to download forms and questionnaires.

The U.S. Department of Education's Office of Civil Rights has issued guidance to schools regarding bullying and harassment. Its *Dear Colleague Letter on Harassment and Bullying* (October 26, 2010) may be found at http://www2.ed.gov/about/offices/list/ocr/letters/colleague-201010.html.

REFERENCES

American Academy of Pediatrics (AAP) Committee on Injury, Violence, and Poison Prevention (2009). Role of the pediatrician in youth violence prevention. *Pediatrics, 124*, 393–403. doi:10.1542/peds.2009-0943.

American Academy of Pediatrics (AAP), O'Keeffe, G. S., Clarke-Pearson, K., & Council on Communications and Media. (2011). The impact of social media on children, adolescents, and families. *Pediatrics, 127*, 800–804. doi:10.1542/peds.2011-0054.

Anthony, B. J., Wessler, S. L., & Sevian, J.K. (2010). Commentary: Guiding a public health approach to bullying. *Journal of Pediatric Psychology, 35*, 1113–1115. doi:10.1093/jpepsy/jsqo83

BeLue, R., Francis, L. A., & Colaco, B. (2009). Mental health problems and overweight in a

nationally representative sample of adolescents: Effects of race and ethnicity. *Pediatrics, 123*, 697–702. doi:10.1542/peds.2008-0687.

Birkett, M., Espelage, D. L., & Koenig, B. (2009). LGB and questioning students in schools: The moderating effects of homophobic bullying and school climate on negative outcomes. *Journal of Youth & Adolescence, 38*, 989–1000. doi:10.1007/s10964-008-9389-1

Conti-Ramsden, G., & Botting, N. (2004). Social difficulties and victimization in children with SLI at 11 years of age. *Journal of Speech, Language, and Hearing Research, 47*, 145–161.

Cooper, G. D., Clements, P. T., & Holt, K. E. (2012). Examining childhood bullying and adolescent suicide: Implications for school nurses. *The Journal of School Nursing, 28*, 275–283. doi:10.1177/1059840512438617

Crothers, L. M., & Levinson, E. M. (2004). Assessment of bullying: A review of methods and instruments. *Journal of Counseling & Development, 82*, 496–503.

Eisenberg, M. E., & Aalsma, M. D. (2005). Bullying and peer victimization: Position paper of the Society for Adolescent Medicine. *Journal of Adolescent Health, 36*, 88–91.

Felix, E. D., Sharkey, J. D., Green, J. G., Furlong, M. J., & Tanigawa, D. (2011). Getting precise and pragmatic about the assessment of bullying: The development of the California Bullying Victimization Scale. *Aggressive Behavior, 37*, 234–247.

Fitzpatrick, K. M., Dulin, A., & Piko, B. (2010). Bullying and depressive symptomatology among low-income, African American youth. *Journal of Youth & Adolescence, 39*, 634–645.

Giletta, M., Scholte, R. H. J., Engels, R. C. M. E., & Larsen, J. K. (2010). Body mass index and victimization during adolescence: The mediation role of depressive symptoms and self-esteem. *Journal of Psychosomatic Research, 69*, 541–547.

Glew, G. M., Fan, M. Y., Katon, W., Rivara, F. P., & Kernic, M. A. (2005). Bullying, psychosocial adjustment, and academic performance in elementary school. *Archives of Pediatric Adolescent Medicine, 159*, 1026–1031.

Goodman, E., & Whitaker, R. C. (2002). A prospective study of the role of depression in the development and persistence of adolescent obesity. *Pediatrics, 110*, 497–504.

Hawker, D. S. J., & Boulton, M. J. (2000). Twenty years' research on peer victimization and psychosocial maladjustment: A meta-analytic review of cross-sectional studies. *Journal of Child Psychology & Psychology, 41*, 441–455.

Heck, N. C., Flentje, A., & Cochran, B. N. (2011). Offsetting risks: High school gay–straight alliances and lesbian, gay, bisexual, and transgender (LGBT) youth. *School Psychology Quarterly, 26*, 161–174. doi:10.1037/a0023226

Hightow-Weidman, L. B., Phillips, G., Jones, K. C., Outlaw, A. Y., Fields, S. D., & Smith, J. C. (2011). Racial and sexual identity-related maltreatment among minority YMSM: Prevalence, perceptions, and the association with emotional distress. *Aids Patient Care and STDs, 25, Supplement 1*, s39–s45.

Hinduja, S., & Patchin, J. W. (2008). Cyberbullying: An exploratory analysis of factors related to offending and victimization. *Deviant Behavior, 29*, 129–156.

Hong, J. S., Espelage, D. L., Grogan-Kaylor, A., & Allen-Meares, P. (2012). Identifying potential mediators and moderators of the association between child maltreatment and bullying perpetration and victimization in school. *Educational Psychology Review, 24,* 167-186. doi:10.1007/s10648-011-9185-4

Hunt, C., Peters, L., & Rapee, R. M. (2012). *Psychological Assessment, 24,* 156–165.

Janssen, I., Craig, W. M., Boyce, W. F., & Pickett, W. (2004). Associations between overweight and obesity with bullying behaviors in school-aged children. *Pediatrics, 113,* 1187–1194.

Katzer, C., Getchenhauer, D., & Belschak, F. (2009). Cyberbullying: Who are the victims? *Journal of Media Psychology, 21,* 25–36.

Klomek, A. B., Kleinman, M., Altschuler, E., Marrocco, F., Amakawa, L., & Gould, M. S. (2011). High school bullying as a risk for later depression and suicidality. *Suicide and Life-Threatening Behavior, 41,* 501–516. doi:10.1111/j.1943-278X.2011.00046.x

Lingam, R., Jongmans, M. J., Ellis, M., Hunt, L. P., Golding, J., & Emond, A. (2012). Mental health difficulties in children with developmental coordination disorder. *Pediatrics, 129,* e882–e891. DOI: 10.1542/peds.2011-1556

Luk, J. W., Wang, J., & Simons-Morton, B. G. (2010). Bullying victimization and substance use among U.S. adolescents: Mediation by depression. *Prevention Science, 11,* 355–359. doi:10.1007/s11121-010-0179-0

Marshal, M. P., Dietz, L. J., Friedman, M. S., Stall, R., Smith, H. A., McGinley, J., …

Brent, D. A. (2011). Suicidality and depression disparities between sexual minority and heterosexual youth: A meta-analytic review. *Journal of Adolescent Health, 49,* 115–123. doi:10.1016/j.jadohealth.2011.02.005

Mouttapa, M., Valente, T., Gallaher, P., Rohrbach, L. A., & Unger, J. B. (2004). Social network predictors of bullying and victimization. *Adolescence, 39,* 315–334.

Nansel, T. R., Overpeck, M., Pilla, R. S., Ruan, W. J., Simons-Morton, B., & Scheidt, P. (2001). Bullying behaviors among US youth: Prevalence and association with psychosocial adjustment. *Journal of the American Medical Association, 285,* 2094–2100.

National Association of School Nurses (NASN). (2011). *Overweight and obesity in youth in schools—the role of the school nurse* [Position paper]. Retrieved from http://www.nasn.org

Nishina, A., Juvonen, J., & Witkow, M. R. (2005). Sticks and stones may break my bones, but names will make me feel sick: The psychosocial, somatic, and scholastic consequences of peer harassment. *Journal of Clinical Child and Adolescent Psychology, 34,* 37–48.

Rigby, K. (1999). Peer victimization at school and the health of secondary school students. *British Journal of Educational Psychology, 69,* 95–104.

Rossen, E., & Cowan, K. C. (2012). *A framework for school-wide bullying prevention and safety* [Brief]. Bethesda, MD: National Association of School Psychologists.

Shields, A., & Cicchetti, D. (2001). Parental maltreatment and emotion dysregulation as risk factors for bullying and victimization in middle childhood. *Journal of Clinical Child Psychology, 30,* 349–363.

Shields, A., Ryan, R. M., & Cicchetti, D. (2001). Narrative representations of caregivers and emotion dysregulation as predictors of maltreated children's rejection by peers. *Developmental Psychology,* 321–337.

Shin, J. Y., D'Antonio, E., Son, H., Kim, S. A., & Park, Y. (2011). Bullying and discrimination experiences among Korean-American adolescents. *Journal of Adolescence, 34,* 873–883.

Sontag, L. M., Clemans, K. H., Graber, J. A., & Lyndon, S. T. (2011). Traditional and cyber aggressors and victims: A comparison of psychosocial characteristics. *Journal of Youth and Adolescence, 40,* 392–404. doi:10.1007/s10964-010-9575-9

Strauss, R. S., & Pollack, H. A. (2003). Social marginalization of overweight children. *Archives in Pediatric Adolescent Medicine, 157,* 1187–1194.

Toomey, R. B., Ryan, C., Diaz, R. M., Card, N. A., & Russell, S. T. (2010). Gender-nonconforming lesbian, gay, bisexual, and transgender youth: School victimization and young adult psychosocial adjustment. *Developmental Psychology, 46*, 1580–1589.

Totura, C. M. W., MacKinnon-Lewis, C., Gesten, E. L., Gadd, R., Divine, K. P., Dunham, S., &

Kamboukos, D. (2008). Bullying and victimization among boys and girls in middle school: The influence of perceived family and school contexts. *The Journal of Early Adolescence, 29,* 571–609. doi:10.1177/0272431608324190

U.S. Department of Education Office of Civil Rights. *Dear colleague letter on harassment and bullying.* (October 26, 2010). Retrieved from http://www2.ed.gov/about/offices/list/ocr/letters/colleague-201010.html

Voelker, R. (2011). Community a factor in Suicide attempts by lesbian, gay, and bisexual teens. *Journal of the American Medical Association, 305,* 1951.

Vreeman, R. C., & Carroll, A. E. (2007). A systematic review of school-based interventions to prevent bullying. *Archives of Pediatric and Adolescent Medicine, 161,* 78–88.

Wang, J., Nansel, T. R., & Iannotti, R. J. (2011). Cyber and traditional bullying: Differential association with depression. *Journal of Adolescent Health, 48,* 415–417.

Wang, J., Iannotti, R. J., Luk, J. W., & Nansel, T. R. (2010). Co-occurrence of victimization from five subtypes of bullying: Physical, verbal, social exclusion, spreading rumors, and cyber. *Journal of Pediatric Psychology, 35,* 1103–1112. doi:10.1016/j.jadohealth.2004.09.004

Williford, A., Boulton, A., Noland, B., Little, T. D., Karna, A., & Salmivalli, C. (2012). Effects of the KiVa anti-bullying program on adolescents' depression, anxiety, and perception of peers. *Journal of Abnormal Child Psychology, 40,* 289–300. doi:10.1007/s10802-011-955-1

Zinner, S. H., Conelea, C. A., Glew, G. M., Woods, D. W., & Budman, C. L. (2012). Peer victimization in youth with Tourette syndrome and other chronic tic disorders. *Child Psychiatry and Human Development, 43,* 124–136. doi:10.1007/s10578-011-0249-y

CHAPTER 15

PHARMACOTHERAPY FOR DEPRESSION

There is considerable controversy about whether there is adequate research on the safety, effectiveness, and appropriate use of psychotropic medications in children and adolescents. Nonetheless, psychiatrists, psychiatric mental health nurse practitioners, and pediatricians frequently prescribe antidepressants for children and adolescents. Therefore, it is imperative that school mental health professionals be informed about antidepressant medications and the recent research about medication and treatment for major depression in order to inform students and their parents, as well as to more effectively provide supportive treatment. At the same time, school personnel should be careful not to recommend medication to students or their parents; this is not within their scope of practice.

"School personnel should be careful not to recommend medication to students or their parents."

Intensive school-based interventions for students with depression should be utilized before a referral to school-based health clinic providers or community-based physicians, nurse practitioners, or therapists is made (Merrell, 2008). Nonetheless, some students with severe depression may receive psychotherapy or psychopharmacological treatment outside of the school, and students at risk for suicide may require hospitalization. However, because of the barriers to children and adolescents receiving specialized mental health services, primary care settings have often become the mental health clinics for this population (Cheung et al., 2007) and the resulting implication is that the treatment is medication. However inadequate primary care providers may feel about providing mental health services, they have become the prescribing clinicians for growing numbers of youth. Furthermore, rates of specialty mental health referral from primary care are low, even when an emotional disorder is recognized (Zuckerbrot, Cheung, Jensen, Stein, & Laraque, 2007). These gaps in services can be and must be filled by school mental health providers.

Although medications can help to resolve the symptoms of depression, they do not address the self-esteem, the social relationships, the thought patterns, or the other personal skills that may have suffered as the depression was developing. To address the consequences of depression or depressive symptoms for the whole student, psychotherapeutic interventions are more useful. Intervention plans for students at this level of need will necessarily be individualized and characterized by the highest levels of integration and collaboration with primary care and other community-based or school-based clinic providers. Individual progress and outcomes need to be carefully monitored for these students.

RESEARCH AND IMPLICATIONS FOR SCHOOL-BASED INTERVENTIONS

Much of what is currently known about the psychopharmacological treatment for adolescent depression comes from research conducted by the National Institutes for Mental Health (NIMH) and the longitudinal, prospective *Treatment for Adolescents with Depression Study (TADS)*. The TADS participants ($N = 439$) were 12 to 17 years old and enrolled in the study from spring 2000 through summer 2003. All adolescents had mild to severe depression, and were assigned to one of three conditions: antidepressant pharmacotherapy (fluoxetine), cognitive behavioral therapy (CBT), or combined treatment of pharmacotherapy and CBT. Several key findings from this research and other studies that assessed the effectiveness of selective seratonin reuptake inhibitors (SSRIs) have influenced prescribers; therefore, knowing the results of this research is important for effective collaboration when providing school-based treatment with students who are depressed.

First, the foundational principle for intervention with middle school and high school students with depression is that identifying adolescents with moderate to severe depression and providing evidence-based treatments will likely have benefit and should be encouraged (March, Silva, Vitiello, & the TADS Team, 2006). Derived from research findings, this conclusion has implications for the responsibilities school mental health professionals hold with respect to middle school and high school students who are depressed. Core responsibilities include:

- Recognition and assessment of depression in students.

- Providing evidence-based interventions in the school setting.

- Collaborating with the students' providers (e.g., school-based health center, primary care, community mental health) if prescribed antidepressants.

"Identifying adolescents with moderate to severe depression and providing evidence-based treatments will likely have benefit and should be encouraged."

Second, the findings from the NIMH study and others converge to make it clear that the combination of cognitive behavior therapy (CBT) and medication is superior to medication alone for major depression in adolescents and should be provided. However, the study also concluded that the remission rates were low for any treatment (Kennard et al., 2006) so that, in the end, any treatment is better that no treatment at all (Hebebrand, 2010; March, 2010).

These findings are useful to have in mind when talking with students or their parents about the benefits of combined therapy (see Table 1), especially when they are reluctant to add psychotherapeutic interventions to their medical treatment. For example, after 3 months, nearly three fourths of those adolescents treated with medication (fluoxetine) combined with CBT

218

had a positive response and, after 9 months, 90% sustained that recovery. Furthermore, in addition to symptom improvement, combining antidepressant medication (fluoxetine) with CBT resulted in superior improvement in overall functioning, global health, and quality of life (Vitiello et al., 2006). For those who do take medication only, improvement after 3 months is likely for almost as many as those who have combined treatment, but only about three fourths of those that initially improve sustain the response to 9 months. Adolescents and their parents may find that engaging in CBT is a challenge because of their schedules or other circumstances. Addressing these challenges is the advantage of having intervention provided in the school setting by school mental health professionals. For those that do not engage in treatment in the school setting, it is important to emphasize that if the improvement on medication begins to plateau, CBT is highly recommended.

ESSENTIALS

■ Treating adolescents with depression is likely to have benefit.

■ Any treatment is more effective than no treatment.

■ Combined cognitive behavior therapy and medication can be more effective than medication alone.

Table 1. Results of the Treatment for Adolescents Depression Study

■ After 12 weeks of treatment, 71% in the combined CBT and medication group improved.

■ 82% that had a positive response by 12 weeks sustained that recovery through 36 weeks (9 months) of treatment.

■ Among those who had a positive response to combined CBT and medication, 89% sustained the response through 36 weeks.

■ Although only 42% of those receiving CBT alone had a positive response at 12 weeks, nearly all (97%) sustained improvement through 36 weeks.

■ For those who respond to medication (fluoxetine) alone, adding CBT to their treatment could enhance their chances for continued improvement.

(March et al., 2006; Kennard et al., 2006; Rohde et al., 2008)

On the other hand, adolescents and their parents may be reluctant to treat with antidepressant medication, particularly given concerns for suicidal ideation and attempts when under treatment. Yet the evidence is clear that medical management of moderate to severe major depression with antidepressant medication should be made available for adolescents, including fluoxetine (e.g., March et al., 2006) and other SSRIs (e.g., Clarke et al., 2005). Although there is a purported increased risk of suicidality with SSRI medication, the evidence actually suggests there is a *lower* risk of suicidality if adolescents are treated with SSRI's (Hebebrand, 2010; March, 2010). Nonetheless, school mental health professionals should monitor suicidal ideation in students with depression undergoing pharmacotherapy, in addition to the monitoring provided by the student's prescriber. For adolescents with a personal or family history of suicidality who are being treated with an SSRI, access to CBT is especially valuable and can reduce the risk of self-harm (March et al., 2006; March, 2010).

"For adolescents with a personal or family history of suicidality who are being treated with an SSRI, access to CBT is especially valuable and can reduce the risk of self-harm."

In the group that received CBT only, less than half had an initial positive response at 12 weeks (42%). However, nearly all (97%) of those sustained the positive response through 36 weeks. In other words, when CBT alone is effective, the recovery is sustained. For students who are reluctant to treat with antidepressant medication, CBT intervention by itself can be very effective. It is thought that CBT has a preventive effect that helps sustain improvement and avoid recurrence of depression (Rohde et al., 2008). This holds true even if, after the initial 12 weeks of treatment, the student engages in CBT less frequently over the next 6 months. This highlights the benefits of adding CBT to treatment with antidepressant medication alone.

Finally, the value of ongoing, long-term treatment cannot be overemphasized: the TADS findings consistently refer to treatment offered over 36 weeks or 9 months. Other research has found benefits of ongoing treatment of up to a year (Clarke et al., 2005). For TADS, the longer-term treatment, regardless of treatment strategy, had lasting benefits for the majority of participants during an additional follow-up year (March & Vitiello, 2009).

"The value of ongoing, long-term treatment cannot be overemphasized."

Adolescents with more severe depression at the onset of treatment were less likely to achieve full remission at 12 weeks, emphasizing the importance of not only longer-term treatment, but also treatment that targets residual symptoms in the continuation phase of treatment (Kennard et al., 2006), whether by adding medication or by focusing the CBT interventions. Even with a positive treatment response, most adolescents with severe depression continue to show signs of substantial functional impairment after 12 weeks of treatment (Vitiello et al., 2006). This underscores the need to provide longer-term treatment efforts that target the functional impairments in adolescents (Vitiello et al., 2006) such as problem-solving and social skills interventions (Kennard et al., 2010).

KEYS TO COLLABORATION

- Students at this level of service call for very high levels of collaboration among families, school mental health professionals, and community-based providers.

- School mental health professionals should work with other providers to ensure that pharmacotherapy occurs in the context of psychotherapy.

- School mental health professionals have a role in helping healthcare providers monitor the effects of medication in school.

Furthermore, more frequent sessions are important in the acute phase of treatment. Combination treatment in the TADS study nominally consisted of 15 CBT sessions in the acute phase, which likely enhanced the positive response after the first 12 weeks. When only 5 to 9 acute CBT sessions were offered in conjunction with SSRI medication, the effect of the CBT sessions was weak (Clarke et al., 2005). In fact, with treatment-resistant adolescents, participants who had more than 9 CBT sessions were two and a half times more likely to have a positive treatment response than those who had nine or fewer CBT sessions (Kennard et al., 2009). Together, the findings point to the importance of at least an adequate number of sessions (9), frequent acute sessions in the first 3 months, and continued sessions for an additional 6 to 9 months, even if on a less frequent basis, for optimal outcomes.

"Together, the findings point to the importance of at least an adequate number of sessions (9), frequent acute sessions in the first 3 months, and continued sessions for an additional 6 to 9 months, even if on a less frequent basis, for optimal outcomes."

ABOUT ANTIDEPRESSANT MEDICATIONS

Students will be prescribed medication for depression outside the school setting unless there is a school-based health center. In that case, psychiatric-mental health nurse practitioners are best positioned to prescribe psychotropic medication and may be employed by the school district or health center. Psychiatrists on occasion may provide consultation and prescribe in high school health centers as well. Primary care providers such as family nurse practitioners and pediatric nurse practitioners also prescribe antidepressants, depending on their area of expertise and experience. It is crucial for school mental health providers to have a collaborative relationship with prescribers in the school setting in order to ensure monitoring of the response to medication treatment and to ensure that pharmacotherapy occurs in the context of psychotherapy. It is best if a baseline of symptoms observed while the student is involved in psychotherapy is used to ascertain the need for the addition of antidepressant medication.

Currently, SSRIs are the first-line medical therapy for depression in adolescents and children because they are well-tolerated, are administered once a day, have fewer side effects than other antidepressants, and are less likely to be harmful if taken in an overdose. The SSRIs include: fluoxetine (Prozac), sertraline (Zoloft), paroxetine (Paxil), cialopram (Clexa), escitalopram (Lexapro), and fluvoxamine (Luvox). Fluvoxamine is not approved for the treatment of depression in any age group but it is approved for obsessive compulsive disorder in children, so it would not be unusual to see a child prescribed that medication.

Fluoxetine is approved for children 8 years of age and older and has had the largest number of studies with findings for positive effects on acute depression (Cheung et al., 2007); thus fluoxetine is the first-line antidepressant medication for children and adolescents. Yet 30% to 40% of children and adolescents with

depression do not respond to the initially prescribed medication. Escitalopram is approved for adolescents aged 12 years and older and is a choice when a switch to another medication is required. Sertraline and citalopram have inconsistent evidence of efficacy for youth (Whittington et al., 2004) but are often prescribed off label when there is a hypersensitivity to fluoxetine, a trial of fluoxetine has failed, or one of these antidepressants has successfully treated a biological relative. Although paroxetine has had inconsistent evidence of efficacy in children and adolescents, it also has had the largest number of studies with negative results (Cheung et al., 2007).

Response rates to medication treatment are higher if treatment begins during the school year and continues throughout the school year (Shamseddeen et al., 2011). Students treated with antidepressants must be closely monitored by the family and the prescribing clinician. School mental health professionals will additionally want to monitor the student given their opportunities to observe him or her in the social and educational context. In the initial first months of treatment and at times of changes in dose, the student should be monitored for worsening depression and suicidality. The family or prescriber should be notified if these occur and if other associated behaviors occur, including restlessness or anxiety, agitation, panic attacks, insomnia, irritability or hostility, impulsivity, or hypomania. In addition to symptoms, side effects should be monitored.

Antidepressant medications should continue for 9 to 12 months. Relapse in depressive symptoms is frequently seen in adolescents who stop their medication once they begin to feel better. Continuation beyond 12 months may be necessary for adolescents with treatment-resistant depression or if tapering off the medication is unsuccessful. Discontinuation and tapering off medication should take place under the supervision of the prescribing clinician. Ideally, medication treatment should be ended during a time of minimal stress, such as during summer vacation, rather than during the school year, particularly if the student reports greater problems at school (Shamseddeen et al., 2011).

INTERVENTIONS FOR SUICIDAL IDEATION

If a student is experiencing suicidal thinking and is not being treated with medication, he or she should be referred to a prescribing clinician for possible pharmacotherapy given the extent to which depression is untreated or undertreated (Mann et al., 2005). Psychotherapy must be initiated if not already in progress. Reduction in suicidal ideation and improved problem-solving has been found for CBT and interpersonal psychotherapy (Mann et al., 2005). Both of these approaches have been described (see Chapter 5) as intensive interventions for depression; they will likely have a preventive benefit with respect to self-harm and suicidal behavior as well. For those who present with suicidal ideation and nonsuicidal self-injury, these interventions will assist with a reduction in the destructive patterns in the short-term and offer improvement in depression in the long-term.

REFERENCES

Cheung, A. H., Zuckerbrot, R. A., Jensen, P. S., Ghalib, K., Laraque, D., & Stein, R. E. K. (2007). Guidelines for adolescent depression in primary care (GLAD-PC): II. Treatment and ongoing management. *Pediatrics, 120,* e1313–e1326. doi:10.1542/peds.2006-1395

Clarke, G., Debar, L., Lynch, F., Powell, J., Gale, J., O'Connor, E., … Hertert, S. (2005). A randomized effectiveness trial of brief cognitive-behavioral therapy for depressed adolescents receiving anitdepressent medication. *Journal of the American Academy of Child and Adolescent Psychiatry, 44:* 888–898. doi:10.1097/10.chi.0000171904.23947.54

Hebebrand, J. (2010). Commentary on 'Forum: use of antidepressants in children and adolescents.' *Current Opinion in Psychiatry, 23,* 62–67. doi:10.1097/YCO.0b013e328334bd2c

Kennard, B. D., Clarke, G. N., Weersing, V. R., Asarnow, J. R., Shamseddeneen, W., Porta, G., … Brent, D. A. (2009). Effective components of TORDIA cognitive-behavioral therapy for adolescent depression: Preliminary findings. *Journal of Consulting and Clinical Psychology, 77,* 1033–1041.

Kennard, B., Silva, S., Vitiello, B., Curry, J., Kratochvil, C., Simons, A. … The TADS Team. (2006). Remission and residual symptoms after short-term treatment in the Treatment of Adolescents with Depression study (TADS). *Journal of the American Academy of Child and Adolescent Psychiatry, 45,* 1404–1411.

Mann, J.J., Apter, A., Berolote, J., Beautrais, A., Currier, D., Haas, A . … Hendin, H. (2005). Suicide prevention strategies: A systematic review. *Journal of the American Medical Association, 294,* 2064–2074.

March, J. S. (2010). Commentary on 'Forum: Use of antidepressants in children and adolescents.' *Current Opinion in Psychiatry, 23,* 62–67. doi:10.1097/YCO.0b013e328334bd2c

March, J. S., & Vitiello, B. (2009). Clinical messages from the Treatment for Adolescents with Depression Study (TADS). *American Journal of Psychiatry, 166,* 1118–1123.

March, J., Silva, S., Vitiello, B., & The TADS Team. (2006). The treatment for adolescents with depression study (TADS): Methods and message at 12 weeks. *Journal of the American Academy of Child and Adolescent Psychiatry, 45,* 1393–1403.

Merrell, K. W. (2008). *Helping students overcome depression and anxiety: A practical guide (2nd ed.).* New York, NY: Guilford.

Rohde, P., Silva, S. G., Tonev, S. T., Kennard, B. D., Vitiello, B., Kratochvil, C. J., … March, J. S. (2008). Achievement and maintenance of sustained improvement during TADS continuation and maintenance therapy. *Archives of General Psychiatry, 65,* 447–455.

Shamseddeen, W., Clarke, G., Wagner, K. D., Ryan, N. D. Birmaher, B., Emslie, G., … Brent, D. A. (2011). Treatment-resistant depressed youth show a higher response rate if treatment ends during summer school break. *Journal of the American Academy of Child and Adolescent Psychiatry, 50,* 1140–1148.

Vitiello, B., Rohde, P., Silva, S., Wells, K., Casat, C., Waslick, B., … The TADS Team. (2006). Functioning and quality of life in the Treatment for Adolescents with Depression study (TADS). *Journal of the American Academy of Child and Adolescent Psychiatry, 45,* 1419–1427.

Whittington, C. J., Kendall, T., Fonagy, P., Cottrell, D., Cotgrove, A., & Boddington, E., (2004). Selective serotonin reuptake inhibitors in childhood depression: Systematic review of published versus unpublished data. *Lancet, 363,* 1341–1345.

Zuckerbrot, R. A., Cheung, A. H., Jensen, P. S., Stein, R. E., & Laraque, D. (2007). Guidelines for depression in primary care (GLAD-PC): I. Identification, assessment, and initial management. *Pediatrics, 120,* e1299–1312. doi:10.1542/peds.2007-1144

CHAPTER 16

Advocating for Comprehensive and Coordinated School Mental Health Services

Kelly Vaillancourt, PhD, NCSP, Katherine C. Cowan, &
Anastasia Kalamaros Skalski, PhD, National Association of School Psychologists

ESSENTIALS

- Only 16% of children who need mental health services receive them. 70%-80% of these children access mental health services at school (Center for Health and Health Care in Schools, 2007).

- Students are more likely to seek help when they need it if school-based mental health services are available (Slade, 2002).

- Expanded school mental health services in elementary schools have been found to reduce special education referrals, improve aspects of the school climate (Bruns, Walrath, Glass-Siegel, & Weist, 2004), and produce declines in disciplinary referrals, suspension, grade retention, and special education referrals and placement among at-risk students (Shonkoff & Phillips, 2000; Substance Abuse and Mental Health Services Administration, 2005).

Previous chapters in this book highlight the relationship between depression and academic and life outcomes. Chapters 3–5 and 9–10 describe specific programs and resources to help assess and intervene with students who are at risk for or suffering from depression, which are effective when properly implemented. However, mental health programs and services will be far more sustainable and effective when incorporated into a comprehensive system of supports. Indeed, there is a broad body of research that supports the effects of providing evidence-based mental health interventions within the context of a multi-tiered system of supports (MTSS), including processes like response to intervention (RTI). Utilizing this framework allows school-employed mental health professionals to reach more students, provide more targeted interventions, and most importantly, link interventions more successfully to improved academic outcomes. Unfortunately, despite the positive outcomes associated with providing comprehensive school-based mental health services, many schools and districts do not consider these services to be a priority for student success when financial resources are tight.

As mentioned in Chapter 1, it is a vital part of our job to advocate for all students. We frequently do this well on an individual level but often are unsure of how to effectively advocate at the systems level for comprehensive and coordinated school mental health services. Advocating for services to meet the needs of students with depression can both benefit students directly and be a catalyst for moving your district toward providing comprehensive and coordinated mental health services within an MTSS framework. This chapter provides the context and strategies to help you determine the best course of action and engage in advocacy effectively. Change will not happen overnight, but with persistence, it will become a reality.

UNDERSTANDING THE BASICS OF ADVOCACY

The relationship between student mental health, academic achievement, and overall life functioning is clear and professional advocacy is instrumental to ensuring that all students have access to effective school services that support all three.

An important first step is to understand the nature of advocacy and its various purposes. First, advocacy involves engaging in coordinated actions and activities designed to promote a cause or an issue of importance. In this case, advocacy can positively influence the lives of students and families by improving and increasing access to needed school mental health services and resources. Second, advocacy can take many forms, takes time, and requires collaboration across various stakeholders. Third, advocacy may vary depending on who and what you are trying to influence. The focus of this chapter is on *professional advocacy*, although many of the tips and strategies apply to *legislative advocacy*. Professional advocacy addresses advocacy for the *settings* in which the issue is important, the *services* critical in response to identified needs, and the *professionals* delivering the desired services. In this case, your immediate focus might be on services to address depression but you will

be most effective in the long run if your professional advocacy encompasses a clear articulation about the role of schools and mental health agencies (settings), the critical benefits of comprehensive school mental health services (prevention, promotion, and intervention services), and the importance of having an adequate supply of qualified school and community mental health professionals to provide the needed services (professionals). If you wish to engage in legislative advocacy, contact your state professional association to determine how you can support each other's efforts. Resources specific to legislative advocacy are provided at the end of this chapter.

ESSENTIALS

- Professional advocacy is: (a) intentional, effective communication or outreach that builds awareness, understanding, and engagement in a particular issue, action, or strategy; and (b) actions that prove effectiveness and value (Cowan, 2011). Professional advocacy should be an integrated, ongoing responsibility for all school mental health professionals and is appropriate for all levels of interaction (individual, classroom, building, district, state, and federal).

- Legislative advocacy is intentional and coordinated efforts to influence the introduction, modification, or enactment of a specific piece of legislation designed to address the goals of an organization or group of organizations or meet the needs of a specific population. Legislative advocacy is generally conducted by organized groups (formal or informal) and is primarily targeted at state and federal legislative bodies.

226

"Advocating for services to meet the needs of students with depression can both benefit students directly and be a catalyst for moving your district toward providing comprehensive and coordinated mental health services within a multi-tiered system of supports. "

Clarifying Your Training, Expertise, and Role

Advocating for school mental health services begins with understanding how to talk about what you do and why it is important. It is critical to establish the connection between the mental health services that you are advocating for and the people who are responsible for providing those services. The scope of practice of school counselors, school nurses, school psychologists, and school social workers varies by district. Although these professionals are commonly the most qualified mental health professionals employed by the school, many times individual practitioners do not consider themselves mental health professionals because the titles used in schools reserves this term for community-employed professionals contracting with a school. In other cases, individual practitioners do not consider themselves to be mental health professionals as a result of the narrow roles they play in the schools they serve.

Additionally, other educators and administrators may not be aware of the breadth of training these professionals have and their ability to provide high quality mental health services to children. The American School Counseling Association, the National Association of School Nurses, the National Association of School Psychologists, and the National Association of Social Workers maintain national standards that outline the scope of training and practice that each of these professions is qualified to deliver. These standards represent clear connections to mental health training, services, and supports.

Linking your skill set to professional standards is important because too much diversity of training and roles for school mental health professionals creates confusion and ambiguity. This confusion can exist among consumers (e.g., parents, community agencies, public officials), across the four professions (e.g., What is the difference between a school counselor and a school psychologist?) and, in some cases, within each profession's areas of specialization (e.g., degree in which a professional is trained to respond to the behavioral needs of a student). As you begin your advocacy work, consult your professional association's resources to help you educate your colleagues about the wide range of mental health services you can provide. Educating consumers (educators and families) on your scope of practice will help clarify the unique services school mental health professionals provide as well as how they collaborate and work together to make sure that every student has access to the services they need both in the school and within the community.

KEY POINTS TO CONSIDER

■ Be clear what the basic training is for your profession and what advanced or specialized training you have as a practitioner.

■ Distinguish the specific roles of the professionals in your district and school(s). This varies from district to district and your stakeholders care most about who is serving them and how.

■ Collaborate with others on the mental health team so that the messaging about roles and responsibilities is clear and consistent.

■ Emphasize how your training helps families and educators to link children's mental health to positive behavior and successful learning.

■ Identify skill areas for professional development that would enhance the team's capacity to provide effective mental health services.

MODELS FOR SCHOOL MENTAL HEALTH SERVICE DELIVERY

Just as there are a variety of roles that school mental health professionals fulfill, there are numerous models of practice that describe how comprehensive school-based mental health services are framed. It is important to understand these models and how they operate within the school context because you will need to articulate how these models improve effectiveness of service delivery, student outcomes, and ultimately, academic achievement.

Several models for comprehensive and coordinated services, in particular, are gaining attention. These models have similar features, as depicted by Figure 1, but approach service integration and delivery from different perspectives. These models are typically grounded in a multi-tiered system. They share elements with RTI systems as described throughout this book, in that they typically include components of universal screening for academic and behavioral barriers to learning, implementing evidence-based interventions in response to these student needs, monitoring the ongoing progress of students in response to implemented interventions, and engaging in systematic data-based decision making about programming and services needed for students based upon specific student outcome data.

Full Service Community Schools

Dryfoos and Maguire (2002) defined the critical elements of full service community schools (FSCS) as (a) being open all of the time, (b) run by a partnership, (c) providing an array of services, (d) responsive to the needs of the family and the community, and (e) focused on overcoming barriers to learning. A FSCS delivers health, mental health, and other services to ensure that the non-curricular needs of the students and their families are being met, using the school as the access point for service delivery. Collaboration between the school and the community is an integral part of this model, with each community determining what services, including after school and weekend services, will be provided at each school. The underlying premise of FSCSs is that the school is an essential part of the community and all students have a right to learn. However, learning cannot take place if the non-curricular needs of the students, and their families are not met.

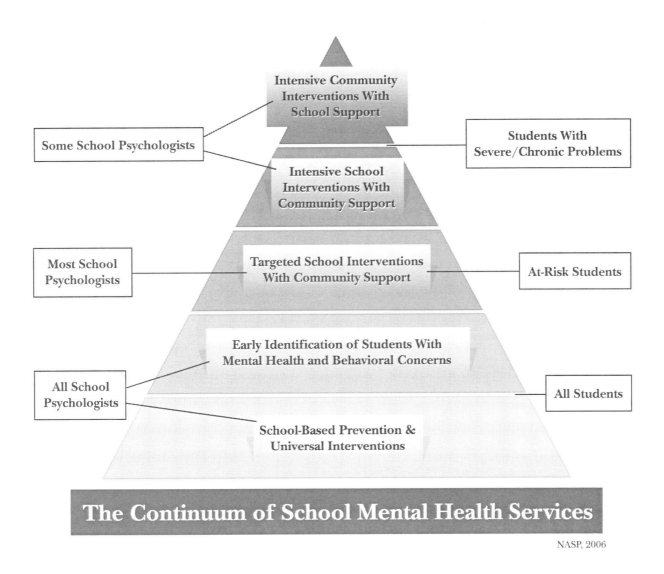

Figure 1. The Continuum of Mental Health Services

Adapted with permission from "Communication Planning and Message
Development: Promoting School-Based Mental Health Services" in *Communiqué*, Vol. 35, No. 1.
National Association of School Psychologists.

School-based health clinics are often linked to this model, emphasizing the connections between the health and wellness of a child and their academic achievement. For more information, visit www.nasbhc.org.

Coordinated School Health Model

The coordinated school health (CSH) model, proposed by the Centers for Disease Control and Prevention (CDC), involves the delivery of services and supports in eight critical areas: health education; physical education; health services; nutrition services; counseling, psychological and social services; policies and practices supporting a healthy and safe school; and health promotion for the staff. The premise of the CSH model is that by coordinating the various parts of the school health system, schools can eliminate gaps and redundancies in service, build effective partnerships across schools and communities, enhance communication, and engage students in healthy lifestyles. For more information, visit http://www.cdc.gov/HealthyYouth/CSHP.

The UCLA Three-Component Model

The UCLA Three-Component Model (see Figure 2), conceptualized by research done at the UCLA Center for Mental Health in Schools, originated from a school-based service delivery perspective and is based upon the development of a comprehensive system of learning supports, which include mental health services. This approach balances instructional components (e.g., teacher quality, standards, curriculum), the organizational/management components (e.g., shared governance, accountability, budget decisions) and a third component of learning supports. This model seeks to reduce fragmentation of services by framing the necessary behavioral, mental health, and social services within the context of school culture and learning. It emphasizes that education policy (ESEA and IDEA) needs to be restructured to support all three components equally in order for effective school reform to be achieved (Adelman & Taylor, 2010). For more information, visit http://smhp.psych.ucla.edu.

"Services to support students with depression can easily be incorporated into the MTSS approach and terminology because, as laid out in this book, they clearly require a multi-tiered approach when implemented comprehensively."

Incorporating Multi-Tiered Systems of Support Terminology

Connecting each of these models is the value of providing a broad range of services to students in need. This process is commonly known as a *multi-tiered system of supports* (MTSS), mentioned above. Utilizing the MTSS terminology in your advocacy efforts provides a framework that can naturally encompass the other conceptual models that have emerged while keeping the focus on meeting student needs within the right settings, with the right services, and the best qualified personnel. Services to support students with depression can easily be incorporated into the MTSS approach and terminology because, as laid out in this book, they clearly require a multi-tiered approach when implemented comprehensively. Some of the key features of MTSS that can contribute to positive advocacy messages are explored in **Handout K.**

Figure 2. The Three-Component Model

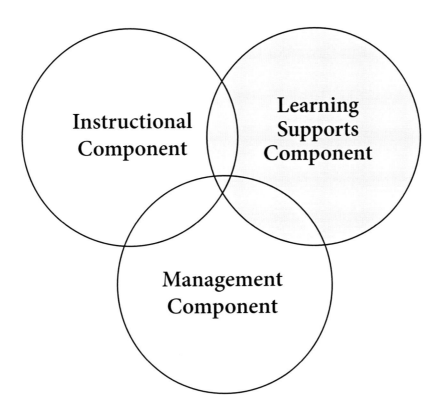

LEARNING SUPPORTS

- Re-engage disconnected students and maintain their engagement

- Provide support for the full range of transitions that students and families encounter

- Respond to and prevent academic, behavioral, and social–emotional problems and crises

- Increase community family involvement and support

- Facilitate student and family access to effective services and special assistance as needed

IDENTIFYING A UNIFIED ADVOCACY VOICE

Once it is clear that your advocacy is unified under a common service delivery model, it is imperative to also unify the voices of the practitioners in the trenches. As Chapter 11 on collaborative and integrated service delivery addresses, it is important for school and community mental health providers to work together to provide comprehensive and coordinated school mental health services. It is also paramount for these professionals to engage public policy and other decision-makers in a unified discussion of the critical importance of these services. Common ground is found in the belief that students are more successful in school when they are able to access the needed services to remedy barriers to learning. Having these services available in the setting in which the student spends the bulk of their day helps to facilitate necessary access by the individuals and their families.

Additionally, there is strong agreement among experts on the basic framework and core components of a comprehensive continuum of services. However, how to implement these frameworks, with which professionals, and in which setting, can often be unclear to decision makers when advocates fail to use common language. Disparate voices advocating for different parts of the continuum or for singular services can be counterproductive to moving a district toward comprehensive systemic change. Advocacy efforts must be rooted in the common points of agreement in order to represent a unified voice. Following are some of general points of agreement that can form the foundation for discussions among school-employed and commu-

nity-based professionals and can help inform your unified advocacy messaging.

DEFINING SERVICES TO ADDRESS DEPRESSION WITHIN AN MTSS FRAMEWORK

- Students suffering from depression are in pain, cannot learn to their highest potential, and may be at risk for harmful behavior.

- Meeting the needs of students with depression is critical to supporting their positive learning and behavior, and schools can play a vital role in doing so.

- Effectively supporting students who are at risk for or struggle with depression requires screening, assessment, and intervention services. Early identification and intervention can minimize the negative effects of depression.

- There are many evidence-based interventions and programs that address depression but they are most effective when integrated with other mental health programming.

- Providing these services within a multi-tiered system of supports helps ensure that they are preventive and responsive, are adjusted appropriately to meet students' specific needs, and appropriately linked to the learning environment.

- A comprehensive multi-tiered system facilitates appropriate coordination of services between school and community practitioners, which minimizes gaps in services, reduces waste, and improves student mental health and academic outcomes.

KEYS TO COLLABORATION

- Invite all interested and impacted stakeholders to the table.

- Maintain open communication among all parties.

- Address all concerns.

- Focus on the shared goal of advocacy.

- Foster respect among all professionals.

- Students achieve better when they are able to access a broad range of services and supports that build resilience and directly remedy barriers to learning.

- Access to needed services and supports is improved when these services are provided in a school setting. A broad range of services and supports will include health, mental health, and social services including prevention, promotion, and intervention.

- Services and supports that are selected in response to the unique needs of the school and the community will be more effective and efficient.

- School-employed professionals are well trained and knowledgeable about the unique features of school systems, including their mission and purpose, and are able to identify the most successful strategies that can be utilized during the school day to help engage students and remedy barriers to learning.

- Community-employed professionals are well trained and knowledgeable about individualized interventions and community systems and, in coordination with school- employed professionals, are able to connect students and their families to a broad range of community-based and intensive supports in order to remedy the barriers to learning and personal success.

- An adequate supply of school and community professionals working in a collaborative and coordinated effort to provide a comprehensive system of supports is necessary to produce the greatest outcomes for students.

"Disparate voices advocating for different parts of the continuum or for singular services can be counterproductive to moving a district toward comprehensive systemic change. Advocacy efforts must be rooted in the common points of agreement in order to represent a unified voice."

THE ADVOCACY PROCESS

It is helpful to establish an advocacy team who will take the lead on developing and implementing an advocacy plan. Without a set group of people taking on this responsibility, it is too easy to lose focus and miss opportunities. Ideally, the team will comprise people who are, at least in combination, knowledgeable about the issues (e.g., work with students suffering depression), good writers, comfortable presenting ideas and data, and skilled at building and maintaining positive relationships. They will help establish clear objectives based on an assessment of needs, opportunities, and resources. It is important to identify who, outside this team, needs to be kept informed of plans and actions (e.g., supervisors, leaders of local professional organizations). Following a few basic steps can help you organize and implement a successful advocacy campaign (see Figure 3).

Step 1: Assess the Situation and Define Your Objectives

As you plan your advocacy campaign, consider the current priorities and challenges of your school building or district and how your goals align with those priorities. For example, is your principal or district superintendent struggling to reduce absenteeism and keep students en-

gaged in learning? Is absenteeism connected to student mental health concerns including depression? Are there new district or school policies that you could use to support your arguments related to increasing access to school-based mental health services? This step may involve administering needs assessment surveys, reviewing existing student performance data, and consulting with school administrators about priorities for school improvement. Based on your assessment and data gathering, it will be important for you to consider what your objective is and how your advocacy efforts can be most effective. If you discover that your target audience is not aware of the link between mental health and academic achievement, you may want to focus your initial efforts on raising awareness and education before advocating for implementation of strategies to address student mental health needs. You also should be

Figure 3. Steps for Effective Professional Advocacy

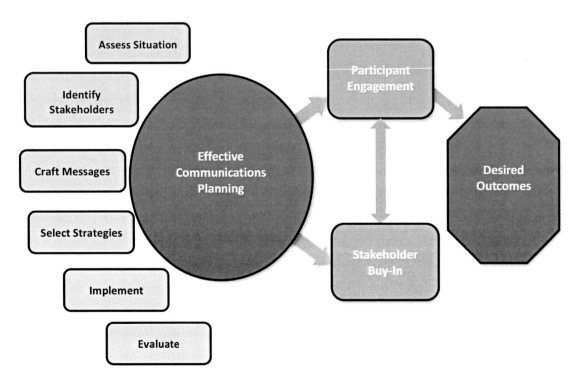

realistic about the obstacles you will face, the time line you have to reach your goal, and the resources that you have available.

Consult Professional Resources

This book has a wealth of research information, and the end of this chapter contains references to additional fact sheets that can be used to provide practical and evidence-based research that documents the importance of providing school-based mental health services. In addition, it will be helpful to reference national practice models (e.g., the NASP or ASCA practice model) to reassure administrators that they already have the personnel necessary to begin implementing this kind of framework.

Become Familiar With the Jurisdiction of the School Board

Each school district is governed in a unique way. It will be helpful for you to identify the key decision makers in your district. In some cities it is the mayor and the city council; in other cities, the school board has complete authority over the school district.

POSSIBLE OPENINGS TO DISCUSS THE BENEFITS OF COMPREHENSIVE MENTAL HEALTH SERVICES

- Crisis or trauma event involving the school community (or portions of it).

- Increased discipline problems, even after changes in discipline policies.

- Increased student requests to meet with the school counselor for non-academic or scheduling issues.

- Increased reports of bullying or other aggressive behaviors.

- Increased concerns about student absenteeism or psychosomatic complaints shared with the school nurse.

- Increased or persistent dropout rates.

- Persistently poor performance by at-risk students, even with enhanced instructional supports.

- Increased or pervasive student risk behaviors.

- Review of school climate data.

- New law or policy passed at the state level.

Examine Existing School District Policy and State Policy and Legislation

It will be important to familiarize yourself with existing school and district policies related to school-based prevention and intervention services. Examine where the implementation of a multi-tiered system of supports could be incorporated into existing policy. In addition, it will be helpful to determine if your state or school system policy allows community-based providers to deliver mental health services on school grounds or during the school day. Some districts only allow school-employed mental health professionals to deliver services during the school day and community-based supports to be offered before or after school. Becoming familiar with the existing policies that guide the delivery of student mental health services is critical to determining where your advocacy messages should be targeted.

Use Data

Part of this assessment includes identifying and collecting data that support the need for change. This type of data will vary based on your school and district, but below are some suggestions of helpful information to gather.

- **Stakeholder surveys and other school data.** Many schools routinely collect discipline and school climate data. School-wide information systems can provide a breadth of data about student behavior, discipline, academic achievement, attendance, and student engagement. If your school or district administers school climate surveys, examine these to see what teachers, parents, and students report as areas in need of improvement in the school. If your school or district does not collect these data, you may want to informally survey teachers and parents regarding their perceptions of student engagement, behavior, and other concerns they have about the school environment. In addition, your school or district may collect data about the types of concerns that school counselors, school nurses, school psychologists, and school social workers frequently address

with students and families. Many schools participate in the annual Youth Risk Behavior Surveillance System (YRBSS) surveys administered by the Centers for Disease Control and Prevention (http://www.cdc.gov/HealthyYouth/yrbs/index.htm). These surveys can give you a profile of some of the mental health concerns of students. It will be important to maintain confidentiality of this information; however, knowing the number of students and families who sought assistance for depression, or other mental health concerns, could be helpful to your advocacy.

- **Data from neighboring schools or districts.** If there are schools within your district or neighboring school systems that are already implementing a similar framework, see if they would be willing to share some of their outcome data. Administrators are more likely to implement a change if they have evidence that the change has resulted in positive outcomes in other schools.

CONSIDER YOUR AUDIENCE'S ...

- Level of knowledge and awareness

- Primary concerns, hopes, and expectations

- Perspective

- Possible barriers to understanding

- Competing priorities (particularly building and district leaders)

- Ability and likelihood to take action

Step 2: Identify and Mobilize Relevant Stakeholders and Supporters

The voice of many is more effective than the voice of one. Begin by identifying what individual practitioners, or groups of practitioners, will join you in convincing local and district administrators that this type of service delivery model is needed. If you are advocating at the school level, identify other faculty who would be willing to take on this challenge with you. In addition, it will be most helpful to include parents in your efforts. If you are working at the district level, identify groups of professionals and local organizations (e.g., local school psychology associations, parent advocacy groups, school board members, local homeowners associations) who would be willing to share in your advocacy efforts. Community members' voices are extremely important in influencing local policy decisions, and their support will be invaluable.

In addition to identifying those who support your goals, it is also important to identify those who might be the most vocal opponents of your goals. In any advocacy process there are almost always differing opinions on the appropriate role for schools and on the allocation of resources. It will be necessary to identify those who have previously, or who will most likely repeat the most cogent or powerful arguments against enhanced school mental health services. What are those arguments likely to be? How can you counter them without becoming adversarial? What is the relationship between your opponents and key decision-makers?

Whether allies or opponents, you always want to understand your audience's primary concerns and desires. These will vary among audiences. For example, the school board is most likely concerned about costs, legal issues, and high stakes test scores. Principals are often most concerned about support for teachers, use of resources, impact on instruction and test scores, and building safety. Parents care that their child is safe, valued, and getting the instruction and support he or she needs to succeed in school. In the end, these are all similar issues seen from different perspectives. Your job as an advocate is to tailor your communication about comprehensive school mental health services to the perspectives of specific audiences. Doing so helps improves their understanding of the issues.

"Remember that one of your most critical audiences may be other school-based mental health professionals who need to see themselves in the roles you will be describing, understand programs or models being advocated for, and be able to articulate and reinforce the key advocacy messages."

Step 3: Craft Key Messages

Ultimately, school and district administrators and local school boards are focused on ensuring that the students reach their full academic potential, yet many minimize the documented link between behavioral and mental health and school achievement. It is important to frame any advocacy efforts regarding school-based mental health services within the context of improved academic achievement. This requires planned and intentional communication with all relevant stakeholders. You want to ensure that you are presenting your argument in the most efficient way possible, while still getting your message across. Intentional and planful communication and message development:

- helps you target the right audience with the right strategies;

- helps you to organize your ideas and be consistent with your message; and

- makes it easier for your target audience to understand your argument, remember your message, and act on it.

TIPS FOR DEVELOPING YOUR KEY MESSAGES

- Identify three primary (key) messages.

- Tailor your messages to the knowledge level and perspective of your audience.

- Keep objectives relevant to local context.

- Be clear and concise.

- Support your argument with data.

- Provide personal examples (put "a face" on the issue).

- Offer specific suggestions for change.

Developing key messages is an important part of the communication process. They are sound bites that succinctly convey your argument. Key messages are more effective when accompanied with data. If it is available, incorporate school or district-level data into your key messages. It is critically important to keep key messages simple and easy to remember. Having a maximum of two to three key messages with no more than three supporting points for each message is generally ideal. You should tailor your messages to specific audiences.

Sample Key Messages

1. Mentally healthy children are more successful in school and life.

- Research demonstrates that students who receive social–emotional and mental health support achieve better academically.

- School climate, classroom behavior, on-task learning, and students' sense of connectedness and well-being all improve when students receive needed mental health supports.

- Mental health is not simply the absence of mental illness but also encompasses social, emotional, and behavioral wellness and the ability to cope with life's challenges.

2. Schools are an ideal place to provide mental health services to children and youth.

- Unfortunately, too many children and youth with mental health problems are not getting the help they need and, when left unmet, mental health problems are linked to costly negative outcomes such as academic and behavior problems, dropping out, and delinquency.

- Schools are ideal settings to provide mental health services. School-based mental health professionals know the students, parents, and other staff. The learning environment provides the right context for prevention and intervention. And, importantly, school is where children spend most of their day.

- Qualified school-employed mental health professionals are trained to link interventions to learning and can more readily collaborate with teachers and other school on identification, implementation, and monitoring of students' needs and progress.

3. **Providing school-based mental health services within a multi-tiered system of supports is a cost-effective, sustainable strategy to promote student success.**

- Administrators and teachers cannot address these issues alone; schools need adequate access to school mental health professionals and a broad array of comprehensive and coordinated school mental health services.

- Schools and communities can partner to provide collaborative, comprehensive, and coordinated services.

- The impact of social–emotional and mental health promotion and prevention interventions is at least two to three times higher when programs are carefully implemented by qualified personnel who have expert knowledge of

the relevant issues being addressed (Durlak & Dupre, 2008).

These examples can help guide the framing of key messages most appropriate for stakeholders. The most important thing is to be sure to incorporate your key message in all of your advocacy and outreach efforts, including meetings, presentations, and written resources. Remember the exact wording and supporting points should be tailored to each audience. It may take numerous attempts before the benefits of mental health services delivered within the context of a multi-tiered system of support fully resonate with your colleagues, principal, or superintendent. Despite the base of research that documents the positive outcomes associated with providing these intervention and prevention services, there are a number of barriers and challenges that prevent full implementation of this type of model in the school setting.

Step 4: Select and Implement Your Strategies

The strategic activities you employ may vary based on the decision maker(s) you wish to influence and the partners who are joining in your efforts. It is important to think broadly about who may be impacted by your issue and to craft unique messages and strategies for each audience. Below are some tips to help you plan your activities to advocate with your school principal, the parents of the students in your school, your school district administrators, and your elected officials.

When to Advocate With Your Principal

If your objective is to implement or change a set of practices or policies at the school building level, it is most appropriate to begin a conversation with the building principal. In addition, if your goal is to increase the types of services provided at a school, or become more involved in service delivery and decision making within the context of one building, your efforts should begin with the principal. If your objectives involve more systemic change, you should seek the support of your principal, but your advocacy should focus on influencing the school board and the superintendent.

When to Advocate With Families

There are no people that care more deeply about student success than the families of students. Ultimately, every parent desires for their children to be happy, successful, and able to live independent productive lives. Consequently, a focus of most advocacy campaigns should engage the families of students within schools from the very beginning so that they can help champion the causes that will contribute to their child's success. Engaging families requires thoughtful consideration about their culture, traditions, and beliefs, and how these may impact their understanding about the importance of the services and supports you are promoting. Craft your messages in a culturally sensitive and supportive fashion. Educate families about the breadth of supports and the value to the community of students having access to these supports. Reaching out to understand the needs of families; communicating your key messages within this context is the key to having families engaged as advocates with you rather than as adversaries.

When to Advocate With the School Board or Superintendent

If your goal is to change or implement a district level policy, your work should focus on the school board and the superintendent. In addition, if your goal is to prevent reduced funding for an initiative, increase funding for an existing initiative, seek funding for a new initiative, or advocate for additional school mental health personnel, it is most appropriate to focus your efforts with the school board, superintendent, or governing body that makes decisions regarding the school budget. However, it is still important to seek the support of building principals when engaging in district-level advocacy, especially if the changes you are seeking will directly affect building-level practices. Administrator support can be highly influential when seeking district level change.

Strategies for School-Level Advocacy

The principal is the most important stakeholder to influence as he or she makes the final decisions regarding policy and programmatic changes at the school level. As you plan your strategy, be mindful of the time of year you attempt to engage your principal. Your message may be lost if you begin your efforts at the very beginning of the year when families and teachers are overwhelmed with information or during end-of-grade standardized testing.

- ■ **Ask for a meeting with the school administrators.** At this meeting, present whatever data you have gathered and outline your key messages. Offer to be a resource as he or she considers your argument. If you are asked questions to which you do not know the answers, be sure to follow up and provide him or her with whatever information was requested.

- **Arrange a visit to a neighboring school or district.** If you are aware of another school either within or outside your district that is successfully implementing MTSS, attempt to connect your principal with administrators at that school. Principals value the perspective of other administrators when making policy or programmatic decisions in their school.

- **Offer to present at a staff meeting.** In many cases, before a principal implements a new program or framework, they want to ensure that their staff is educated and on board. If your principal is reluctant to agree to implement a multi-tiered system of support (or even if he or she is fully on board) offer to share the data you have gathered at the next staff meeting. You may gain additional supporters of your work and increase buy-in to an upcoming change.

- **Partner with the Parent Teacher Association.** Parents have an influential voice in the school. Ask to be placed on the agenda and prepare a short presentation about the importance of school-based mental health services. Share your resources and ask them to support your efforts.

- **Be persistent.** Some administrators are more reluctant to change than others. Be sure to periodically check in with your administrators to reit-

erate your message, and share any new relevant data you obtain over the course of the school year.

Strategies for District-Level Advocacy

- **Identify the key stakeholders and decision makers.** Research their background and involvement in public education (unfortunately, not all tasked with making education decisions have a background in education). See if there are any connections that you can make with their personal history and background. Connecting your argument with a personal belief or experience of a key decision maker increases the chances that they will make an effort to support your work.

- **Send school board members or other key decision makers an e-mail asking for a meeting.** Provide a brief overview of your concerns and a few key talking points, and ask for an in-person meeting with them or a member of their staff. Following the presentation of your argument and data, ask if they would be willing to support a specific policy proposal.

- **Sign up to speak at a school board meeting.** As mentioned before, some administrators are motivated by mandates as opposed to best practices. In conjunction with your allies, sign up to speak at a school board meeting to educate them about the importance of delivering mental health services in the school setting and the potential cost-benefits of these services. Invite your supporters to join you at the meeting to show a unified voice. You will likely have to keep your comments short, so be sure to prepare a packet of information to provide the board members, and follow up with each member after you speak. If you have not spoken at a school board meeting before, it may be useful to observe one prior to signing up to speak.

- **Invite key decision makers to visit local schools**. Sometimes administrators and decision makers need to see first-hand how a program works in another setting. If you have identified other schools or districts that are successfully implementing a school-based mental health service delivery model, arrange a site visit with those whose opinion you are trying to influence.

- **Follow-up.** Be sure to follow up with each school board member or local policy maker that you meet with. Be sure to provide them with any information they asked for, and periodically e-mail, call, or set up an in-person meeting to reiterate your message.

Step 5: Evaluate Your Progress

Advocacy is a marathon, not a sprint. You need to evaluate each step of the advocacy process. This begins by asking if you have assessed the needs and situation adequately, reviewed the data correctly, and identified the appropriate target goals given the situation. You need to also examine if you have engaged the right stakeholders. Have you invited the right people, worked to try and resolve differences with opponents, and strengthened your base of supporters for your cause? Evaluating your messaging is also critical. Despite coordinated and planful com-

munications and activities, your message may not resonate in the way that you had hoped and change may not come as quickly as you had anticipated. It is important to periodically examine which key messages seemed to be most effective in articulating your goals and which activities were most successful. Focus your time and energy on what is working while continuing to seek out additional supporters and new opportunities for advocacy. Finally, you need to ensure that the strategies that you are using are effective. Measuring the effectiveness of advocacy strategies is highly related to the data you collect and its sensitivity to change over time. Before implementing strategies, determine what the best methods for evaluating those strategies will be. Keep the data collection simple, objective, and measurable. Periodically gather data and measure your steps to success along the way. Be open to adjusting your methods in response to your evaluation findings. It is only too late to modify your approach when your goals have been defeated. Until then, learning from your mistakes and adjusting and revising your approach to effective advocacy is essential.

CHALLENGES TO EFFECTIVE ADVOCACY

Chapter 11 highlights the challenges associated with implementing collaborative and integrated service delivery models; many of these same challenges apply to advocacy. Frequently, the terrible Ts: tradition, turf, (lack of) trust, (lack of) time, and trouble (the difficulty of doing this work and effort required to overcome challenges) impede effective collaboration (Adelman & Taylor, 2004). School personnel are sometimes wary of advocating for models that incorporate community-based personnel within school-based service delivery models due to the perception that community agencies have a hidden agenda or will benefit financially from providing targeted services to students and families. Additionally, some school staff members have difficulty letting go of traditional school models, which narrowly define their roles. School staff members may also be concerned that addressing depression and other mental health difficulties will overwhelm limited resources. This may be even more true for schools or districts where school mental health professionals serve multiple schools and have high case loads and additional staff would be needed in order to implement MTSS with fidelity and success. Collaboration among teachers, staff, mental health professionals, parents, administrators, and the community is vital to effective advocacy; these and other concerns should be addressed before moving forward.

In addition to facing challenges associated with collaboration, you may face challenges identifying partners to support your advocacy and obtaining buy-in from decision makers. As mentioned previously, many still hold the belief that mental health is not the responsibility of the schools. However, the fact is that schools have the responsibility to ensure that all students are learning and reaching their academic potential. This requires providing a wide range of learning supports, including mental health services, to ensure that students are engaged and ready to learn when they enter the classroom.

Finally, the political climate of a school or district may not be conducive to change, despite buy-in from local policy makers. Although implementing a multi-tiered system of supports does not require legislation or a policy change at the local level, some educators are more likely to pursue these services if directed by policy and legislation.

CHALLENGES TO EFFECTIVE ADVOCACY

- Lack of cohesion among school-employed mental health professionals within a district.

- Stakeholders' lack of awareness or understanding of the link between mental health and learning.

- Stigma related to mental health problems.

- Poor communication and collaboration between school and community providers.

- Territorialism.

- Competition for financial and human resources.

A Bit on Legislative Advocacy

The primary focus of this chapter has been the importance of having active, intentional professional advocacy for school mental health services. However, as previously noted, there are times when legislative advocacy may be a more powerful influence for change. When a problem has reached a crisis point where the frequency or intensity of the issue is such that immediate large-scale change is necessary, advocating for legislation that directs actions or provides incentives via grant funding to act in a certain manner, may be the best course of action. As mentioned, legislative advocacy is generally most effective when coordinated with or by your professional association or a coalition of organizations.

The steps involved in pursuing legislative advocacy are similar to those involved in professional advocacy. One difference is that the messaging for legislative advocacy must be crafted to respond to the political realities of the state or local community. It is imperative to fit your issue into the political passions and priorities of the elected officials. Elected officials depend upon the votes of the people to get elected so it is only human nature that the voice of their constituents would have the greatest effect on their actions. Another difference is that most of the strategies that are utilized will focus on generating grassroots support for an issue. This will require that a message clearly articulates what the problem is that the proposed legislation seeks to solve and why fixing this problem is of benefit to everyone. Legislators typically respond to the issues with the largest, most vocal, and most active set of supporters. To get the attention of elected officials, the issues must be personalized for them. The most important thing to remember in legislative advocacy is to put a face on an issue or to tell the story. Research, best practices, and data can serve as the foundation and framework for a proposed bill but they rarely serve as the primary force behind it being proposed. And they are almost never the reason a bill is passed. People's stories, whether tragedies or triumphs, serve as the fuel that drives legislation. Every bill has a political champion who will carry it through the legislative body. And every *passed* bill carries the faces of the people and their stories that inspired the need for change.

CONCLUSION

Schools are increasingly becoming the primary source of mental health services for children. These school health and mental health services include increasing levels of service delivery ranging from school-wide prevention to intensive individual intervention services delivered through a comprehensive and coordinated effort between the school and community with the goal of keeping students engaged and in school. As a result, a variety of models have emerged that although different in their origin, maintain the essential features of a multi-tiered system of support. Despite research that supports the positive outcomes associated with providing mental health services within this framework, many administrators, educators, and policy makers continue to resist the idea that these types of services are the responsibility of the school. With continued advocacy, we can make progress toward the goal of ensuring that all students have access to the mental health services they need to be successful in school.

RESOURCES

The National Association of School Psychologists has additional resources to support professional and legislative advocacy. These resources are available online to users of this book at www.nasponline.org/depressionand-schoolagechildren

The website of the Centers for Disease Control and Prevention (http://www.cdc.gov) offers two sections of particular relevance to this chapter:

- Coordinated School Health (http://www.cdc.gov/HealthyYouth/CSHP) is the home page for the coordinated school health model. Pages found here explain the model and its rationale, and provides resources, data, publications, and other material to assist schools to improve their school health programs.

- The Youth Risk Behavior Surveillance System (YRBSS) monitors health-risk behaviors associated with the leading causes of death and disability among youth (http://www.cdc.gov/HealthyYouth/yrbs/index.htm).

The websites of the University of California-Los Angeles, Center for Mental Health in Schools (http://smhp.psych.ucla.edu) and the University of Maryland, School of Medicine, Center for School Mental Health (http://csmh.umaryland.edu) contain a wealth of resources, tools, and publications to support advocacy for mental health policies and programs in schools.

Enhancing the Blueprint for School Improvement in the ESEA Reauthorization: Moving From a Two- to a Three-Component Approach (http://www.nasponline.org/advocacy/UCLA_NASP_Brief_FINAL.pdf) is a policy analysis coauthored by the National Center for Mental Health in Schools at UCLA and the National Association of School Psychologists that defines a comprehensive system of learning supports (including services for social, emotional, and behavioral problems) integrated with the instructional and management components of school operations.

The website of the Office of Special Education Programs, IDEA Partnership, maintains a collection of resources on Communities of Practice (http://ideapartnership.org/index.php?option=com_content&view=section&id=11&Itemid=45)

The Office of Special Education Programs, Technical Assistance Center on Positive Behavior and Interventions and Supports (www.pbis.org) offers an array of resources on best-practice behavioral practices for improving behavioral and academic outcomes for students.

The RTI Action Network (http://www.rti-network.org) and the National Center on Response to Intervention (http://www.rti-4success.org) are two outstanding source of information and resources about effective implementation of response-to-intervention in schools.

REFERENCES

Adelman, H. S., & Taylor, L. (2004). Mental health in schools: A shared agenda. *Emotional & Behavioral Disorders in Youth, 4*(3), 59–78.

Adelman, H. S., & Taylor, L. (2010). *Mental health in schools: Engaging learners, preventing problems, and improving schools*. Thousand Oaks, CA: Corwin Press.

Bruns, E. J., Walrath, C., Glass-Siegel, M., & Weist, M. D. (2004). School-based mental health services in Baltimore: Association with school climate and special education referrals. *Behavior Modification, 28*, 491–512.

Center for Health and Health Care in Schools. (2007). *Children's mental health needs, disparities, and school-based services: A fact sheet*. Retrieved from http://www.behavioralinstitute.org/FreeDownloads/TIPS/school-based%20mental%20health%20facts.pdf

Cowan, K. C. (2011, Month). *Communication matters: Promoting and preserving your role in a tough professional climate*. Paper presented at the meeting of the National Association of School Psychologists, Philadelphia, PA.

Dryfoos, J., & Maguire, S. (2002). *Inside full service schools*. Thousand Oaks, CA: Corwin Press.

Durlak, J. A., & Dupre, E. P. (2008). Implementation matters: A review of research on the influence of implementation on program outcomes and the factors affecting implementation. *American Journal of Community Psychology, 41*, 327–350.

Shonkoff, J. P., & Phillips, D. A. (Eds). (2000). *From neurons to neighborhoods: The science of early childhood development*. Committee on Integrating the Science of Early Childhood Development, Board on Children, Youth, and Families, National Research Council and the Institute of Medicine. Washington, DC: National Academy Press.

Slade, E. P. (2002). Effects of school-based mental health programs on mental health service use by adolescents at school and in the community. *Mental Health Service Research, 4*, 151–166.

Substance Abuse and Mental Health Services Administration. (2005). *Project ACHIEVE*. Retrieved from www.modelprograms.samhsa.gov/template_cf.cfm?page=model&pkProgramID=31

Appendix: Handouts

All of these handouts are archived on the websites of the National Association of School Nurses (NASN) and the National Association of School Psychologists (NASP), fully formatted for printing. They can be accessed via the QR codes below. Scanning the QR code with your mobile devise will lead you directly to either the NASN or NASP archive page.

A. Universal Interventions for Preventing Depression

B. Targeted Interventions for Students at Risk for Depression

C. Intensive Interventions for Students With Depression

D. Building Effective Programs to Prevent Depression

E. Approaches to Temperament Risk Factors for Depression

F. Students and Grief

G. Signs of Depression in Children and Adolescents

H. Mental Health Screening in Schools

I. Talking With Students About Depression

J. Talking With Parents About Their Adolescent With Depression

K. Providing Mental Health Services Within a Multi-Tiered System of Supports

L. Professional Advocacy Planning Worksheet

www.nasponline.org/depressionandschoolagechildren

http://www.nasn.org/mentalhealth

Universal Interventions for Preventing Depression
By John E. Desrochers & Gail Houck

Universal preventive interventions target a whole population group, such as an entire classroom, school, or district. In other words, universal preventive interventions are not targeted specifically to students identified as at risk for depression, although these students also participate and benefit. Within a response-to-intervention (RTI) framework, these would be considered Tier 1 interventions. School-based universal interventions emphasize: building resilience within students, building protective schools, and raising awareness about depression.

SPECIFIC UNIVERSAL PROGRAMS
A wide range of prevention programs are available that are effective in contributing to the prevention of many student mental health problems, including depression. Examples are provided in Table 1. (see reverse)

BUILDING PROTECTIVE SCHOOLS
A more comprehensive, ecological approach to prevention considers the context or environment of the student as a contributor to the student's problems, including depression. Rather than focusing primarily on the individual characteristics of students, ecologically focused programs address the contextual (risk and protective) factors in the school as an indirect means to build resilience. Protective factors within the school include such things as school security and safety, social support, positive relationships with teachers and peers, and a sense of connectedness and belonging. Risk factors include such things as troubled relationships with peers and teachers, poor school climate, and inadequate classroom management. Activities that enhance protective factors and reduce risk factors within the school contribute to the prevention of depression and other mental health problems.

- The quality of students' relationships with peers and school staff has been found to be important for engagement with learning and connectedness to school, both important protective factors against depression. It is important that every student has a positive relationship with at least one caring adult in the school.

ACTION PLAN

- ❏ Create, join, or support a collaborative family–school–community problem-solving team in your school or district and use it to advocate for the implementation of a universal prevention program.

- ❏ Educate school personnel, parents, and community leaders about the role of protective factors in counteracting risk factors, building resilience, and promoting positive life outcomes for students. Emphasize the preventability of depression and the need for school-based prevention programs.

- ❏ Investigate several prevention programs. Choose one that most closely matches the needs of your school or district in terms of the skills it teaches and its affordability, feasibility, and acceptance. Consider this program as one segment on a continuum of interventions for depression that also includes targeted interventions for students at risk for depression and intensive intervention for those identified as depressed. Consider integrating such a program into the school's RTI framework.

- ❏ Develop a process designed to assess protective and risk factors for your students, determine which ones you can impact, and implement a plan to do so.

National Association of School Nurses

NATIONAL ASSOCIATION OF SCHOOL PSYCHOLOGISTS

Table 1. Examples of Universal School-Based Programs for Preventing Depression

Name	Age/Grade Range	Access
Resourceful Adolescent Program (RAP) Classroom lessons built on cognitive behavior principles significantly reduce depressive symptoms with improvements maintained over 10–18 months	Grades 7–10	http://www.rap.qut.edu.au
Beyondblue Enhances resilience by teaching skills (problem solving, coping, emotional regulation, stress reduction, social competence, conflict resolution, assertiveness) and building social support	Grades K–12	http://beyondblue.org.au
Children and Youth Resiliency Program Produces cohesive peer-group, classroom, and school communities and a reduction in the number and severity of disruptive incidents and suspensions.	Ages 12–18	http://www.corstone.org/html/solutions/programs.cfm
Program in Education, Afterschool, and Resiliency Emphasizes building social competence and resilience through relationships with positive adults	Grades K–12	http://www.pearweb.org
Second Step (Student Success Through Prevention) Classroom-based lessons provide social and emotional education to children from the preschool years through middle school	Grades K–8	http://www.cfchildren.org/second-step.aspx
Adolescent Depression Awareness Program (ADAP) Provides education about the identification and treatment of adolescent depression to reduce the associated stigma, morbidity, and suicide	High School	http://www.hopkinsmedicine.org/psychiatry/specialty_areas/moods/ADAP
School Transitional Environment Project (STEP) Restructures the school environment to facilitate transition and reduce stress, anxiety, depression, and delinquent behavior	Ages 12–18	http://www.ojjdp.gov/mpg/STEP%20(School%20Transitional%20Environmental%20Program)-MPGProgramDetail-428.aspx
Caring School Community To enhance school connectedness, creates a caring community of learners through class meetings, a buddy program, parent involvement, and school-wide components	Grades 1–6	www.devstu.org

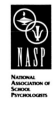

Targeted Interventions for Students at Risk for Depression
By John E. Desrochers & Gail Houck

Targeted interventions are designed to support students who are at risk for depression and need more intensive interventions than are available in the general education program. Within a response-to-intervention (RTI) framework, these would be considered Tier 2 interventions. These interventions help prevent depression by treating students' individual vulnerabilities (including risk factors that may predict or contribute to depression) or addressing contextual risk factors that affect students (e.g., loss and bereavement or divorce).

CHARACTERISTICS OF TARGETED INTERVENTIONS

- Targeted programs are most effective when offered to at-risk youth, over a relatively brief duration, using homework assignments to facilitate application of skills to everyday life.
- Services are most often delivered in a small-group format.
- Students require little formal assessment. In many cases, a life event or specific vulnerability will define the need for intervention.
- Targeted interventions generally require few additional resources and can be implemented by any of the school mental health professionals.

TARGETED PROGRAMS FOR ADDRESSING INDIVIDUAL RISK FACTORS

Intervention for individual risk factors or vulnerabilities for depression are largely based on the premise that addressing those vulnerabilities will prevent the onset of depression. Such targeted intervention involves teaching at-risk students new ways of thinking, social and emotional problem-solving skills, and strengthening their repertoire of coping strategies. A variety of programs are available that are effective in contributing to preventing depression among at-risk students. Examples are provided in Table 1.

Table 1. Examples of Targeted Intervention Programs Addressing Individual Risk Factors

Name	Age/Grade Range	Access
Penn Resiliency Program **Based on principles of cognitive behavior therapy and teaching of social problem-solving skills. Students learn impact of thoughts on emotions and behavior, as well as assertiveness, negotiation skills, decision-making, social problem-solving, and relaxation skills.**	Ages 8–15	http://www.ppc.sas.upenn.edu/prpsum.htm
Strong Kids Series **Teaches social, emotional, and coping skills and promotes resilience through an integration of behavioral, affective, and cognitive approaches.**	Grades preK–12	http://www.brookespublishing.com
Adolescent Coping With Stress Class (ACWS) **Teaches coping skills and new ways of thinking. Designed for the classroom setting during school hours, as an adjunct to health class, or as an after-school workshop or group.**	Ages 9–18	http://www.kpchr.org/research/public/acwd/acwd.html

National Association of School Nurses

NATIONAL ASSOCIATION OF SCHOOL PSYCHOLOGISTS

TARGETED PROGRAMS FOR ADDRESSING CONTEXTUAL RISK FACTORS

Although the focus of targeted interventions is on the prevention of depression in children and adolescents with individual risk factors for depression, general principles of these programs have been applied to the prevention of depression and other negative outcomes in students who face difficult life events such as parental death and divorce. Table 2 provides an example of some of these kinds of programs.

Table 2. Examples of Targeted Intervention Programs Addressing Contextual Risk Factors

Name	Age Range	Access
New Beginnings Program Divorced parents learn skills to improve parent–child relationship quality, improve effectiveness of discipline, reduce exposure to conflict between parents, and increase access between the nonresidential parent and child.	Ages 3–17	http://www.nrepp.samhsa.gov/ViewIntervention
Children of Divorce Intervention Program (CODIP) The key components of the program are group support and coping skill enhancement. Program provides skills that enhance children's resilience and healthy adjustment over time.	Ages 5–13	http://www.childrensinstitute.net/programs/codip
Cognitive–Behavioral Intervention for Trauma in Schools (CBITS) Group sessions allow students to process the traumatic memories and express their grief. Six cognitive–behavioral skill areas are addressed. Improves depressive symptoms and posttraumatic stress symptoms.	Ages 9–18	http://www.soprislearning.com

National Association of School Nurses

NATIONAL ASSOCIATION OF SCHOOL PSYCHOLOGISTS

Intensive Interventions for Students With Depression
By John E. Desrochers &Gail Houck

Intensive interventions for depression are provided to students who are (a) at very high risk of developing depression or already diagnosed with a depressive disorder and (b) not responding adequately to less intensive interventions. Within a response-to-intervention (RTI) framework, these would be considered Tier 3 interventions. School-based interventions typically are similar to targeted (Tier 2) interventions but are specifically designed for students with depression, and include psychotherapeutic approaches. Integrated into these more intensive efforts are strategies designed to enhance protective factors and build skills that are important components of therapeutic intervention. Examples of approaches that are considered evidence-based are cognitive–behavior therapy, the Adolescent Coping with Depression Course, and interpersonal psychotherapy for depressed adolescents (IPT-A).

INTERVENTIONS FOR DEPRESSION IN ADOLESCENTS

Cognitive–Behavior Therapy
Cognitive–behavior therapy (CBT) is the most researched school-based intervention and has yielded the strongest and longest lasting benefits for students with depression. Some of the most frequently implemented CBT techniques include the following.
- *Cognitive restructuring:* teaching students to challenge distorted and negative cognitions about themselves and their environment, and to replace these with more realistic ones.
- *Problem-solving*: teaching students to evaluate situations or problems by gathering relevant information, considering alternative responses or options, and choosing the best response.
- *Pleasant activity scheduling:* the student's systematic planning of daily activities to include pleasant and desirable events.
- *Anxiety management/relaxation training*: is not as well researched, but promising.
- *Social skills training:* teaching students social problem-solving skills and self-assertion.

General Findings About Cognitive–Behavior Therapy
- School-based CBT delivered in a group format minimizes the time and resources required to effectively reduce depression.
- For school-based intervention, 10 hours of CBT intervention appears to be the minimum required to have a meaningful impact on student depression. The more sessions provided, the better the response to CBT. It is best for schools to make intervention available throughout the school year.
- If the student is on an antidepressant, delivering 10 or more CBT sessions more than doubled the likelihood of an adequate response.
- The treatment effects of CBT alone, without medication, can last for more than 9 months.

The Adolescent Coping With Depression Course
The Adolescent Coping With Depression Course is a cost-effective, nonstigmatizing, CBT-based psychoeducational intervention for depression that can be delivered in schools. Skills taught include progressive relaxation, increasing pleasant activities, using positive thoughts to counter negative ones, social skills, communication skills, and goal setting. All materials are free and may be downloaded at http://www.kpchr.org.

Interpersonal Psychotherapy-Adolescents
Interpersonal psychotherapy for adolescents (IPT-A) with depression is designed for individuals, making it helpful for students who are more introverted and less comfortable in group settings. Some research suggests that it may be preferable to CBT for low-income individuals or in cases where there is family or parent–child conflict. The IPT-A treatment manuals and workbooks can be purchased from the developer (Laura Mufson, PhD; lhm3@columbia.edu).

NASN
*National
Association of
School Nurses*

NASP
NATIONAL
ASSOCIATION OF
SCHOOL
PSYCHOLOGISTS

INTERVENTIONS FOR DEPRESSION IN CHILDREN

Because the rate of depression in younger children is low, less is known about intensive treatments and their efficacy in this population. However, given the adverse psychosocial and educational impacts of depression on young students, school mental health providers must provide intervention. Both CBT and interpersonal psychotherapy can be adapted for elementary school students but attention must be paid to the developmental challenges with which school mental health providers in elementary schools are familiar.

- Young children are more concrete and have fewer meta-cognition skills than middle school or high school students.
- They are generally less verbally articulate about feelings.
- Young children are not as readily engaged in a discussion of thoughts.

With this developmental context in mind, adaptation of the basic elements of CBT and interpersonal psychotherapy can be made according to the younger student's developmental level, attention span, verbal skills, and reading abilities.

The ACTION Program

This CBT program is a developmentally and gender-sensitive group intervention for students as young as 9 years old that has been used extensively and effectively in public schools. It includes cognitive, self-control, behavioral, and parent-training procedures. The workbooks and a video are relatively inexpensive and available at http://www.workbookpublishing.com/depression.html. The sessions are designed to be fun and engaging for younger children while teaching them about their depressive symptoms, stressors, and relationship difficulties.

Interpersonal Psychotherapy

The basic premise of IPT is that the onset of depression is linked to conflicts and problems in interpersonal relationships, especially for those who are biologically vulnerable. Since young children are particularly embedded in family relationships, addressing interpersonal interactions is a central effort in this approach. This focus on interpersonal interactions is actually more concrete than a focus on cognitions. Although the phases of individual treatment can be readily adapted for younger children, parental involvement is critical.

COLLABORATION AND CASE MANAGEMENT

Students with severe depression and those who have depression with substance use, history of child abuse, suicidal ideation, and complex family involvement often need all services available in the school and in the community. Intensive interventions in these cases require school mental health professionals to engage in collaboration with community-based providers and partnerships with parents in order to provide a comprehensive, integrated program for the student.

National
Association of
School Nurses

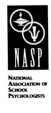

NATIONAL
ASSOCIATION OF
SCHOOL
PSYCHOLOGISTS

Building Effective Programs to Prevent Depression
By John E. Desrochers & Gail Houck

There is mounting evidence that carefully designed and implemented programs are effective in preventing depression and many of the mental health problems facing children and adolescents (National Research Council and Institute of Medicine, 2009). Moreover, engaging students in their environmental context is the most effective way to produce change (Nation et al., 2003). Including social, emotional, and behavioral components in a school's curriculum improves student outcomes in those areas and in academic achievement as well.

CHARACTERISTICS OF EFFECTIVE PROGRAMS

Researchers have identified nine characteristics of effective prevention programs (Durlak, Weissman, & Pachan, 2010; Nation et al., 2003). Incorporating these characteristics in school-based programs for the prevention of depression and other mental health problems is likely to improve their effectiveness.

Comprehensiveness
- Does the program include multiple components addressing domains that influence the development of the problem?
- For example, a school-based program to prevent depression could include peer relationships, student social competence and coping skills, and family education.

Varied Teaching Methods
- Are diverse teaching methods involved?
- Effective programs typically use a variety of teaching approaches that focus on increasing awareness and understanding the problem behaviors, as well as acquiring or enhancing skills.
- Each of these—increasing awareness, understanding the problem, and skill acquisition or enhancement—can employ several strategies.

Sufficient Dosage
- What are the program duration, frequency of sessions, and the nature of follow-up sessions?
- Sufficient dosage means that the programs provide enough of the program or intervention to achieve the desired results as well as follow-up to maintain them.

Theory Driven
- What is the theory that frames the understanding of depression and the design of the intervention program?
- Effective programs are based on accurate information and are supported by research, so there is a theoretical justification.

Positive Relationships
- How are positive relationships provided and modeled?
- A key component should be the opportunity to be with adults and peers in ways that promote strong relationships and support positive outcomes.

Appropriate Timing
- Does the program target developmentally appropriate assets or skills that are known to be preventive?
- The timing needs to be appropriate to the developmental needs of the students and early enough to be preventive.
- For example, enhancing social skills is much more preventive for second graders than for high school students, because the earlier intervention prevents an accumulation of negative experiences.

Socio-culturally Relevant
- How involved are members of the school cultural and ethnic groups in the selection of the program, modification of its features, and design of implementation in ways that consider the community and cultural norms?
- Programs need to be tailored to the community and cultural norms of the students and need to include the students in program planning and implementation.

National Association of School Nurses

NATIONAL ASSOCIATION OF SCHOOL PSYCHOLOGISTS

Outcome Evaluation

- What results are reported for the program, and after what period of time?
- Effective programs have clear goals and objectives, and systematically document their results, not just at the end of the program but up to 3 years later or after a developmental transition (elementary to middle school, middle school to high school).

Well-Trained Staff

- How are those that implement the intervention trained to do so? Effective programs are supported by staff members (teachers, administrators, and school mental health professionals), and staff members are provided with the necessary training to implement the intervention.
- For example, if teachers were asked to implement a school-based intervention, they should be provided the necessary training.

CHARACTERISTICS OF EFFECTIVE INTERVENTIONS

Research also provides guidelines for the ways that interventions can most effectively delivered to students. The best student outcomes are obtained when the interventions are monitored to ensure that they are delivered correctly and when they incorporate SAFE (Sequenced, Active, Focused, Explicit) procedures (Durlak et al., 2010):

Sequenced

- The program or curriculum breaks complex skills into more easily mastered steps and comprises a series of activities that are coordinated, connected to each other, and presented in a coherent sequence culminating in the learning of a specific skill.

Active

- The program incorporates active learning approaches (e.g., role-play) that involve the practice of specific social, emotional, or behavioral skills.
- Feedback on performance is built into the teaching process and mastery of one step leads to the next step in the sequence of learning.

Focused

- The program, in whole or in part, has a specific and significant part of the program devoted to improving social, emotional, and behavioral skills.
- Specific and sufficient time is allocated within the program for skills training.

Explicit

- The program is designed to accomplish goals related to improving specific social, emotional, or behavioral skills rather than more general skills or outcomes having to do with general development.
- The goals of the program are clear and explicitly identify the skills students are expected to learn.

School-based programs designed to prevent depression and other student mental health problems will be more effective to the extent that they are designed according to the above guidelines. All members of the community must learn about and disseminate the research showing that depression (and other mental health problems) can be alleviated and that student grades, test scores, and school performance significantly increased by providing programs that teach social–emotional–behavioral skills and support student mental health. Key stakeholders include school administrators, school mental health professionals, teachers, parents, and community leaders.

REFERENCES

Durlak, J. A., Weissberg, R. P., & Pachan, M. (2010). A meta-analysis of after-school programs that seek to promote personal and social skills in children and adolescents. *American Journal of Community Psychology, 45*(3-4), 294-309. doi:10.1007/s10464-010-9300-6

Nation, M., Crusto, C., Wandersman, A., Kumpfer, K. L., Seybolt, D., Morrissey-Kane, E., & Davino, K. (2003). What works in prevention: Principles of effective prevention programs. *American Psychologist, 58*, 449–456.

National Research Council and Institute of Medicine. (2009). *Preventing mental, emotional, and behavioral disorders among young people: Progress and possibilities.* Washington, DC: National Academies Press. Retrieved from http://www.nap.edu/catalog.php?record_id=12480

National Association of School Nurses

NATIONAL ASSOCIATION OF SCHOOL PSYCHOLOGISTS

Signs of Depression in Children and Adolescents
By John E. Desrochers & Gail Houck

Adults, children, and adolescents with depression usually share the common feelings of sadness and hopelessness, but children may express depression in a number of ways that are not the same as adults—irritability and vague physical complaints (e.g., recurrent stomach aches) are classic examples. Other signs that a child might be experiencing depression are listed below.

PHYSICAL SIGNS OF DEPRESSION IN CHILDREN AND ADOLESCENTS

- Changes in sleep patterns: Difficulty falling asleep or staying asleep; sleeping much more than is typical for the child's age.
- Unusually low energy; fatigue; sluggishness in moving, talking, reacting; reduced amount of activity or playing.
- Restlessness and agitation: increased fidgeting, squirming; reduced ability to sit still.
- Changes in eating patterns: increased or decreased appetite; weight gain or loss.
- Frequent physical complaints: complaints about illness symptoms, especially vague ones such as headaches, stomachaches, muscle aches, and tiredness.

COGNITIVE SIGNS OF DEPRESSION IN CHILDREN AND ADOLESCENTS

- Poor attention and concentration.
- Poor memory.
- Difficulty taking tasks to completion.
- Difficulty making decisions.
- Pessimistic world-view; perceiving things as worse than they are; negative attributions.
- Negative view of self, life, world, and future.
- Helplessness and hopelessness; belief that there is nothing that can be done about their depression and that this is the way it always will be.
- Low self-esteem; over focus on one's deficiencies and failures.
- Thoughts of suicide or death; self-destructive thoughts

SOCIAL–EMOTIONAL–BEHAVIORAL SIGNS OF DEPRESSION IN CHILDREN AND ADOLESCENTS

- Disengagement from friends, family, teachers; seeking solitude; difficulty with interpersonal relationships.
- Excessive time alone with videogames and other solo activities.
- Reduced participation in previously enjoyed activities; dropping sports and clubs.
- Classroom misbehavior; lack of cooperation.
- Decreased performance in school.
- Tardiness and absence from school.
- Running away or talking about running away.
- Suicidal talk or attempts; reckless behavior; self-injurious behavior.
- Alcohol and/or drug abuse.
- Lack of grooming and self-care.
- Decreased ability to appropriately cope with social events, extracurricular activities, hobbies, and family events.
- Decreased ability to cope with responsibilities.
- In young children: regression, clinginess, avoidance of new situations, accident proneness, and fears.
- Increased sensitivity to failure, rejection, and criticism.
- Increased irritability, anger, brooding, or hostility.
- Increased dependency and insecurity.
- Apathy and boredom.
- Feelings of sadness, isolation, hopelessness, worthlessness, or guilt.
- Crying or verbal outbursts without apparent cause.

Remember that not every child or adolescent who exhibits these signs is depressed; nor do those who are depressed exhibit all these signs. Judging whether a young person is depressed is sometimes very difficult to do. Consulting with a school psychologist, school social worker, school counselor, or school nurse is a good first step for teachers or parents who have concerns. Such a professional will be able to advise you as to whether further assessment or intervention might be warranted.

NASN
National Association of School Nurses

NASP
NATIONAL ASSOCIATION OF SCHOOL PSYCHOLOGISTS

Approaches to Temperament Risk Factors for Depression
By John E. Desrochers & Gail Houck

Temperament is considered to be a biologically based coping style. A student's temperament is characterized by such features as activity level, prevailing mood, intensity of response, adaptability to new experiences, and distractibility. Temperament is relatively stable by 3 years of age and persists through school age and adolescence. Characteristic patterns of these behaviors are classified as three basic temperament types: easy, difficult, and slow-to-warm-up. Children classified having an easy temperament typically have a positive mood, low to moderate activity level, moderate persistence, and high tolerance level. They are usually adaptable, sociable, outgoing, and mellow. These characteristics act as protective factors for these children. In contrast, having a difficult or slow-to-warm up temperament can be a risk factor for depression.

DIFFICULT TEMPERAMENT

Students classified as having difficult temperament tend to have a more negative mood, high activity level, and irregular or unpredictable biorhythms. They are typically not readily adaptable, tend to be reactive to new situations, and react with high intensity. They tend to be easily frustrated, with difficulty recognizing their needs and appropriately expressing them. In other words, children with a difficult temperament are considered difficult to interact with, which constitutes the basis of their typically poor social adjustment and vulnerability to depression.

WORKING WITH STUDENTS WITH DIFFICULT TEMPERAMENT

- Teach alternative behaviors: patience, using words to deal with anger and frustration, temper control.
- Modulate the student's level of stimulation, especially when faced with new students, crowds, exciting events, or new situations.
- Transitions are best tolerated when managed slowly.
- Students with a high activity level need physical outlets on the playground or through athletic or other physical activities.

SLOW-TO-WARM-UP TEMPERAMENT

Children classified as slow to warm up are considered shy. They are slow to approach people, tend to observe others, are socially reticent, and tend to withdraw from social demands and new social situations. These children can be considered "too much work to interact with," at least initially, and may be ignored by peers or become socially withdrawn.

WORKING WITH STUDENTS WITH SLOW-TO-WARM-UP TEMPERAMENT

- Avoid criticism, impatience, and pressure for sociability.
- Prepare the student for new situations.
- Allow time for the student to observe others and engage with them at his or her own pace.
- Facilitate the student's expression of needs so that they are not ignored.
- Provide opportunities for the student to have responsibility for a younger student and to experience social leadership.

National Association of School Nurses

NATIONAL ASSOCIATION OF SCHOOL PSYCHOLOGISTS

MATCHING CLASSROOMS TO STUDENT TEMPERAMENT

In relation to temperament, the central issue for the student's success is the fit of his or her behavioral style with the classroom setting and the school social environment. The teacher is the key determinant of this fit in the classroom.

- Poor student–teacher relationships represent a vulnerability for behavior problems and depression.

- Teachers can interrupt the cycle of conflicted relationships with students who have a difficult temperament and intervene constructively with their social and emotional problems, thereby reducing attendant problems in the classroom.

- Teachers are facilitators of students' social interactions, opportunities, and general classroom dynamics and can assist students with a slow-to-warm-up temperament in their interactions with peers.

- In addition to establishing the overall classroom climate and a relationship with the students as a group, the distinct relationships teachers have with individual students are also important.

National
Association of
School Nurses

NATIONAL
ASSOCIATION OF
SCHOOL
PSYCHOLOGISTS

Students and Grief
By John E. Desrochers & Gail Houck

The primary task is to create a safe school environment for grieving.

Depending on the wishes of the family, information about the family's loss should be shared personally and directly with the student's teacher and, in turn, the teacher or school mental health professional can inform the student's classmates and other close friends. School mental health professionals can be a source of support for the entire home–school community.

INFORMING CLASSMATES AND FRIENDS

- The information should be factual and brief, yet sensitively delivered.

- Acknowledge your own feelings about the loss or a similar loss, and your feelings of sadness for the student.

- Allow students to express their feelings and reactions, even if harsh (e.g., anger, fear, relief it did not happen to them). Validate those feelings.

- Provide developmentally appropriate education about the feelings that go with grieving, such as irritability or anger, sadness, guilt, self-blame, or denial.

- Prepare staff members and students to welcome the student back to school and to acknowledge the loss.

- Encourage teachers and students to invite the bereaved student to talk about the loss if he or she feels ready.

- A key role for the classroom teacher is to provide a nurturing environment.

THE ROLE OF SCHOOL MENTAL HEALTH PROFESSIONALS

- Discuss with teachers the student's usual level of functioning in terms of affect, academic performance, and social interaction.

- Alert school staff members to any potential signs and symptoms of traumatic or complicated grieving.

- Regularly consult with teachers and other school staff regarding their observations of the student's emotional responses, especially as manifested in mood, academics, and social relations.

National Association of School Nurses

National Association of School Psychologists

SCHOOL-WIDE TRAGIC EVENTS

Tragic events, from bus accidents to school shootings to natural disasters that may result in student and/or teacher deaths impact the entire home–school community. Deaths during adolescence typically occur because of accidents and interpersonal or self-inflicted violence. Thus, nearly all schools in the United States have a crisis plan in place to guide emergency response.

Crisis Teams

- Most schools have crisis plans and crisis teams in place.
- School communities rely on well-trained crisis teams comprising school mental health professionals, administrative and teaching staff, and outside professionals as needed to help them respond to the death of a student or staff member.
- The primary goal following a crisis is to help students feel safe.
- In addition to helping students to feel safe, it is important to help them to remain engaged with supportive peers, school staff, and family, and to cope with the resulting thoughts, feelings, and behavior.
- Providing information, support groups, and individual counseling is an important part of the school's response. The initial emphasis is on general education about trauma, loss, and bereavement.
- Support groups can be made available for students who choose to participate.
- Individual grief counseling can be provided for students who self-identify or who are referred by teachers or parents for more intensive help.

Support for Family and Staff

- A designated school mental health professional should reach out to the family of the deceased student or teacher to offer condolences and to learn what information can be shared with the school community, particularly the student's classmates and friends or the teacher's students. A prepared statement, developed and reviewed by a school mental health professional with the family, may be a useful way for teachers to disseminate information to classrooms.
- Formal rituals for the participation of the school community that the family would prefer can be identified: funeral, memorial service, flowers, school-based memorial site, or donations in the name of the deceased.
- Staff meetings with teachers, administrators, and other school personnel should be scheduled in order to keep them informed and to process their feelings.
- Staff members should be taught to observe the signs and symptoms of complicated grieving. Changes in academic performance, social interaction, or affect may signal potential difficulty with grief.
- Information about grief and coping with loss can be distributed to parents, teachers, and adolescents.
- Developmentally appropriate ways of sharing memories about the student or staff member can be used to facilitate bereavement (e.g., through writing or art).
- Classroom discussion should make students aware of personal strengths and coping skills and leave them feeling they are not alone.
- A safe space in designated health offices, school counseling rooms, guidance office, or other spaces in the school can be made available for support to students, family, and staff members during the school day. These spaces should be staffed by school mental health professionals.

National Association of School Nurses

NATIONAL ASSOCIATION OF SCHOOL PSYCHOLOGISTS

Mental Health Screening in Schools
By John E. Desrochers & Gail Houck

An increasingly large number of medical and mental health associations, state and federal agencies, and advocacy groups support mental health screening for students.

- The evidence for the value of screening for depression and suicide is overwhelming.
- Universal screening for depression and other behavioral health problems in youth is considered best practice.
- Universal screening for students at risk for academic problems is already a part of the response-to-intervention (RTI) process. Integrating social, emotional, and behavioral screening in this process is an efficient use of resources.

KEY MESSAGES ABOUT SCREENING

- Screening will not occur without the consent of parents and assent of students.
- Screening can identify students at risk for emotional and behavioral problems that can have lifelong implications if left untreated.
- Mental health problems do not simply go away by themselves.
- School mental health professionals can implement interventions that improve student outcomes.
- In the case of depression and its close link to suicide, screening can even save lives.
- Screening and talking about depression and suicide do not cause distress among students.
- Some version of universal screening for depression and other mental disorders should be established in each school district.

A MENTAL HEALTH SCREENING ACTION PLAN

- Establish a collaborative team comprising key family–school–community stakeholders to investigate, develop, and implement a mental health screening process for the school or district. Plan screening as part of a comprehensive, coordinated continuum of support for the social, emotional, and behavioral development of students.
- Begin to incorporate universal screening for mental health problems into the school's RTI process.
- Decide what you want to screen for: protective or risk factors, depression alone, depression plus suicide, or a broader array of mental health risks.
- Choose an appropriate screening procedure on the basis of affordability, feasibility, and acceptance.
- Consider legal and ethical issues and consult with the district's attorney to ensure that any procedures developed meet legal requirements.
- Provide professional development for school personnel on risk factors, signs, symptoms, outcomes, and methods of referral for students exhibiting depressive symptoms.
- Dispel any misunderstandings about mental health screening and promote buy-in among teachers and administrative staff.
- Conduct parent education sessions on risk factors, signs, symptoms, outcomes, and methods of referral for students exhibiting depressed behavior. Discuss the benefits of mental health screening, how it is to be conducted, and how the results are to be used. Dispel any misunderstandings about mental health screening.
- Implement the screening process and use the results to plan individual and school-wide interventions.

National
Association of
School Nurses

NATIONAL
ASSOCIATION OF
SCHOOL
PSYCHOLOGISTS

Talking With Students About Depression
By John E. Desrochers & Gail Houck

Adolescent students who are experiencing depression often want information about their condition. At the same time, they are often cautious about talking to adults because they are unsure of the reaction they might get and what the consequences might be. Talking with adolescents about their depression requires adults to strike a balance between providing guidance and promoting the autonomy of the student.

HOW STUDENTS MAY PRESENT TO SCHOOL MENTAL HEALTH PROFESSIONALS
- Most adolescents have a pressing desire to be normal, and often minimize their symptoms. They may have fears of being considered more depressed than they are or being considered weird, stupid, or crazy.
- They are likely to be very cautious about disclosing depressive symptoms in order to avoid negative and unwanted consequences. For example, they may fear being singled out for special programs, being prescribed an antidepressant, or having their parents or peers find out about their condition.
- Alternatively, they may also carefully disclose in order to minimize the risk of not being treated or not having their symptoms legitimized.

CONFIDENTIALITY, CONNECTION, AND THE NEED FOR INFORMATION
To offset the concerns and to create a context of safety in which depression can be identified and treatment discussed, school mental health professionals must address three main issues: confidentiality, connection, and a need for information

Confidentiality
- Three situations are commonly recognized as requiring a breach of confidentiality: (a) when a student requests it, (b) when there is a risk of harm to the student or others, and (c) when required by a court.
- Know state and school district regulations about mandated reporting.
- Appreciate that many students view their disclosures of distress and feelings of inadequacy as privileged information.
- Discuss confidentiality and explain at the beginning of a relationship with a student what information will be shared, why and with whom it will be shared, and how it will be shared. Make sure the student understands what will and will not be shared with the parent or caregiver.

WHAT ADOLESCENTS WANT
Despite their caution, adolescents with depression generally want a connection with a professional they can trust and who will work with them to find solutions. They need information about what they are experiencing and what can be done about it.

Connection
Students want a connection and are astute observers of verbal and nonverbal cues; they will withhold information and withdraw from interaction if they are not picking up the right cues from the professional. School mental health professionals who develop a relationship with adolescents are more likely to engage them in treatment than those who do not.
- Actively listen to the student.
- Convey concern about the student's well-being.
- Do not simply process complaints.
- Express empathy.
- Communicate an authentic understanding of the experience of depression.
- Respect the adolescent's desire to be normal.
- Use the *student's* words to describe symptoms.
- Acknowledge that feelings are important to discuss and that it takes strength to seek help.
- Accept the symptoms of depression; do not try to talk the student out of these feelings.

National
Association of
School Nurses

NATIONAL
ASSOCIATION OF
SCHOOL
PSYCHOLOGISTS

Information

Adolescents want feedback and information about depression from the professionals they work with. They want professionals to collaborate with them to find solutions. Adolescents who are more informed about treatment options are more likely to engage in treatment.

- Validate the student's experience and convey a legitimate concern.
- Point out (*notice* rather than accuse) behavior that seems different from the student's usual behavior or that may indicate depression.
- Keep in mind that adolescents view depression as caused by external stressors and as something to be solved by personal actions. Discuss depression as a normal consequence of stressful or abnormal experiences.
- Biological and technical explanations of depression are not likely to be helpful.
- Discuss depression in the context of the personal history and experience that the student shares with you.
- Stay solution-focused.
- Present options that are congruent with solving the problems they identify.
- Enhance the student's feeling of being understood.
- Confirm the student's autonomy to make decisions for themselves.

National
Association of
School Nurses

NATIONAL
ASSOCIATION OF
SCHOOL
PSYCHOLOGISTS

Talking With Parents About Their Adolescent With Depression
By John E. Desrochers & Gail Houck

Collaboration between parents and school mental health professionals is crucial for students with serious depression. It is usually helpful to include adolescents in conversations with parents in order to respect the student's confidentiality and autonomy and to help maintain the connection with the adolescent.

PREPARING THE ADOLESCENT

- ❏ Discuss with the student about arranging to talk with his or her parents.

- ❏ Talk with the student about the goals of the meeting and preview what will be discussed with parents.

- ❏ Rehearse a conversation between the student and the parents about the student's experience of depression, what he or she is doing about it, and what is needed from the parents.

DURING THE MEETING
The following elements should be covered when talking with parents about their child's depression.

- ❏ Share the student's experience and symptoms of depression.

- ❏ Elicit parental observations.

- ❏ Describe the student's perception of contributing factors.

- ❏ Elicit parental perceptions of contributing factors.

- ❏ Provide an explanation of depression.

- ❏ Identify treatment options.

- ❏ Share the student's preferences and choices.

- ❏ Identify what is needed from the parents.

- ❏ Clarify the role of school mental health professionals in monitoring symptoms, providing interventions in the school setting, and optimizing the student's academic and social experience.

National Association of School Nurses

NATIONAL ASSOCIATION OF SCHOOL PSYCHOLOGISTS

Providing Mental Health Services Within a Multi-Tiered System of Supports

By Kelly Vaillancourt, Katherine C. Cowan, & Anastasia Kalamaros Skalski
National Association of School Psychologists

Supporting children's mental health is critical to their success in school and life. Mental health services for children and youth are most effective when provided as a continuum of care that integrates schools, families, and communities. This continuum of care is most commonly known as a *multi-tiered system of supports* (MTSS). School-based and community-based providers bring specific expertise and levels of service to the process, and MTSS keeps the focus on meeting student needs within the right settings, with the right services, and with the best qualified personnel. The MTSS framework encompasses prevention and wellness promotion, universal screening for academic and behavioral barriers to learning, implementing evidence-based interventions that increase in intensity as needed, monitoring the ongoing progress of students in response to implemented interventions, and engaging in systematic decision making about programming and services needed for students based upon specific student outcome data.

School mental health professionals can be effective advocates for moving toward an MTSS approach for school-based mental health services at the systems level. Knowing and being able to articulate the benefits of MTSS and the steps toward implementation is critical to such advocacy.

BENEFITS OF AN MTSS FRAMEWORK FOR SCHOOL MENTAL HEALTH SERVICES

Multi-tiered systems of support that include prevention and intervention services improve behavior. Teachers frequently cite student behavior as a barrier to effective instruction. Among interventions and supports is one example of an evidence-based multi-tiered system of support in which students have access to a wide range of behavioral and mental health interventions by highly trained school-employed and community-based personnel. This type of whole-school intervention has been shown to decrease behavior problems while improving academic success (Luiselli, Putnam, Handler, M. W., & Feinberg, 2005; Nelson, Martella, & Marchand-Martella, 2002). When students are engaged and demonstrating appropriate behavior, teachers are able to focus on what they do best, which is to provide high quality and rigorous instruction to students.

Multi-tiered systems of support improve access to needed services and resources.
Comprehensive and collaborative mental health services within an MTSS model involves collaborating with a variety of professionals, including community-based professionals. Although schools do have a responsibility to address mental health concerns that impede a student's ability to learn, there may be circumstances in which a continuum of supports are necessary that include both school-based services and services within the community. Sometimes these services are co-located within the school. Sometimes they are located at community mental health agencies or other

teachers who leave the profession, a significant percentage cites student discipline problems (Ingersoll, 2001) as a reason for their dissatisfaction and decision to leave. Positive behavioral

community settings. In either case, in an MTSS model, these services are collaborative and involve active coordination between school- and community-employed professionals. Implementing MTSS in the school increases student access to school-based services, and provides an avenue for identification of available resources in the community. Coordination of these services and resources can address additional needs of students and families and help them be successful in all aspects of their lives.

Multi-tiered systems of support improved engagement and collaboration.
The very nature of MTSS encourages collaboration among the home, school, and community. In fact, many models mentioned in this chapter emphasize the role of the community in determining specific services needed at each individual school.

MTSS improves collaboration among staff members in the school and with parents. One key component of a response-to-intervention (RTI) framework is creating partnerships between the school and family. Research indicates that family–school partnerships positively impact children's school success (Christenson, 2004) and that school-based behavioral consultation helps to remediate both behavioral and academic difficulties for children (MacLeod, Jones, Somer, & Harvey, 2001).

One of the best ways to attain buy-in for a new initiative or for changes in existing programs is to seek input from all those who will be effected by the change. MTSS is not driven by one person's opinion about what may work. All teachers, administrators, specialized instructional support personnel, and other staff are involved in identifying students who may need extra support, collaborating with parents to determine the most appropriate interventions, and monitoring the progress of the

*National
Association of*

intervention. Utilizing this framework helps to make sure everyone's voice is heard and ultimately results in better outcomes for all students.

Service delivery within a multi-tiered system of supports increases student engagement and improves achievement. The ultimate goal of building principals and district superintendents is to maximize achievement so that students can achieve scholastic and career goals. Comprehensive school-based mental health programs provide a wide range of prevention and intervention services that are based on student need and that address students' behavioral, emotional, mental, and social functioning. Rigorous instruction and effective leadership contribute to student achievement; however, students who receive social–emotional support and prevention services achieve better academic outcomes (Greenberg et al., 2003). These types of whole-school interventions, delivered within an RTI framework, have also been shown to improve school climate. Improving school climate and student engagement and connectedness is associated with increased achievement in reading, writing, and math (Spier, Cai, & Osher, 2007).

TIPS FOR BUILDING AN MTSS MODEL

Understanding the benefits of an MTSS model is only valuable when the model is adopted and implemented in reality. There are several important steps for advocates of this model to consider in the quest for its adoption.

1. **Convene an MTSS Community of Practice (COP) with a shared commitment of working toward the implementation of a comprehensive and coordinated system of comprehensive and coordinated learning supports.** Given the complexity of relationships involved in developing effective partnerships across complex systems (schools and communities), it is necessary to utilize a model for working together and can bring together a variety of stakeholders on a level playing field. Based on the work of Wenger (2006), a community of practice brings together a group of people who share a concern or passion for something they do and, through their interactions with one another, learn how to do it better. A key feature of establishing the COP is engaging a broad base of stakeholders impacted by this work and empowering them as collaborative decision makers.

2. **Assess existing needs, resources, and conduct a gap analysis.** The COP will examine the existing needs and resources in the system and then analyze these data to determine where needs are not matched by available resources.

3. **Determine the infrastructure goals, objectives, and desired outcomes.** After studying the assessment and analysis, the COP can set a shared mission, vision, and goals to drive their work. These goals should speak to the current and needed investments of the systems and what it will take in order to achieve the desired outcomes.

4. **Determine strategies for effective collaboration.** One critical feature of an effective MTSS system is that the services and supports are truly collaborative and coordinated. These services should include investing in the school's infrastructure while also supplementing the existing resources and services available in the schools. Open communication, active coordination, shared decision making, and shared accountability are all critical elements to effective collaboration.

5. **Implement comprehensive and coordinated services and supports.** Most systems adopting an MTSS approach will benefit from having written agreements (Memorandums of understanding (MOU), and will guide the collaborative work. These MOUs could include agreements related to a variety of issues including finances, settings, services, roles, and responsibilities.

6. **Monitor progress and evaluate system strengths and needs. Revise and reevaluate as warranted.** An effective MTSS system will include regular monitoring of student and program outcome data and analyses focused on continual improvement. This process will be ongoing and adopted within the operations of the COP as normal part of interacting.

REFERENCES

Christenson, S. L. (2004). The family–school partnership: An opportunity to promote the learning competence of all students. *School Psychology Review, 33,* 83–104.

Greenberg, M. T., Weissberg, R. P., O'Brien, M. U., Zins, J. E., Fredericks, L., Resnick, H., & Elias, M. J. (2003). Enhancing school-based prevention and youth development through coordinated social, emotional, and academic learning. *American Psychologist, 58,* 466–474.

Ingersoll, R. M. (2001). *Teacher turnover, teacher shortages, and the organization of schools.* Seattle, WA: Center for the Study of Teaching and Policy, University of Washington.

Luiselli, J. K., Putnam, R. F., Handler, M. W., & Feinberg, A. B. (2005). Whole-school positive behavior support: Effects on student discipline problems and academic performance. *Educational Psychology, 25,* 183–198.

MacLeod, I. R., Jones, K. M., Somer, C. L., & Havey, J. M. (2001). An evaluation of school-based behavioral consultation. *Journal of Educational and Psychological Consultation, 12,* 203–216.

Nelson, J. R., Martella, R. M., & Marchand-Martell, N. (2002). Maximizing student learning: The effects of a comprehensive school-based program for preventing problem behaviors. *Journal of Emotional and Behavior Disorders, 10,* 136–148.

Spier, E., Cai, C., & Osher, D. (2007, December). *School climate and connectedness and student achievement in the Anchorage School District.* Unpublished report, American Institutes for Research.

Wenger, E. (2006) Communities of practice: An introduction. Retrieved from http://www.ewenger.com/theory

Professional Advocacy Planning Worksheet

Assess the Situation	Findings	Next Steps/Who is Responsible
To Do: Determine who might help conduct the assessment. *Eventually you might want to establish an advocacy team, depending on the situation/goals.* • What are your school/district's current priorities and how are mental health services relevant? • What is the status of and perceptions regarding school-based interventions to address depression or other mental health issues? • What are the relevant school/district/state policies and legislation? • What data do you have to support your argument? • What data do you need? • Are there events or other opportunities that could act as a catalyst for moving this forward?		

Define Benefits/Outcomes	How Will You Demonstrate Benefit?	Who Needs to Be Kept Informed?
To Do: Establish clear objectives. *Base on assessment of needs, opportunities, and resources.* • What are your objectives (short- and long-term)? • What are the barriers to achieving your goals? • How will students benefit? • How will other stakeholders benefit? • Why should they care? • What data or research do you have?		

Identify Relevant Stakeholders	Key Stakeholders and Decision Makers	Possible Supporters/Opponents
To Do: Build relationships. *Start with areas of common ground and think long-term.* • Who are the key stakeholders you need to influence to meet your objectives (e.g. parents, principal, school board)? • Who are the key decision makers? • Who might/will support your efforts? • How will you reach out to them? • Who might oppose your efforts? • How will you prepare for their opposition?		

National Association of

NASP
NATIONAL
ASSOCIATION OF

	Key Messages	Supporting Facts

To Do: Identify 3 most critical arguments. *Make them simple; support them with data.*

- Do you have data or scholarly research to support your arguments?
- Who can help you "put a face" on this issue?
- What personal experiences can be shared about the issue and why it needs to be resolved now?
- How will you target your messages to your key audiences?
- Are your messages adapted for your different stakeholder groups?

1.

2.

3.

Select and Implement Your Strategies

	Strategy/Implementation Details	Person Responsible/Timelines

To Do: Identify who needs to be in the loop. *Determine what information will be communicated and how, and specific roles and responsibilities.*

- What strategies will be most effective with each stakeholder group?
- How will you continue to engage your stakeholders and supporters?
- What ongoing communication strategies will you use to strengthen your base of supporters and address concerns of your opponents?
- What is your timeline for implementation?
- What data do you need to collect during the implementation to demonstrate effectiveness?

Evaluate Your Progress

	Short Term Objectives	Long Term Objectives

To Do: Incorporate ongoing evaluation into planning and implementation. *Regularly review progress and be prepared to adjust your efforts as you go based on effectiveness.*

- What activities were effective in meeting your objectives?
- What could be done differently?
- Were your messages effective?
- Have you reached out to all possible allies?
- What is your follow up plan?
- What resources are needed to move forward?

Depression in Children and Adolescents: *Guidelines for School Practice,* **Handout L.**

National Association of School Nurses

NATIONAL ASSOCIATION OF SCHOOL PSYCHOLOGISTS